80°   75°   70°

ATLANTIC

CUBA

20°

HAITI

SANTO DOMINGO

JAMAICA

PORT-AU-PRINCE

SAVANNE ZOMBIE

15°

CARIBBEAN

80°   75°   70°

Living Treasure

SAVANNAH BASILISK (Coryopthanes cristatus)

IVAN T. SANDERSON

LIVING TREASURE

WITH THIRTY-TWO

ILLUSTRATIONS BY THE AUTHOR

THE VIKING PRESS · NEW YORK

1945

TO MY LITERARY AGENTS,

Paul Reynolds,

MY STAUNCH ADVISER IN AMERICA,

AND

Innes Rose,

MY CLOSEST FRIEND IN ENGLAND

FIRST PUBLISHED IN APRIL 1941

SECOND PRINTING APRIL 1945

COPYRIGHT 1941 BY IVAN T. SANDERSON

PRINTED IN THE UNITED STATES OF AMERICA

PUBLISHED ON THE SAME DAY IN THE DOMINION OF CANADA

BY THE MACMILLAN COMPANY OF CANADA LIMITED

CONTENTS

Part Three: To Yucatan

ILLUSTRATIONS

ILLUSTRATIONS

INTRODUCTORY

THE following string of little histories, reproduced as far as possible in their natural settings, was never intended to constitute a tale of adventure, a travelogue, or its bastard offspring, a "tropical travel diary." Furthermore, this is neither the history of an expedition nor a scientific report upon a zoological project.

If I could be sure that I had made this quite clear, I should feel satisfied; if I could also show convincingly that we are not, and have no desire to claim to be, either explorers, adventurers—in the strict sense of the word—or any other form of professional travellers, I would live in utter contentment for the rest of my life.

One naturally appreciates and congratulates all those who add spice to the life of the work-weary by sparkling accounts of travels and adventures in far-away places. One can but stand in awe of talents so admirably employed for the enjoyment of all and the furtherance of what is after all a business requiring acumen, fortitude, and courage. Praise should be bestowed where it is due and it is undeniably due to the explorers. But what we cannot quite understand is why everybody who travels more than two boundaries away from his homeland should invariably be dubbed an explorer. Further, we are quite definitely puzzled in observing that any of these most ordinary mortals who try to refute the accusation are instantly treated with suspicion—as if they were hiding some frightfully deep publicity plot!

People seem to forget that far-away places, even Africa (darkest) and South America (the impenetrable), are inhabited by other people. There are, in fact, millions of the latter. There they are, scrambling about on ice-floes, cutting their way through steaming jungles, serving afternoon tea to tribesmen, but they aren't explorer-author-lecturers. No; indeed no! They simply happen to live in those places. Nor are they all deeply pigmented, with feathers in their hair; there are intelligent, bleached-looking families whose only homes are in the most unlikely and most popularly "explored" countries in the world. Yet should one of these happen to write or speak interestingly of the many fascinations of his homeland—and more especially if it happen to be a tropical one with a romantic name— he will instantly be dubbed an explorer and probably be reported as having been on an "expedition."

We also are so labelled, when all we do is travel by some comfortable floating hotel to a country that is rather far away from some other countries and there live for a time in order to carry on our work—or studies, or business, if you prefer—because that is the most convenient place to do so.

An introduction to a narrative is a nuisance to the reader, the publisher, and everybody else, but it is at the same time the only real opportunity the author has to express himself on a number of rankling questions.

The position, then, is this. My wife and I are irrepressibly interested in natural history and this pursuit happens also to be our profession. The work entails studying certain specific groups of animals in their natural surroundings, collecting specimens of these animals, and examining, recording, and tabulating the physical features of those surroundings. This is a very fascinating job for any interested in such things and, withal—it seems to us at least—a decent, honest, and fairly rational life. Moreover, it must rather naturally be prosecuted in the countries where the specific groups of animals are found. We therefore go and live in these countries ourselves, and we cannot see what is so odd about that.

Our objects are neither to explore, nor particularly to travel, nor even to gather material to write books. They are primarily scientific or—might one say?—a simple thirst for knowledge; secondarily, they are economic though not in the private sense. The economic aspects come in through the requirements of public health, medicine, agriculture, and forestry—"things" that have much to do with animal parasites, pests, and habits. This opus purports to be nothing more than the descriptions of a life that thousands of those "other people" might and often do lead in the countries we visit. Its only tentative claim to distinction is that it is single-mindedly zoological, which the average inhabitant of Jamaica, British Honduras, or Yucatan necessarily is not.

My aim has been merely to state as clearly and truthfully as possible the life of and the life in the tropical forests and jungles. In attempting this, the most difficult part has been stating what I have called below "pomposities." These large, underlying conceptions are so elementary and obvious that they are easily overlooked and yet without them the jungles might appear on paper like Hollywood fantasies and our own work dangerously like that practically worthless form of enterprise, "a collecting trip."

To explain these things calls for some statement of elementary biological truths. The putting of these into a book for some reason appears to prompt many people who know them all already to imagine that the author thinks he is stating them for the first time! Clarification of the obvious is, none the less, often very essential especially in tropical biology—*vide* Charles Darwin and the theory or practice of evolution—and we personally are more than fortunate in having had the support of a certain institution for several years now in doing just this in our work.

The Trustees of the Percy Sladen Memorial Fund—which is a fund bequeathed by the late benefactor of that name to biological science and which is now administered through the Linnean Society of London—generously backed the studies which were prosecuted during the period herein described with the principal object of making it possible for us to clarify and record just these obvious underlying features of wild life. I would not go into such intimate details of our professional activities were it not for the fact that I desire very greatly to express publicly my real appreciation to the said Trustees.

That these underlying principles can bear practical fruit of a very concrete nature will, I think, become quite clear below. It is as easy for the bench-worker to sneer at a roving theoretician as it is for a practical field-worker to laugh at a sedentary theorist. Both pursuits are senseless, for there is place for theory and practice in the home laboratory as in the untrammelled jungles. If, moreover, practical results can be obtained from theoretical suppositions such as is the case of the mosquito called "*darlingi*" which is mentioned later, one cannot but feel that such obscurer studies are indeed of first importance. Our sorest trials are met in attempting to explain these pomposities without being pompous and in stating them concisely and simply.

Finally, there are just two other things I should like to mention.

The first is a point made by a great literary pundit. Since he *is* a great pundit, I have the utmost respect for his pronouncements even upon matters that are not strictly literary; besides, he was right. This pundit said that little histories about bats and frogs and rats could apparently be whisked back and forth across the Atlantic from equatorial Africa to equatorial America, or vice versa, without altering anything more than the author's word for the locale. This is indeed true from the point of view of pundits and all others except horribly systematic zoologists and, perhaps, botanists. In defence of my little host of frogs and bats and rats that herewith patter along I should, however, like to say that it is just this remarkable similarity that makes their lives so fascinating. That they are different, systematic zoologists, they themselves, or even I can clearly demonstrate, but that is not the point. Of real import is the manner in which they are woven into the essential unity of natural life—a unity which is often so sadly overlooked and which so sorely needs laying bare.

The second matter is quite different. One might suppose that there was no need to mention it at all but, forsooth, this is not the case. The fact is, I find it necessary to state in plain language that (a) we take our work very seriously, but that (b) we do not take ourselves at all seriously. It seems inconceivable, yet there undeniably exist those who are not only doubtful but wholly incredulous of (b)!

I.T.S.

Part One

VIA JAMAICA

MYTHS AND REALITIES

Round-Mouthed Ones, a Cave Monster, and Coneys

IT all began years ago while we were on holiday in the green
island of Jamaica. The incident seemed so trivial that it passed
almost unnoticed, and left no impression upon us at the time.
We had been cooped up in London for two years, and were conse-
quently luxuriating in the tropical sunlight. We rode about in a shiny
car, swam in the warm sea, viewed the Blue Mountains from every
possible angle, and spent our afternoons collecting and examining
the small fauna of the island. This last was really our greatest relaxa-
tion; for Alma and me it was a matchless pleasure to hold a living
creature in the hand after months of probing in glass jars for alcohol-
soaked corpses.

At the outset we were intrigued by anything alive. Our enthusiasm, as invariably happens, swiftly infected the hotel staff, and the
usual stream of small creatures dangling from nooses of fine grass
soon began to flow towards our bungalow.

Then one day a tall man wearing blue jeans and an intelligent
smile presented himself. He evinced great interest in our activities,
which at that moment consisted in efforts, mostly on Alma's part, to
take colour photographs of a somewhat irritated and exceedingly
agile lizard. A wonderful co-operativeness is inspired by zoological
endeavour. Let a specimen escape the clutches of a zoologist anywhere in the world, and I guarantee that whatever onlookers may
be on hand will join the chase with a wholeheartedness that is rarely
to be witnessed otherwise.

On this occasion our captive—a fine example of the beautiful

green lizard named *Anolis garmani*, which spends its life messing
about on the higher branches of large trees and turns brown with
fright, bad weather, or the embrace of a hot hand—not only got
loose, but made for bush with a speed untoward in an arboreal animal on the ground. The only onlooker ran true to form and at great
speed. He overtook the fugitive and caught it in his cap, but unfortunately this treatment prompted the animal to turn dark brown
in messy patches, so that Alma's colour photography had to be temporarily abandoned until her subject should go green again under the
influence of sunlight and absolute quiet.

While waiting, we got acquainted with our visitor. He was a
carpenter by trade, and also acted as general handyman on a near-by
property. Having heard of our queer habits, he had come to inquire
whether we were interested in bats, because there was a shallow
cave within his jurisdiction that housed many.

Now, asking us whether we are interested in bats is equivalent to
asking a child if it likes sweets. We listened avidly, and insisted upon
being led to the cave without delay.

This abode of bats turned out to be an overhanging cliff into
the base of which road workers had burrowed to get stones and lime.
The place was full of daylight, but nevertheless several dozen large
bats hung chattering in clusters or wheeled silently back and forth.
We spent some time swatting at these with a long pole, as we were
not in those days properly equipped for bat-hunting. We knocked
down four, all of a fruit-eating species known as *Artibeus jamaicensis
jamaicensis*—presumably so that future students may be doubly sure.
We carried our prizes back to the hotel, to the horror of a party of
visiting Anglo-Saxons who were just starting their afternoon tea.
The anti-bat juju seems to be particularly strong among blond
Nordics.

We spent the evening getting our hands in, working on the bats.
One soon gets out of practice in skinning, and forgets the innumerable little things that must be done with specimens in the field, such
as searching for external parasites before skinning, dissecting out
the uterus before throwing away the corpse, and so forth. The

niceties and the routine of these field operations can become badly blurred in the mind of even the most ardent collector during two years of super-civilization, so it was only with much fumbling, and overlooking of the details of procedure, that I finally managed a rather bedraggled-looking stuffed specimen. Alma then pointed out, to my chagrin, that I had neglected to make our customary search for external parasites.

We have a special catalogue-form for these, one which bears innumerable columns and takes a very long time to fill in. Alma finds perverse pleasure in getting a lot of items for this catalogue, because it so often lags behind the others. I had therefore to begin a careful search of the already stuffed bat.

Not for one moment did I expect to find anything, but I continued blowing apart the fur and grubbing around with a needle. I was about to give up when I perceived a small tick adhering to the naked upright tragus of the left ear. With the greatest difficulty this tiny creature was detached intact and transferred to one of our smallest corked tubes, in which it was as lost as a single tadpole would be in a ten-gallon tank. Assured, with the aid of a lens, that it was indeed there, we duly added a label giving the circumstances of its capture and the name and number of its host, sealed the tube, and put it away. Hidden at the bottom of our collecting case, it passed completely out of our minds. As I have said, it seemed so trivial that it went by almost unnoticed, and left no impression on us at the time.

A year later we were leaving Haiti, clearing up the work of one trip and embarking upon another. We packed all our specimens and shipped them off to England. None of us for an instant gave thought to the small tube containing the specimen marked "Number 1 PA."; but it must have gone off bravely with the rest.

Several months later we were camped in the more remote jungles of Dutch Guiana, not too remote, however, for the periodic arrival of mail. One day a large envelope arrived from which tumbled a cascade of papers, typed sheets, pamphlets, and diagrams. The principal enclosure was a twice-folded sheet of heavy tracing paper bearing a most detailed plan and elevation of a revolting, hairy beast without a noticeable head. The covering letter plainly showed that the Assistant Keeper of Arachnida at the British Museum was in a state of considerable zoological excitement.

There was a specimen among our recent shipment from the Antilles, the letter announced, that called for special comment and, it seemed, the straining of every zoological nerve. This beast was none other than *Sphærorhynchus*. The epistle seemed to pause at that point as if to allow for our intake of breath and fervid comment. Then it went on.

This creature—of the utmost zoological interest—held a position as yet ill defined but somewhere between the ticks and the mites. It was not represented in the national collections, in fact it was represented hardly anywhere; it had been recorded only from the left ears of some three or four bats in Brazil; the Nazis had got it in Berlin! Furthermore, we were told, its presence had never been suspected in Central America. We were then asked what we proposed to do about it.

This terrific find was, of course, our Number 1 PA. We were told that all our bats preserved in spirit had been "critically" examined, but had failed to yield other specimens of the parasite; the tanks and containers which had held the bats had been rinsed into fine muslin and all the spirit strained, but no detached specimens were found.

You can hardly conceive of the enthusiasm of the scientist on such occasions. We at once caught the fever and forthwith examined all the bats we had on hand and strained the soupy liquid that bathed them. We also slaughtered more bats and "critically" examined their fur and their ears, but we failed to capture a single additional specimen of *Sphærorhynchus*. Then we had to go home to England.

There the excitement swelled to a crescendo. We pored over the little brute magnified to colossal dimensions on a ground-glass screen. We discussed it and read about it and commented on it over afternoon tea. Enthusiasm increased on all sides.

Now, when we went home we had in mind a project for research and collecting in the Orient. Preliminaries had been completed, but several difficulties cropped up, and all the time this *Sphærorhynchus* business went on as an overtone. It eventually became the central point about which all our other plans revolved. However we looked at any project, it always seemed that somebody sooner or later said, "and then we might have another crack at *Sphærorhyn-chus*." The creature seemed to become irresistible by virtue of its very minuteness; somehow the problem seemed almost to take on the character of a challenge to the honour of the British Empire. And so it came about that all the more important considerations swept around and clustered spear-head fashion behind the quest for this most rare and dismal little aberrant arachnid, and in due course we sailed for the New World again, to reach which—for us, at least—one is almost compelled to go via Jamaica.

Thus we presently found ourselves again in the hotel bungalow talking to the same smiling man in blue jeans. Once again we entered the shallow cave and stood listening to the high-pitched chatter of probably the very same bats.

This time, however, we brought a formidable array of bat-catching apparatus, and rapidly cleaned up the whole resident population. As each bat fell to the cave floor, we fell upon it with probes and lenses and delved into the recesses of its much-convoluted ears. We pored over every bat to the point of exhaustion, but there were no *Sphærorhynchus* or Round-Mouthed Ones.

It is an excellent rule to begin a trip with a failure. Not only is it stimulating, but the eagerness to recoup invariably leads to discoveries of unsuspected interest and importance. This failure proved no exception.

You will have wondered whether seeking this bat-infesting parasite was the only object of our trip or even its major purpose. It was not, though its influence had been so great. There were other objects, some of which were concrete and individual while still others were more general in scope and might be described as "theories requiring factual proof and hypotheses needing theoretical exposition." Of the latter pomposities, more later.

Among the concrete desiderata were some very special rats, two guinea-pig-like creatures, a porcupine, certain minute opossums in an interesting condition, another dismal arachnid which was an old friend of ours, and a particular horse. Since for the moment we had reached a dead end in our search for *Sphærorhynchus*, the last-named now claimed our attention.

This horse business had also started some three years previously when we were in Haiti and had visited the mountain pine forests there. I mentioned the matter in an earlier account of that trip, but left the horse part open with the remark that somebody armed with something more lethal than a shotgun loaded with Number Six shot would have to go up into the mountains to obtain a specimen. Our stop in Jamaica now offered this opportunity, and we arranged that my long-suffering and painstaking assistant, Fred, should go over because he liked flying (which is the only way to get there), knew everybody in Haiti, thanks to his long residence in that country, and spoke the lingo with fluency. Alma and I, we decided, would only be a hindrance and an unnecessary expense, since the sole object of the trip was a single specimen. Our disappointment over the Round-Mouthed Ones was thus dulled with the business of getting Fred off at the quite unnecessary hour of five o'clock the following morning.

That feat accomplished, Alma and I became intolerable pests to the landed proprietors of the eastern end of Jamaica. We got a car and buzzed about the countryside inquiring of all and sundry for caves, and, once we had located one, we descended upon its owner demanding permission to rid it of bats. On one occasion, I must confess to having posed as some ill-defined sanitary official and having got away with it as well as with a dozen bats. But all our efforts were of no avail. We could not find a *Sphærorhynchus*. Reluctantly we turned to the next of our special desiderata: one of the guinea-pig-like creatures which happen to inhabit Jamaica.

This fast-disappearing animal, *Geocapromys brownii*, known locally as the coney, is very rightly protected. It used to be fairly common in the island at all higher elevations, but is now unknown in most places. We got permission to take a few specimens.

If one excludes the bats, the mammalian fauna of the West Indies is meagre and remarkably patchy. Each of the larger Antilles, and several of the lesser, possess either one or two species that are found neither on any of the other islands nor on the mainland of the Americas. The insectivorous Solenodons of Cuba and Haiti have no relatives nearer than Madagascar. The rodents, which comprise all but a few of these truly indigenous mammals of the West Indies, have relatives on the continents of North and South America, but these are, at best, distant-cousin types. Excluding bats, Jamaica to-day supports but one purely indigenous land mammal, and this is the local coney.

It would appear from perusal of some early books, such as the famed *Voyage to the Islands of Madera, Barbados, Nieves, Snt. Christophers, and Jamaica* of Sir Hans Sloane, that before the coming of Europeans, the raccoon—judged by unearthed skulls to be of the North American *Procyon lotor* type—was extremely common around the Jamaican coasts, and that there was also a wild dog called the "alco" that couldn't bark and was tamed by the indigenous Amerindians.

The rising and sinking of the land masses throughout the Caribbean, or alterations in the general level of the seas due to changes in the size of the polar caps in the ice ages, or both, made possible the arrival in earlier geological periods of such truly indigenous creatures as the coney. Subsequently such forces also cut them off, and isolated them like living fossils. Such species as the raccoon doubt-less came later in one of those mysterious ways by which animals arrive upon minute islands hundreds of miles from other land. Some say they arrive on floating logs, or by swimming, though both sug-gestions strain belief. The raccoon may have come with early man.

As we set about preparing for our coney-hunt, we encountered persistent rumours among the country people that there was an-other native rodent clearly distinct from the imported house rats and mice. It was called locally the garden mouse and was described as being smaller than a house rat and having close, shiny, sleek fur of an ochre-brown colour above and bright golden-yellow below. It seemed to be agreed that the eyes were surrounded by black or dark brown "spectacles," and that its tail was very long and slightly hairy. It was said to be arboreal.

There was only one objection to accepting the existence of such an animal, for its description suited many arboreal rats, and that was that it had not so far been collected. This is an almost insurmountable disqualification in an island upon which so many serious naturalists have worked for so many years. At the same time, the remoter areas in the mountains contain many big tracts that have never been systematically examined—and a new mouse was discovered in the British Isles in 1923!

Indeed, once we began to inquire into the fauna of Jamaica, we were beset with vivid accounts from all sides offering intimate details about a seemingly inexhaustible list of small mammals. The majority turned out to be one or another of the imported species: the mongoose, black or brown rat, house mouse, or agouti—all of which we found in practically every type of habitat throughout the island and at all elevations. We even trapped house mice in the fern forest six thousand feet up in the Blue Mountains! Most of the remaining tales seemed to centre on the coney or the alleged garden mouse. Yet there still remained a few unaccountable records. Among these was one that might interest palæontologists or archæologists.

A strange people known as the Maroons inhabit two districts of upland Jamaica. Ethnologists have never ceased wrangling over them, and apparently find their meagre customs of unending interest. I myself know nothing about them except that a certain story emanates from those who live in the Blue Mountains at the eastern end of the island. The story is to the effect that somewhere in the neighbourhood of their settlement, high in the mountains, there is a cave into which, in early days, either the Maroons or their Amerindian predecessors pushed human sacrifices. What gives this rather commonplace legend some substantiality is that the cave is said to have had a wall barrier across its lower recesses and that behind the wall was once water which rose and fell periodically. This is a very specific although not uncommon cave phenomenon. The story continues that when the water topped the wall, a great beast came forth and snatched up the luckless offering. The Maroons declare that the wall is now broken and the enclosed waters dispersed, and that in their place may be seen an immense skeleton in a good state of preservation.

This tale prompted me to ask the obvious question, namely, has anybody seen the skeleton or the cave, and if not, why not? Upon the three occasions that we have visited Jamaica, I have gone around dandling this question with little concrete result. Mr. Cundall, the late curator of the Jamaica Institute, confirmed the legend with enthusiasm, and country people from the John Crow Mountains area repeat it without prompting. One man even declared he had got an eye-witness version from a Maroon. You may therefore well ask, "Why haven't you gone to see for yourself?" I am afraid I have only two weak-sounding excuses to offer. First, I haven't had time and, second, it's all very difficult. Let me try to explain.

Certain parts of the high ranges of Jamaica are practically, if not altogether, unknown; they are not quite but very nearly real jungle, and would be a match for anything in Africa or South America for impenetrability. I refer disbelievers to any of the schoolboys who were lost on the Blue Mountains in the summer of 1939, or to any of the army of rescuers who went out to search for them.

Penetration into such country to look for a cave (or even to collect rats) requires organization no less elaborate than an expedition into the interior of South America. In fact, it demands more, for in Jamaica one cannot motorboat up placid rivers or even pound along behind a line of Livingstonian porters. There are no paths, nor are there people who know how or where to make them. The climate is vile and the ground surface normally nearer the vertical than the horizontal. Such considerations make a fully equipped, tent-encumbered *safari* necessary for any worth-while investigation of the Blue Mountain country. We had not the time for this.

There are other difficulties in the way of investigating this reported cave. The Blue Mountains are rather extensive, and apparently riddled with caves. Then, too, there is the problem of the Maroons themselves, who alone are supposed to know where this cave is. But they won't talk!

All of this *may* go to show that the cave and its skeleton are myth rather than fact. There is nothing like natural obstacles for creating a good myth; at the same time, from the point of view of the zoologist this story presents a decidedly provocative question, namely, what might the skeleton be?

The suggestion that a prehistoric monster had lived in a Jamaican cave until recently seems absurd. Local suggestions of a large caiman are equally improbable. What appears much more probable is that the cave-deposits in the Blue Mountains contain well-preserved, semi-fossil bones of large, extinct, late-tertiary mammals, and that the discovery of one of these, along with evidence of much later Amerindian cave dwellings, prompted the superstitious Maroons to create the myth to explain the things seen. This explanation of the legend carries implications which are the real reason that I mention the matter at some length. Cave exploration by palæontologists might be exceedingly profitable in this area, which is one of igneous rock masses. Deposits on the floors of caves in such older rock formations might well contain remains of much earlier faunas than those of caves in the comparatively recent limestones that cover the greater part of the rest of the island.

It was the perennial question of this cave, coupled with our desire for some specimens of the coneys, that led us one brilliant morning to a magnificent green valley at the eastern end of the island which bore the noble name of Sherwood Forest.

We arrived over a bumpy road in our shiny car with a most charming and competent young man who knew "all about the people and the district." Having made a solid breakfast from our food basket, we set out with some trepidation upon alarmingly big mules for the ill-famed John Crow Mountains. The mules gave up before we did, and by eleven o'clock we were on foot and, shortly afterwards, on hands and knees. With us were three taciturn men and an uncertain number of doubtful-looking dogs. It was a very ordinary sort of hunt, marred only by one of the hunters' wearing throughout an immaculate straw hat with an old Etonian ribbon-band.

The general idea was to hunt coneys, which apparently live in hollow trees in the upper parts of these mountains—where, incidentally, there is no standing or running water, since the country rock is highly porous limestone. We didn't get far because the going was very bad, and I dislike excessive travel unless it is absolutely necessary. Of course, the hunters had looked forward to taking us for a very long walk, as hunters always do, but when one of them incautiously mentioned, quite early in the proceedings, that we were in good coney country, I called a halt. We got down to business, which consisted chiefly in the dogs' and the men's delving and probing into small trees that had holes around their bases.

The vegetation was very odd up there. The whole area was roofed with a more or less interlocking mass of the so-called mountain mangrove (*Clusia*), which has roundish, very decent-looking, clean, dark green leaves affording plenty of dappled shade. Needless to say, no coneys appeared, though the dogs worked overtime and made a furious pother. Something else did appear, however, and I still suffer acutely when I think of it, for it came out of a hole not three inches from my nose, went up the tree in leisurely fashion, and disappeared for ever.

It was a largish, very pale grey rat with a pure white underside and a tail that I still contend was white.

Once before I had had an almost identical encounter. It was in a dense thorn forest at the eastern edge of the plateau of Hinche in central Haiti. A similar rat suddenly popped out of a hole right into my face and, before I could do anything sensible, it jumped to the ground and shot off through a bed of small lilies and down a hole. Extensive trapping around that area resulted in the capture of some so-called black rats (the ordinary *Rattus rattus* fellow) which were grey above and white below. The capture of the latter, despite the colour similarity, failed to convince me that this was what I had seen. I have been even more dubious since this second encounter in Jamaica. I suppose it is merely that I have a rodent in my bonnet about there being as yet undescribed small mammals in the Antilles.

This disappointment rather spoilt my interest in this hunt, and we presently retraced our steps without having seen any coneys. On the way down, I reverted to the question of the monster's cave. Everybody confirmed the story, but there was no specific information forthcoming as to its whereabouts. We were asked whether we would care to see some other caves, and, having answered in the affirmative, altered our course and finally came out into a narrow, banana-choked valley, on the farther side of which we were presently shown a perfectly enormous cave.

In this we grubbed around in search of small life while the hunters threw stones at bats as I refused to permit the discharging of shotguns amid the crumbling limestone walls. One of the lads must have been a cricketer, for he clipped bats on the wing right and left, and soon brought me a handful. I turned them over casually to make sure that they were *Artibeus*, as we had imagined.

There is no need to make a fuss about what we found. Of course, both right and left ears of all of them were positively bristling with Round-Mouthed Ones. Operations were instantly renewed with quite fresh enthusiasm, and we carried on until all the bats had either been bagged or driven from the cave. We then set out for the village.

Arriving there, we found a very downcast-looking old gentleman seated on the running-board of our car. One hand held a bag and the other a dog with an expression only a little less dejected than his own. At our approach he opened the bag and extracted therefrom four coneys.

"Where did you get them?" we asked.

"I don't know; the dog gets them," he said. "He brings them home from somewhere hereabouts. Oh, you needn't go up into the hills for them," he added, staring fixedly at our erstwhile hunters.

"In fact," he went on in the florid Jamaican patois, which cannot be translated with any degree of fidelity, "my daughter has quite a lot of tame ones in her garden."

We quietly paid the price he asked and climbed into the car. We rewarded the alleged hunters, finished off the contents of the tea basket, and left as quickly as possible.

Collecting animals in the tropics need not be attended by crippling adventures or serious difficulties, provided one keeps away from one's fellow-men. Much valuable and useful zoological work, even elementary collecting, can be done in civilization's back yards and vacant lots, though it is undeniably more pleasant and much more romantic to carry out such enterprises beyond the confines of man-infested territory. Do not let it be supposed, though, that the latter is always so profitable.

It is certain, however, that the more opened-up be the area in which such activities are prosecuted, the more the collector's difficulties will increase and the more adventurous and complicated will his life become. Consider what our position would have been had this day's activities around Sherwood Forest been pursued in darkest South America.

We should not have required ready cash; we should have been home when we reached the spot occupied on this occasion by the shiny car; we should not have had the charming and competent young man who "knew all the people and the country"; we should have had on hand fluids and bottles and all our other equipment essential for preserving rare and precious specimens; we should have had fewer dogs and hunters; we might not have had the coneys, but we should probably have had the Round-Mouthed Ones. In short, we should have been very happily and comfortably situated and well fed by our own staff from our box of special delicacies and, upon such an auspicious occasion, probably have opened a treasured bottle to celebrate. As it was, and due solely to the so-called "blessings of civilization," we were in a very different position.

Actually we were some fifteen miles east of Morant Bay on the southeast coast of the over-populated and progressive colony. We

were in the dark both literally and figuratively, for the lighting system of the car had failed. We were rather wet because it was raining
and you can't fiddle effectively with a car from inside. We were
extremely hungry. We had no cigarettes or matches. Finally, we
had no prospect of any immediate improvement in our plight, for
the car would not budge even in the dark and there was an extraordinary dearth of late wayfarers on that road. As this narration is in
imminent danger of becoming a travelogue, suffice it to say that it
was after midnight when we finally reached Kingston, where we
were staying. Here the better face of man showed itself.

These *Sphærorhynchus* had by their timely appearance in no way
fulfilled their obligations to science. Oh, no! They were much too
important for that.

Amid the uproar about them in England, a persistent little technical melody had been heard that now rang very true. Several years
ago, we had had the good fortune to procure a number of the dismal
but priceless little arachnids known as *Podogona*. Their tale has
previously been told, and it was there mentioned that these little
beasts at first defied all efforts to carve them up into thin slices so that
their internal anatomy and histology could be studied under micro-
scopes. They were eventually sectioned, I believe, by someone
adopting the technique used for sectioning rock—which is to say, by
grinding them down. So hard were their outer coats, indeed, that
they not only defied the knife and the microtome but also proved
quite impervious to the infiltration of the alcohol in which they had
been immersed with a view to preservation. Thus, when they were
eventually opened up, they were found to be hollow because decomposition had proceeded unchecked within their impervious
husks.

To obviate this unhappy state of affairs in the future, methods
were devised whereby such small, precious, hard-skinned creatures
could be satisfactorily preserved for subsequent anatomical examination. A preservative that would enter the hard outer coats of these
animals was, after considerable experimentation, compounded from
several chemicals that possessed penetrative qualities of a high po-

tency. We carried only the formulæ for these, since we had had dire experience of travelling with already-mixed fluids in our cases.

True, many if not most arachnids, especially ticks and their ilk, can and will live for days, weeks, or even months without food, provided the atmospheric conditions are suitable. Live ticks have recently been sent on journeys of many weeks' duration, arranged in serried ranks upon damp sand. The dumb things just lay there and lived. We were not sure of *Sphærorhynchus*, however, there being no precedent to guide us and no information on its special predilections. And here we were in Kingston, after midnight, with a whole precious crop clinging to dead bats' ears in a candy jar that we had purchased from a Chinaman, and no fixatives.

I say humanity showed its better face that night and I truly mean it, for the chief dispenser at the hospital ungrumblingly left his bed and clambered about in his pharmacy in search of the essential ingredients. He helped me mix them and he timed the Round-Mouthed Ones as they floated slowly up and down in the various fixative fluids.

Most people, especially in the western hemisphere, know what a tick looks like: a very small, hard, squashed spider with a spike sticking out in front. *Sphærorhynchus* fits this description, but lacks the frontal spike. In fact, the whole front of the animal, where there should be a head, is only a large spherical hole opening downwards and slightly forwards. This is a powerful sucker, by which *Sphærorhynchus* clings to its unlucky host. When the creature is thus attached, the four pairs of pointed legs are not used at all, but stick up into the air so that the whole animal looks as if it had taken a headlong dive into the skin of its host and sunk in up to its neck. It proved much more difficult to pry these little creatures with their sucker mouths from the ears of the bats than to remove a large tick with its barbed spike from the thickest animal skin. Matters were further complicated by the small size of *Sphærorhynchus* and by the fact that one never knows whether he is dead or alive.

While on the host, they remain perfectly immobile; when removed, they either start running away with great rapidity or lie inert for hours. We left some of them attached to portions of a dead bat's ear to see whether they would eventually leave of their own volition. They did not, and we became rather bored with waiting, so we tried to stir them up, and were amazed to find that they were dead and brittle. This was three days after their bat host had died.

There was another point that interested us about these animals. They were all taken from only this one kind of bat, though there were other bats living in close proximity. The young and immature *Artibeus* were parasitized like their elders, but the *Sphærorhynchus* on them were invariably immature themselves, being six- instead of eight-legged, and paler, pinkish-brown in colour. Most of the bats bore more than one parasite, and in one instance there were no less than twenty-seven in and about one ear and thirteen on the other ear. We never found any adhering to any other part of the bats' bodies.

When the last lot had been safely transferred to the final preservative, we repaired to our hotel and indulged in a round meal and a bath. Then we had to turn our attention to the coneys, because they were unmistakably making their presence known. There was nothing to do but forgo sleep and set to work skinning them.

The Jamaican coneys are well known to science but probably beyond the ken of anyone else. Certainly it seems that even the majority of Jamaicans are very hazy as to what they are or what they look like. These rodents are neither rats nor rabbits, but belong to the porcupine group. Their nearest relatives are the South American coypu (*Myocastor coypu*) and a bloated, tailless, rat-like creature in Africa called *Thyronomys swinderianus* or, more appropriately, the "Cutting-grass." These creatures, together with other groups of equally ordinary-looking beasts bearing even more extraordinary names, make up a "family" called the *Octodontidæ*, of equal importance and coming next in the scheme of life to the guinea pigs.

The little animals themselves are rather delightful. They have round, fat, hunched little bodies about the size of rabbits, being fourteen inches long. Their heads are rat-shaped but rather deep,

JAMAICAN CONEYS (*Geocapromys brownii*)

and the face wears a disdainful expression. The tail is at the most an inch and a half long and rather unnecessary. The animals walk flat on their feet and the ears are small and pressed close to the head. In colour they are a drab olive-brown, and the fur is short, hard, and brindled. The underside is a yellowish grey. Their tummies are squashy and usually bloated with the barks, leaves, and other vegetable food that they crowd into them by the pint. Internally the stomachs are worthy of note, being divided into three compartments. Their teeth are what get zoologists really steamed up, but this need not concern us beyond an assurance that they are very complex—which we are sorely tempted to say merely indicates specialization in diet.

In habits they do not appear to be very outstanding. They make nests in shallow holes in or under trees. They bear litters of six to eight helpless but well-haired young. They appear to have no fixed breeding season, though there are a great many small immature yet independent animals in late August and September. They apparently can climb some trees, with difficulty, but prefer to dash about the ground in a kind of headlong skelter.

Our interest in them would doubtless have been greater had we had the time to live in their territory and watch them at their daily life. As it was, we desired only a few specimens for preservation. This done, we turned to other matters.

OTHER ANTILLEAN
ODDITIES

Haitian Wild Horses, Worms to the Power of Two,
and Lizard Conundrums

ON returning from our trip to Sherwood Forest, we found a
wire from Fred saying that he was coming back because
he had been so completely unsuccessful in his attempts to
obtain a specimen of the Haitian wild horse that he did not consider
further expenditure on the enterprise worth while. This was a bitter
disappointment. We went off to meet the plane in one of the lower
stages of despondency.

Fred, however, stepped aground looking aggressively cheerful
and self-important. This suited the circumstances so poorly that it
was fortunate he was kept behind a customs barrier for some time.
I felt like being very rude indeed. When he finally got through, our
greetings were rather formal. We at once began firing questions at
him. He hedged by recounting the innumerable difficulties that he
had run into, so we silenced him and proceeded to recount our
successes with the Round-Mouthed Ones and the coneys.

Then we were distracted by a pother which arose on the plane.
Two white-overalled members of the ground staff were atop the
fuselage struggling with a vast package at the baggage door. They
heaved mightily, the bundle came free, and we returned to our
diatribe.

34

"Mr. Allsop," bawled the airport clerk, "check express, please." Fred bolted to answer the summons.

After a long delay he reappeared, staggering under the shapeless and vast brown paper package that we had seen hauled from the plane.

"One Haitian wild horse; male; skin, skull, and skeleton," he announced, plonking the load at our feet.

This time we *did* have the special dinner and the bottle. Nor was that all, for Fred had much to tell.

It appeared that through the kindness and interest of the Haitian authorities, who are most progressive in such matters, Fred had been permitted to borrow an army rifle and the services of two members of the Haitian Guard who were acquainted with the high pine forests where the horses dwell. Fred himself already knew the locale well, for we had camped there for some weeks on our previous visit. After various preliminaries had been arranged in Port-au-Prince, he had set off in that light-hearted way which one tends to adopt under tropic skies. He established his base at the home of the agricultural officer at Savanne Zombie, a settlement for repatriated refugees from the Santo Domingo border, on the south side of the Morne La Selle range, which was the nearest accessible point to the rather limited area which the horses were known to inhabit.

Fred's efforts to obtain a specimen lasted three weeks and were fraught with difficulties. His story was as follows.

Knowing the topography of the highland plateau between the peaks of Morne La Selle and Mont Commissar, where we had previously encountered the horses, he set out the first morning after his arrival accompanied by a guard armed with an army rifle and a largish boy bearing a similar weapon for his own use.

The party soon reached a wide valley in which the horses used to graze almost every morning and evening, but they found that this place had recently been cleared by a ground fire and was without cover. There were no horses, so the party scaled the next ridge and descended into a gully full of pine seedlings. After this Fred's narrative becomes somewhat foggy. It began to rain sometime in the

afternoon and they finally returned to Savanne Zombie late the following afternoon.

In no way daunted, my dogged colleague set out the next day in
a truck and, with what must be regarded as characteristic British
unemotionalism, entered the forest by the same path with the same
guard and the same boy. Again they had no luck, but this time they
got back to Savanne Zombie at nine-thirty p.m. on the same day.

Quite undeterred by these and subsequent failures, the amazing
fellow continued in this wise for the next ten days, arriving home in
ever-shorter time and with greater assurance each day—but always
without seeing a horse. By this time he had covered all the country
to the west of the only road. He then turned his attention to the east
side.

On the first day he was rewarded by encountering a herd of
horses, but they were of all colours and shapes, being merely a
chance aggregation of ordinary feral animals. Returning home the
next day, he was met by a very enthusiastic lad from a two-man
settlement called The Refuge, which was situated on the far side of
the mountains to the north. This fellow said that he had seen the wild
horses in an open grass savannah. Fred promptly set out and spent a
good part of the moonlit night—as far as I could make out—looking
for the horses and then trying to locate the two-man settlement. In
both respects he was unsuccessful, and reached home the following
day after locating the road and being given a lift on a truck.

My respected assistant certainly lacked nothing in determination,
for even the fact that he found he had to return the hundred-odd
miles to Port-au-Prince did not deter him. After three days at the
capital, his host was returning to the pine forest, so back he went,
this time bearing permission to ask assistance from the members
of the Garde d'Haïti actually stationed within the boundaries of
the forest itself. This apparently did the trick.

The very next day, accompanied by two of these guards, he
set out upon a hunt the course of which he tried to trace for me
upon a map with the aid of salient points that we both knew. The

area he covered, and the distance he travelled back and forth within that area, appear to have been stupendous. Fred's enthusiasm was further aroused, if that were possible, by seeing a group of seven of the wild horses early in the morning at the edge of a grass swamp, the only place where anything approaching water is to be found on that whole plateau. They made off in the silent and extraordinarily oily manner which we had noted before. He tried to track them, but the ground soon became too firm to show spoor.

Fred then divided his forces. He and one guard went to one side, the other guard and the faithful boy (who had proved himself little less determined than Fred) to the other. They portioned out the area and kept up the hunt all day. At about four o'clock both parties, unknown to each other, spotted the same group of three wild horses. Both crept up on a stallion that was grazing somewhat apart on a small knoll. Guard Number Two, accompanied by the boy, let go first and, like most Haitians, being a very fair shot, closely missed the heart and hit the animal in the forequarters. He had been instructed to avoid damaging the head. It so happened that Guard Number One was standing on the opposite side, almost exactly in the line of fire, endeavouring to simulate a dead pine sapling as he had a look round. He naturally fell flat and let out a yell.

Fred, who was lying some way off, thought the guard had been hit, and jumped up. He was met by a positive fusillade from a third and quite unexpected quarter. Thereupon he also fell flat, and at the same instant the boy and the guard who had first shot jumped up. Instantly another fusillade broke out and they too went down into the grass yelling. Fred tells me that he was convinced that they had blundered upon an advance guard of Santo Domingans intent upon invading Haiti. The other two horses had in the meantime fled. Their going was accompanied by further sporadic firing. Then silence reigned.

After due pause for reconnoitring, the four original hunters crawled towards each other and allayed their respective fears about homicide and so forth. Then they *all* started yelling. There were answering shouts, and soon a diminutive figure came gallivanting through the grass brandishing a rifle and shouting, "*M'tué li!*" It was manifestly not a Santo Domingan advance patrol.

Having cross-questioned this lone marksman, they discovered that he was a Port-au-Prince taxi-driver who by some typically inexplicable Haitian means happened to be in Savanne Zombie and, hearing that a horse-hunt was in progress, had borrowed a rifle from a brother who was in the Guard and set out to bag the trophy. By one of those coincidences that are so likely to occur when loaded firearms are about, all three "*safaris*" had reached the same point, spotted the same herd of horses, and singled out the same individual upon which to draw a bead at the same instant. By good fortune, the best marksman had fired first, otherwise there would have been no specimen except perhaps one fit for a coroner's inquest.

As Fred observed, there is just nothing to be done about such incidents in Haiti. You ask the taxi-driver how he got there and he answers, "*M'pas connais*"; you ask him why he got there and get the same answer; you call him every kind of an idiot and he is as likely as not to grin broadly, bow elegantly, and affirm, "*Mais évidemment, monsieur,*" in his very best throaty French.

Now here was Fred in some ill-defined part of the pine forest two hours before sundown with a very important specimen of no mean dimensions, two men and a boy, and a grinning menace. It was a Thursday evening and he had already booked passage on the plane leaving Haiti the following Monday morning, having wired me that he could not get the horse.

However, the party turned to and did a very commendable job, in which the chauffeur-sharpshooter co-operated heartily. They skinned the animal, severing the neck and lower portions of the limbs and leaving them in the skin, then gutted and partly cleaned the carcass, placing piles of meat and guts around to attract and, if possible, keep occupied for the night, the many semi-wild dogs that roam this strange, cold, tropical country. They then slung the skeleton in one piece from the tallest tree they could climb and finally achieved the crowning glory of finding their way home.

The rest of Fred's story smacked rather overmuch of a travelogue to repeat here. Suffice it to add that they somehow got the skin and skeleton so well dried and prepared that it altogether lacked odour on reaching Jamaica three days later and was suitable for immediate packing. We treasure the invoice handed out by the airline. It states: "Express package; one horse in paper. Personal effect. Freight $5.75."

Dinner over, we stretched out the skin of the horse in our hotel bedroom. It was the first close view that we had had of one of these remarkable animals.

We were naturally somewhat disappointed upon discovering that it had neither three toes nor anything else that we could spot as being definitely primitive or different from other ordinary horses. We had almost persuaded ourselves during the two years that we had waited and hoped to obtain a specimen that this would turn out to be a living example of *Protohippus* or some other equally fantastic type of extinct ancestral American horse.

Such speculation, moreover, need not be regarded as quite so silly as it sounds, for there are several matters needing explanation about these animals. To reiterate: although groups of completely feral horses are found in the Haitian pine forests, they do not appear to interbreed with the peculiar pinkish-grey animals of which we now had an example. The feral herds are of all shapes, colours, and sizes whereas these are all identical in colour and form. Feral and even domesticated horses are mortally terrified of the true wild groups, which attack them on sight, without provocation, and with surprising ferocity.

Secondly, there is a body of evidence both from the mainland of Central America and even from rock drawings in Haiti itself tending to show that the horse may have been known to man in the Americas before the coming of the Spaniards. There is, of course, abundant fossil evidence of horse-like creatures in tertiary deposits in the Americas, but it had been supposed that the whole group had completely died out even before the advent of earliest man in the western hemisphere. This may have been true in North America, but is it not conceivable that isolated small populations of horses or horse-like animals continued to exist until much later times in out-lying corners of the two continents where conditions were suitable to their requirements and where they were free from whatever animal foes or parasitic diseases caused their extermination else-where?

The pine forests of Haiti might be just such a spot, for there is geological evidence to show that the block of land which now forms the southern half of Hispaniola was in lower middle miocene times a peninsula connected with Jamaica and thence with the mainland. These pine forests have a temperate climate and were once much more extensive. It appears that the original Amerindian indigenes of Hispaniola were not numerous and probably did not dwell in these forests, more especially as there is no standing or running water within their boundaries. The arrival of the colonists with their multi-tudinous slaves from the Old World resulted in the conditions ob-taining today in Haiti, where every bit of habitable land supports a family. The only places not so affected are the pine forests on the summits of the southern range and some similar areas in the centre of the island about the border between Haiti and Santo Domingo. These areas have never been inhabited nor have they been exploited commercially in any way. Their fauna has been unmolested.

Having reported the presence of these wild horses to scientists at home well qualified to give an opinion as to whether they might be remnants of original American stocks, and having been encouraged rather than squelched, we had determined to get some concrete evidence. Now we had the evidence before us.

I would not for a moment pretend to sufficient anatomical, osteo-logical, or even general knowledge to have determined from the examination we could then make whether this specimen displayed any sufficiently primitive or unusual characters to warrant a state-ment upon its ancestry or affinities. But it was certainly an unusual-looking horse.

The general colour of the coat was pinkish-brown interspersed with silvery-grey hairs. On the neck the grey predominated, while

HAITIAN WILD HORSES

on that side covered by the mane it was nearly twice as light. The head was slightly darker than the neck but lighter than the body, and a dull white dagger-shaped mark extended from between the eyes to the muzzle, occupying a median position. The mane was silvery-grey with rich reddish-brown hairs basally, but became entirely dark rich brown terminally. The lower flanks and a wide band across the chest were a light reddish-brown. The limbs were as the dorsal surfaces, but the lower limbs became grey which rapidly darkened to black. There were small, short-furred, dirty-white socks on all the feet. The tail, which was so long as to reach the ground, was a medium silvery-grey turning almost black terminally.

The skeleton has now been examined by experts, and we hear that it is an ordinary horse from the technical viewpoint but notably slender in its bony structure—which is interesting, because this animal, like all its brethren, was so fat in life that Fred had at first thought it was a pregnant female.

Fred's efforts had therefore resulted in something quite contrary to the disappointment he had prepared us for. The second two-year-old query had been cleared up and the third item in our hunt for widespread treasure trove was in the bag. Other booty soon came to hand.

We went up to investigate the forests on the Blue Mountains of Jamaica at higher altitudes above a delightful and quite preposterous botanical garden at a place called Cinchona. This used to be the headquarters of the Agricultural Department, where the staff resided in comfortable cottage quarters amid the imported gum trees, flowering shrubs, quinine bushes, and early morning mists some five thousand feet above and twenty-one miles distant from all the active life of the rest of the colony. It was evident here that things used to be done in style in the old days, and that many departments were apparently run for the benefit of their principal executives, who came out from England, rather than for the betterment of the colony. Since the abandonment of cinchona cultivation (because of the collapse of the price of quinine when its production became dominated by the East Indian Dutch), this beautiful place has become a local resort for the few active people who will bother to climb up to it. The gardens and unique collection of plants and trees have been well tended for years, and the cottages recently repaired, so that a more delightful spot could not be found in the western tropics.

Some thousand feet above and three miles distant from this place, a type of forest or flora peculiar to the Antilles may be encountered. This growth of gnarled, twisted trees and feathery tree-ferns shrouded in mist is the island representative of the "mist forest" of all higher tropical mountains. Its fauna has not been fully or adequately examined. Although we knew well enough that we could not hope to rectify this on the present occasion, we nevertheless decided to risk irresistible temptations by making a brief excursion into the region. This proved to be well worth the doing and was where we received a considerable jolt.

The prevailing, moisture-carrying winds are from the north of the island, so that the northern slope of the mountains is the damper. This is very noticeable at the point known as Morce's Gap, which we visited. Approaching it from the south slope, one passes through tall scrub comprising giant heathers and other well-known forms requiring moderate but not excessive moisture. Stepping over the watershed—literally—one immediately enters a sombre, misty, moisture-laden world of gnarled trees, festooned with mosses and lichens and loaded down with epiphytes, bromeliads, and ferns. The soil also changes immediately to deep, soft, sodden, reddish loam. Magnificent tree-ferns spread their heads everywhere and the ground is rank with mosses.

Zoologically speaking, the first impression is that of entering a strange, dark aviary. Quite new bird-calls sound from all sides, and there is a difference even in the dripping silence of the whole place. We had spent some days collecting the lizards and small whistling frogs (*Eleutherodactylus*) on the drier side at and above Cinchona. Now we fairly dived into the mossy, boulder-strewn torrent beds and deep-mould-covered banks in search of small life and bent primarily upon gathering as much evidence as possible of the zoological dissimilarity between the two vegetational zones.

We found plenty. The small frogs were of a different species; the only lizard we captured was of a type we had never seen in Jamaica before, and all the invertebrates were entirely new to us. It was, moreover, while making the first exciting search that we brought to light the singularly obscure animals that gave us the jolt.

In a clay loam under large stones on the steep mountainside we found a number of big, stout earthworms, iridescent bluish-green in colour on the back, mauvish-grey below. We take considerable trouble over earthworms, because we have found that their study is of great use to soil experts and agriculturists generally; therefore, since these were altogether different from any species collected in the drier zones, we gathered them up.

Earthworms are normally covered by slimy, clear mucus. These were no exception, and much of it stuck to my hands. I had popped the worms into a small bottle and was about to wipe off the mucus when, to my amazement, a small blob of it on my thumb slowly began to rise at one end. It took me some seconds to realize what was happening, and several minutes to decide what to do, as I had no lens with me. The blob continued to rise majestically. The light was very dim in this tangled forest so, in order to get a better view of this phenomenon, I had to scramble back to the path, which was more open. There I made a further examination, probing the small mass with a pair of forceps.

Imagine my surprise when I detached a small, oblong, transparent, flat, animated object and found that there were more adhering to my fingers. These things were obviously tiny flatworms, i.e., creatures belonging to the group known as Platyhelminthes which contains the well-known *Planaria*. I then turned my attention to the captive earthworms.

On each of these, except the specimen I had handled last, I discovered two parasitic—or should we call them epiphytic?—flatworms. Upon the last specimen there were, in addition to the two parasites, some dozen smaller ones. I showed my find to Alma and we set to work getting more earthworms. We collected seventeen, eight of which bore a pair of the parasites each.

These external parasites were normally about eight millimetres long, but could contract or elongate themselves to a considerable extent. The young ones were less than half this size, and much more active. They glided about the surface of their smooth, slippery hosts like transparent ghosts. They moved all over the worms and were very tenacious, being completely flat and more or less edgeless. Removed from their normal environment, they lived for several hours but gradually shrivelled up, first becoming smaller and smaller and finally drying up with a rush quite regardless of the humidity of the air in the container in which they were kept. A surprising fact we noted was that they immediately fell off their hosts if sprinkled with water or totally submerged. Yet the soil from which we collected the earthworms was completely sodden and must often have been flooded during the downpours that are a regular feature of this habitat.

Such obscure creatures are by no means unknown to science, but somehow encountering them for oneself conjures up multitudinous speculations of a highly philosophical albeit an impractical variety. Why is it that men must seek reasons and uses for everything in nature? Yet is there anything in this wide world for which at least an excuse cannot be found? (Having read that, you will understand why I speak of such speculations as being impractical!)

Nothing would ever convince me that there can be any place on earth which does not provide almost unlimited scope for zoological investigation. The more closely you look into the small life of any locale, the more you find that is not only of academic interest, but also of a nature worthy of non-technical record and is, furthermore, provocative of serious thought. I seem to remember having myself made the puerile remark that Jamaica was already too well "collected" to warrant its choice as a field for a zoological expedition. It is true enough that no expedition is needed; all that's necessary is time and enthusiasm and residence on the island. I have mentioned somewhere that a certain eminent conchologist retired to this country and ended up by collecting 564 species and sub-species of land snails from its 4450 square miles of territory and even then admitted the job was uncompleted!

There are zoological goings-on even in the most thickly populated parts of Jamaica that are worthy of investigation and that may upset certain of our basic concepts of animal life quite radically. It is not really my business to go into these matters, especially since they are still mainly in the theoretical stage and were brought to my notice by Mr. C. Bernard Lewis, the Curator of the Jamaica Institute Museum. We have, however, become entangled in this business through the chance circumstance that we have spent much time during the past three years collecting and working upon another aspect of the same problem. In fact, it is of the very essence of our work.

To be more specific, the commonest group of lizards inhabiting the Antilles is that containing the innumerable species of the genus *Anolis* which belongs to the iguanid group of saurians. I should not like to hazard a guess as to how many species and sub-species of this genus have been described from the islands of the West Indies. Every year there is a new rash of them. However that may be, these dainty little lizards are incredibly plentiful both in mere numbers and in distinct forms. Furthermore, many of the forms display a huge range of colour variation, which in some cases is more or less permanent while in others it occurs swiftly by chameleonism such as was noted in the brown blotching of the *Anolis garmani* above.

The study of these colour variations and their causes has kept us busy whenever the lizards have been to hand. Among other things, we have ourselves noted what others have already recorded, namely, that although any given species has a definite possible range of coats, as regards both colours and patterns, populations of this species in different areas often prefer their own particular colour phase or pattern for normal wear. This choice may differ considerably from that of another population only a few miles distant, and yet both lots will adopt identical appearance if required or prompted to do so by similar influences.

The matter became bewildering when we came upon populations of one clearly defined species clad, temporarily, in coats that exactly matched certain colour phases of quite another species— or at least technically so called. In fact, by grappling with such conundrums, we went around almost the entire eastern half of the island of Jamaica along the coastal plain, tracing the colour phases of one lizard *species* into that of the next and thence, via other phases of that one, to a third, and so on. Having got from Kingston, which is on the southern coast towards the eastern end of the island, right around the eastern tip to Ocho Rios, on the northern coast, at a point due north of Kingston, we found we were among the fourth so-called *species* of *Anolis*. We then collected across the island back to Kingston as nearly as possible along the supposed line of the crow's flight, which seemed to fool not only accepted systematic zoology and ourselves but also the lizards.

Discussing our findings with Mr. Lewis, we were delighted to learn that he had carried out similar investigations on the Cayman Islands with similar results. But a disturbing fact then emerged. Mr. Lewis pointed out that published descriptions of certain lizards that he knew well in life were obviously based on preserved material, in which state the animals had adopted one of the less common of their colour coats. In fact, following colour descriptions alone, these lizards could be identified only if one had studied and was conversant with the more unusual colour coats of the animals. There are even worse complications. Some of the *rarer* colour phases in old descriptions seem to fit the normal phases of *other* species today, although there can be little doubt which animals were being described, as shown by the other more permanent features of form, scales, etc.

This business, which is a regular zoologist's brain-teaser, you will perceive means something rather disturbing. It means, in fact, that local animal populations can change within relatively brief periods and that, while doing so, colour features by which they were originally defined may become simply "unfashionable" or may even appear as characteristics of other related so-called species which are themselves similarly changing. It is even more distressing to contemplate the possibility of these related species' changing at different speeds or perhaps not at all.

How are we ever going to pin down for purposes of colour description animals that behave like this unless we keep them under constant surveillance? What strange developments may not be going on behind the backs of zoologists in little-visited places, and how much of this sort of thing is going on among other creatures less noticeable than gaily coloured lizards? Are there not also economic implications in such possibilities?

The whole matter is undoubtedly of the smallest importance except to ourselves, who alone are to blame for choosing just this question as a principal feature of our life-work!

Part Two

AND BRITISH HONDURAS

LOW LIFE AROUND BELIZE

The Fauna of Cays, Urban Animals,
and Toad Parasites

A SHIP'S approach to a new coast, more particularly in the tropics, is always inestimably thrilling. The sensation is enhanced if it is one's first visit to the particular shore. If, in addition, one happens to be a zoologist, a tremendous eagerness is added to the general excitement. Our approach to British Honduras, however, was somewhat impaired by a curtain of fine Scotch mist speckled with innumerable pelicans, distinctly reminiscent of the effects of acute liver disorders.

We were rather distressed, for Belize, the capital and port for which we were heading, was for us a romantic name that we had long ago gazed hopefully upon in maps, together with Calabar and Macassar. Nobody had been able to give us any concrete description of this place, and we were very eager to see it from the sea, lest occasion to do so later should not arise. The British, through some unerring faculty that must surely be hereditary, have almost without exception chosen damp, mist-enshrouded mud-flats upon which to situate the principal towns of their colonies. Kingston, Georgetown, Bathurst, Lagos, Singapore—the list is interminable, and Belize proved no exception. We suspected it even before the mist lifted.

As a matter of fact, this mist was so sodden that it fell rather than lifted, and our first view of the country was therefore unusually striking. Without warning the pale grey curtain dropped on the port beam and, behold, the land appeared up in the sky.

This skyline consisted of a very long row of low, uneven, abrupt humps, which looked for all the world as if the lower mandible of a gigantic crocodile had been laid along the horizon. The day was utterly colourless, and these bluntly sharp protuberances glowed with the cold light that is sometimes seen upon drenched oilskins. The mirror-like surface of the sea melted imperceptibly into the white mist out of which this distant apparition emerged like a mirage. The hard white sky above was formless and depthless.

After some gentle steaming, the mist rose again and the long, denticulate skyline disappeared. Instead, pancake-shaped islands materialized ahead. These seemed to float towards us, then pause, and finally drift away aft. The pelicans became more numerous and it began to rain. We went below for lunch.

When we came on deck again, the islands were still gliding by, but the mist had dissolved. The long rank of toothy hills now lay far astern, while ahead stretched an interminable, very thin line bisecting white sky from white sea. This was broken at only one point by two vertical black strokes, at a distance sufficient to make them appear considerably smaller than matchsticks. Somebody pointed these out and commented simply: "Belize."

Belize is indeed built on a mud-flat; in fact, so flat and so muddy is it that it averages a foot above sea level. The town itself is also rather flat, with the exception of the two vertical radio masts, but do not suppose for a moment that it is invariably shrouded in Britannic mists. We had our next view from the sea about a week later. We were tossing jauntily about in a sturdy and competent small craft under a cloudless sky which was intensely blue in the east and suffused with gold and pink and all the rest of the hot end of the spectrum in the west. We were whaling.

While awaiting the tender to take us off the small liner on which we had arrived in this land of promise we had been greatly stirred to see four sleek bodies suddenly roll out of the still and shining waters, blow stentoriously, and then roll on into the great underneath once more. They were so close that there was no doubt about our pre-liminary identification. They were bottle-nosed dolphins of some species, and we determined there and then to have the skeleton of at least one and we wasted no time in getting round to this once we were ashore.

Thus it came about that we had congregated a motley crew of locals connected with the hire of a motorboat, with its engines, with the construction, furnishing, and employment of harpoons, with the simple business of helping and with that ill-defined but ever-recurring tropical phenomenon of just "coming look-see." We were quite a company all told, for some friends had come along into the bargain. We set out into the muddy sea and proceeded to cruise back and forth where we had seen the dolphins disporting them-selves.

Naturally, this signalled the immediate disappearance of these marine mammals from those points. We therefore took the various advices of boatmen, enginemen, harpooners, helpers, and friends and cruised in other localities each evening for a week, covering a re-markable nautical mileage. We caught many beautiful fish, mostly of the streamlined variety known locally as mackerel; we bathed on two occasions in safe places and we saw a wonderful parade of sun-sets. We also got a good suntan. Then we decided to stop this non-sense and get on with the work on shore.

To round off this story, certain interludes that occurred through-out the next month must be condensed. We availed ourselves of every opportunity of putting to sea from this delightful colony, which is really a marine settlement in a truer sense than are many islands. We went sailing, we went fishing, we went to visit the cays, and we went out upon more seriously zoological errands. The ob-jects were as diverse as the bottoms in which we sailed, yet they all complied with a single law. Simply stated, this was that if harpoons were taken along, dolphins, porpoises, and all other kinds of whales were absent; if they were not taken, bottle-nosed dolphins preceded, swam parallel to, or followed the craft for at least a third of the cruising distance. We did not obtain a specimen.

The northern half of British Honduras is composed of parallel subdued ridges with subdued depressions between them. Actually the land surface is quite flat, the ridges being noticeable only by reason of the differences of soil and vegetation. These ridges and the intervening gullies run parallel to the present seacoast and continue into and under the sea. They are, in fact, the backbones of old coral reefs. At the present day the seacoast proper lies just a little to seaward of one of these reefs. Mangroves, rivers, and the rain on the one hand, and the wind, various animals, and ocean currents on the other are still busily employed today, as in ages past, in adding to this coastline.

The result will probably be that these inexorable natural processes will in time fill in with low, muddy land the next shallow trough, upon which these operations have already begun, and so engulf the next ridge, which at the present time consists of a nearly continuous string of mangrove-covered islands lying a few miles off shore—if pieces of land about three inches below sea level can be rightly called islands. We have been unable to ascertain whether these islands are known locally as "cays," but those formed by the next ridge, which appears above the surface of the waters only very tentatively from time to time, certainly are. The few small islands on this second ridge to seaward are variously written "cays," "cuays," "quays," or even "keys."

At an almost equal distance beyond these again there is a third ridge which may be traced for hundreds of miles north and south. Opposite Belize it is represented by a sprawling mass of muddy islands appearing on a map like a giant's footprint and known as Turneffe. To the north this ridge gives rise to the Banco Chinchorro and Cozumel Island off the coast of Mexican Quintana Roo. Beyond this is a fourth, for the most part submerged, and beyond that is still another one even more deeply submerged.

During our whaling expeditions we visited several of the first line of mangrove-covered islands and also some of the minute sandy cays on the ridge beyond. On both there was a considerable fauna, not only littoral-marine but also purely terrestrial. We enumerated the land fauna of one small cay—not very scientifically, I fear, for we embarked upon it only because we spent some hours of unavoidable confinement on the three-hundred-foot blob of sand with nothing else to do. The results, nevertheless, were rather unexpected.

First, we got two mammals in the form of introduced house mice. The birds consisted of three humming-birds, a motmot, a pair of minute black-and-white finches, and two little vivid golden tree-birds. There was one very windswept turkey-vulture. Among reptiles there were lizards of three species: a large gecko in cracks in the coconut palms, a small brown *Anolis*, and iguanas. We found one toad under a water butt. In addition we collected three species of land snails, at least four of centipedes and millepedes, woodlice—apart from many crabs that were only partly terrestrial—representing the Crustacea, two earthworms, twenty-four species of spiders, and insects of more species than we could count, as we had no method of confining or killing them so that they could be laid out and compared. This tiny sandy island, upon which grew only seventy-nine coconut palms, two large and thirty-four small bushes, and a bed of creeping herbs, was thus supporting a life of quite considerable profusion and abundance. Yet it is on record that this islet, along with most of the other cays and islands, was swept clean by the hurricane of 1931!

It would seem unwise to state that this varied fauna arrived on this small cay by means of floating logs and coconuts, for although there are many such objects drifting in these seas, the journeying of mice by such means is hard to conceive. The same goes for toads, yet they cannot suddenly appear out of thin air. Also, one may be led to wonder what possible good one toad could do to nature or itself majestically squatting on a three-hundred-foot desert island, however paradisaical. Perhaps there were other toads deeply hidden in crab holes; if so, I for one would like to know how long they have been there, whether they breed, and whether they can survive a hurricane.

Though the face of Belize is turned so steadfastly towards the sea, the principal part of our work lay, or was supposed to lie, to land-

ward. Therefore we had to turn our backs upon the lively blue
waters that swished and slopped over the coral reefs against the
sandy isles. We always find it difficult to turn our backs to any sea,
and the cay-girt Caribbean on the coast of Honduras is one of the
most frivolous and interesting waters that have ever tempted us.

Our first days at Belize were a busy time. Apart from the gay but
unsuccessful whaling expeditions and the visits to the cays that occupied many evenings, we pushed forward with two other routine
matters. First, we had to unpack our heavy gear and knock it into
shape for future more extensive and less civilized travels. This need
not detain us, but the other matter must.

The initial period in any new country is of the utmost importance
to us not only because it is employed in getting to know about
local conditions, learning the native names and prices of animals,
hiring a staff, training a skinner, and preparing one's equipment.
Coincident with such preparatory activities, we devote much time
to actual collecting of the common animal life, especially the fauna
of those districts that have been longest opened up by cultivation
and even of the town itself.

Animals that are seen every day in the meat market or in gardens
and ditches in the urban area might be considered of negligible interest to science, and yet these very creatures are often the key to
much that will later be encountered in the wilds. Time and time
again we have made collections of such animals, only to discover
to our surprise on getting home that our specimens are of the utmost
value. The commoner the animal, the more likely it seems to be that
it will turn out to have been overlooked and so be unrepresented in
collections.

A short while ago, for example, some tremendously enthusiastic
scientists arrived in London from a certain Baltic state. They descended upon the British Museum with wide eyes, continental enthusiasm, and an overwhelming desire to study the seasonal variations in English dormice. An unusual but none the less ardent wish,
since these gentlemen had got the dormice of practically every other
country in Europe "taped," down to the very last variation. They

were let loose in our national home of zoological science, which contains by far the most extensive and complete collection of rodents in the world, comprising nobody knows how many thousand specimens from every quarter of the globe. Unfortunately, however, the Baltic gentlemen were unable to find there any worthwhile specimens of British dormice, though they did discover three totally unknown varieties from other countries!

Our procedure in regard to this matter is as follows. Upon arrival, we divide our forces and start poking around, avoiding, as far as possible, disturbing the residents. This is not easy, for although a stranger on the plea of tourism may several times invade the meat market, where many animals are found, without exciting undue comment, fishing in people's water tanks and drains calls for ready answers and prompt explanations. These are two of our principal occupations. Others are to prowl around back yards with torches at night and to gain admission to all barns, warehouses, and church steeples. Our object is to gather concrete examples of all the wild life of the place, which can then be shown to enthusiastic amateurs.

I have remarked upon the willingness of humanity as a whole to co-operate with zoologists. This singular human trait, though an inestimable boon, can also be rather troublesome. This becomes apparent immediately your zoologist arrives in a new country and usually occurs somewhat as follows.

An eager personage of somewhat doubtful mien presents himself at the back door of the domain of the new arrival. He asks permission to speak with the master, and is duly ushered in, since strict instructions have been given that nobody is to be turned away. The caller then opens the conversation in a self-assured but rather conspiratorial manner, somewhat like this:

"I hear in the town that you will purchase animals."

"Yes, that is so," you reply, adding, if adept, "but only certain ones."

This usually scores a point, but your advantage is only temporary, as the visitor continues:

"What ones? Because I will bring you all kind of animals."

To this you either explain in detail or present a written list, though both are useless because there is no way of finding out the local names of animals before you have been in the new country some time.

"Ah," says the visitor, picking at random upon any animal you have mentioned the name of which he can pronounce, "there are many of those. I will bring you many. How many do you want?"

"Well," you answer, "you see, that's rather a common thing and I want only a few and can't pay much for them."

"But," says the visitor with much cunning, "we have two kinds here, a black one and a white one."

"Really! That's strange," you reply, having just remembered that the animal in question has not been recorded from this country at all.

"Which would you like?" you are asked. "One is much harder to get than the other."

"Which one?" you come back, and the reply, I find, is invariably the same, namely, the black one. This probably has something to do with psychology.

"Well, look," you say, perceiving that the whole interview begins to lack reality, "you just bring me anything you get."

"How much will you pay?" is the prompt query.

"All different prices according to what the animal is," you rejoin, if wise.

Then the visitor, if really dangerous, breaks down completely and evinces tremendous interest in natural history. He displays, withal, considerable knowledge of the local fauna, describing several animals with great clarity and precision. Your hopes rise; promises are made on both sides; a list of animals is drawn up; enthusiasm runs high; a monetary advance is sought and refused; and finally a time is fixed on the next day for the delivery of a specified number of particular animals. The visitor accepts a cigarette and takes his departure with politeness and business-like alacrity.

Three weeks later you obtain the first specimen of the first species on the list—but not from your visitor. You either buy it in the meat market or get it from one of your own traps. In the interval you have said about eighteen good-mornings and half a dozen good-nights to the said visitor in the streets of the town.

This problem became a little worse than usual in Belize, but not because the locals were unusually over-optimistic or unreliable, for they very definitely were not; it was rather because of three small boys with exceptional business abilities. These young persons actually fulfilled their promises so well that we came to a working agreement with them—an agreement that finally involved us in quite high finance. As a result we got into a nasty jam on two or three occasions when our rooms were literally groaning with imprisoned beasts not in ones and twos, but in hundreds. We erected large tables below the house and there worked furiously amid a welter of tanks, jars, hypodermics, catalogues, and what-not.

In the middle of all this, an old lady appeared carrying a huge, dilapidated cardboard box. From this box arose a cacophony of squeaks. It was brim-full of bats. How many there were we will never know, for while we were getting them out, countless numbers flew away. Those at the bottom were squashed flat. The old lady accepted our price stoically and departed, leaving us with another hundred-odd specimens on our hands.

In due course Fred laid these out, arranged them according to the three species they comprised and according to sex, and began measuring them. Alma recorded the figures and I occupied myself with other matters until Fred gave a shout.

"What's this lot?" he inquired, indicating a mess on the ear of one of the bats.

I looked closer. Then I grabbed a lens.

"By cracky, I believe they're *Sphærorhynchus!*" I yelled, and a closer inspection proved that it was so.

Almost every bat had both ears crowded with them. There were so many that despite all our excitement and enthusiasm extending over three years, these dismal parasites began rather to bore us. After half an hour we tired of teasing them off their hosts and going through the laborious process of making them rise and fall in the special preservative fluids. But the interesting fact was that these little treasures had come from the town.

The wild life of any town great or small is unbelievably diverse and plentiful. Large cities, more especially those with many parks and gardens, have a fauna only a little less extensive than the surrounding countryside. I cannot speak for American cities, though I was once shown a book entitled something like *The Fauna of New York* which I remember reading for some time before I discovered it to be not an account of the wild life of the state but of the city!

If you are ever in London, it will be well worth your while taking some kind of conveyance to the top of Hampstead Heath, and having a look at the city from above. There is a magnificent view from a corner by a round pond. From this vantage point you see what is not apparent either from below or from an airplane. You are at just the right height to see, stretching away as far as the eye can reach, what appears to be a more or less unbroken green forest. (I am assuming that you make your visit on one of the clear summer days which occasionally occur in April.) If you investigate the matter further, you will discover that you can indeed travel from one end of London to the other in almost any direction without ever being more than a hundred yards, and seldom more than a hundred feet, from some garden, line of trees, square, or park.

This may account for some of the animals that turn up in London from time to time. A park-keeper once told me that he had discovered a litter of fox cubs in Hyde Park, and gave it as his solemn opinion that the individuals of this shy species that are occasionally seen or caught there are actually indigenous, and not tame ones released by citizens who don't wish to take them away on their summer holidays. However that may be, most of the wild mammalian fauna of England has turned up in the parks of London at one time or another.

If you add to these mammals the normal rats and mice and the not inconsiderable list of resident birds, then the occasional bird visitors, the odd reptiles and amphibians, and a long list of fishes, the urban fauna begins to reach considerable dimensions. The invertebrate animals are in every way more numerous. There are worms, spiders, centipedes and insects, snails, woodlice, and a great host of lesser animals. Quite apart from these, there is a whole gamut of creatures to be found in every town that can in no way be classed as truly indigenous.

I wonder how many people have any conception of the droll variety of the pets kept in a large city. Full-grown lions, enormous pythons, lemurs, rattlesnakes, hairy spiders, fleas, octopuses, and almost any other animal you can think of live contentedly behind the placid façades along our streets. Moreover, it seems that many of these strange pets get loose or are abandoned, for the most extraordinary assortment has been gathered in London and other cities. A fair-sized elephant once turned up in a coal yard in Liverpool and was never claimed; the first specimen of a certain Australian flying phalanger ever seen was found on the roof of a house in London; and I once read of a man who one morning found a newborn sea-lion wrapped in a newspaper in his front garden in Putney.

If these are the conditions obtaining in a great northern city, you can imagine the state of affairs in a tropical township. Belize swarms with lizards, snakes, toads, frogs, and bats. Every garden is riddled with water-filled crab holes. Humming-birds whir about every flowering bush, the housetops are lined with turkey-vultures, and a multitude of other birds whistle, fizz, bang, and plop in all the trees. The water-storage butts are miniature aquaria and beneath every piece of wood or tin or canvas is an invertebrate menagerie.

Though it was not so varied in Belize as in a great metropolis, the list of pets was proportionately just as extensive. Through constant inquiry and personal visits we discovered a good proportion of the fauna of the whole country represented by tame individuals in the back yards of the town. At first we could unearth only a few imported rabbits, one or two agoutis, and some parrots but, though the town is a very small one, perseverance rewarded us with peccaries, foxes, ocelots, and other animals in an array that seemed infinite. For the most part we were not interested in the purchase of these pets. Only one or two animals that we wished to preserve in a particular manner for a special purpose, or which we desired to dissect in the fresh condition, were worth the price put upon them. However, we avidly accumulated the indigenous small life. In this category were two animals that proved of especial interest.

The first was a common toad from the roadside ditches, one *Bufo valliceps*, which trills away loudly and happily after rain. There is always a common and rather uninteresting toad in every country, and it always seems to be the first animal we encounter. One collects it in a desultory manner, pickles it, and puts it away, only to discover later that it is of immense interest for some unforeseen reason. We have several times been caught out this way. Deceived by the toad's prevalence, we had not collected enough, or had not recorded its variations in sufficient detail, and lived to curse our perfunctoriness. In Belize, therefore, we determined to do the thing properly and get plenty of the common toads.

To this end we got our enterprising small boys to spend an afternoon grubbing in ditches. The results were a basketful of the small toads, some of which, when we came to examine them in detail, gazed back at us with most quizzical expressions. These individuals had one disdainfully raised "eyebrow."

These toads were suffering from an infection of the eye. We killed one and opened its distended eyeball from above. Inside was a coiled yellow mass, which we teased out and slowly unravelled with considerable difficulty. This proved to be a five-inch tapeworm, but the tiny head-segment, or scolex, was buried deep in the muscular tissue behind the eye. A more thorough scrutiny disclosed more worms in the thighs of the toads.

These were not bundled up and moribund like those in the ocular swellings, but were very active, gliding between the muscles hither and thither and roundabout so that it became almost impossible to trace them. We were more than an hour getting one out whole, and in order to do so the whole musculature of the host's leg had to be removed layer by layer and in some cases strand by

BELIZE FENCE LIZARD (Anolis sagrei) IN FULL DISPLAY

strand. The scolex again was not attached, but lay free in a pocket in the muscles of the abdomen.

Of all the many types of parasitic worms I have seen, these were among the most peculiar. Some, like those under the skin of the eye-balls, were in a resting condition, having formed a cyst around them-selves, rolled their bodies into neat balls, and filled the sac with a clear fluid like water-glass. The skin of the toad above these encysted worms was roughened, darkened, and perforated by a number of enlarged pores.

Tapeworms can extend or contract their bodies to a very great degree. These were no exception, but what gave them distinction was that when contracted they turned a very intense yellowish-orange hue. Near the heads of some of them was a bunch of small, circular, reddish-orange bodies, and scattered through the tissues of the host were many rectangular, flat, white objects—presumably the egg-filled, cast-off terminal segments of the worms, called proglot-tids. The toads seemed to be entirely unaffected by these loathsomely ticklish guests, but then a toad is one of the most patient of beasts.

We wondered about the life-history of these parasitic worms. If the proglottids, which are modified segments of the tapeworm filled with ripe eggs, are cast off among the muscles of the host, do they develop there or do they reach the outside world? Perhaps they are in readiness for the time when their host, the toad, is eaten by some snake or other animal, in the stomach of which they will be released and which they will then infest. Perhaps, on the other hand, they may be only released by such means, and then pass out of the toad-eater with the fæces and finally get into new toads, either directly or through parasitizing some small animal that the toads eat. If only we have the time we are determined to go back and try to find out just what does happen.

The other worth-while item that emerged from our collection of the common animals of the town was a large series of the little fence lizards (*Anolis sagrei*) that swarm in all the gardens and are called locally "maklala." These were ordinary brown lizards with yellow so-called gular pouches. These structures are not really pouches, but rounded, median, fore-and-aft fins of gaily coloured skin that can be raised at will from the underside of the neck by means of bones corresponding to those of our Adam's apples that extend backwards under the skin from a point between the angle of the mandible almost to the chest. Each species of *Anolis* has a different-coloured "fin," and in most species it is much longer in the male. In this particular Belize type it was plain yellow, with the scales also of the same colour. We collected many of these lizards and became, as usual, much interested in the great variety of colours and colour patterns that they could adopt. These ranged from grey with bold brown and silver stripes to almost black throughout or to pale ochre or even to a pattern of rusty-edged cream chevrons along a median black belt. These colour patterns came and went in a few minutes, but all, when dead, assumed an even, light olive-brown tint all over.

We recorded all this as a matter of course. The details passed into the limbo of notebooks, photograph albums, and sketchbooks along with the occurrence of *Sphærorhynchus*, the changing coats of the Jamaican *Anolis*, and other such matters. We did not at that time recognize the importance of these commonest of local lizards.

DEAD HOUSES
AND MUD

In Re Crocodiles; "Self-Starters," Crab Migrations, and a Raccoon-Hunt

SATISFIED with regard to the common fauna of Belize and the animals that we could purchase from the host of household pets, and having done our utmost about the dolphins, we started going farther afield. This entailed primarily a search for "dead" houses. There is nothing like a derelict and collapsed wooden house or shack in overgrown, tropical, cultivated land as a hunting-ground for a zoologist. Why this should be is hard to say, and the fact that it is so, often proves rather annoying.

Wild animals are supposed to be wild, so that collecting them—especially the rarer ones—should, one might assume, involve scouring the wilds. It is therefore rather mortifying to spend a whole day's hard work in an intensive search in swamps thick with mosquitoes, in woods full of prickles and spikes, in caves full of bad air, or on grass-fields roasted by a blazing sun, and catch nothing, and then come upon an abandoned house and find congregated there an assorted army of rare and curious beasts never seen elsewhere, more particularly in "live" houses. It is also rather disconcerting when someone says to you, "What an amazing and beautiful specimen! Where did you get it?" and you have to answer, "Underneath a door fallen from a tumble-down shack on the so-and-so road."

But we have become callous about this sort of thing, and now set out boldly in search of dead houses. In Belize, we employed a plutocratic-looking automobile in which to conduct the search, and we found many. Needless to say, we stumbled across the first by accident and it proved to be the best.

The road passed through an area of low, flat land to the south of Belize. This part of the country is covered with mangrove swamps interspersed with another type of vegetation which is no less watery but supports a more varied floral growth. In some places land had been cleared, and quite reasonable grass pastures meandered between banks of low trees and wild shrubbery, choked with succulent herbs and sedges. We had stopped the car by one of these pastures and were chasing lizards, of which there were many species. There were green iguanas (*Ctenosaurus similis*) on the tree limbs and on the ground that invariably shot into holes at the bases of the trees; there were ground lizards (*Ameiva undulata*) with bright blue or salmon-pink undersides; there were the little maklalas and countless wild-eyed basilisks (*Basilicus vittatus*), which the locals very reasonably call "cock maklalas."

These basilisks are very beautiful lizards of the iguanid family. The males bear tall, fin-like combs or crests on the backs of their heads. They change colour continuously, developing intense greenish-yellow lines along the upper flanks. They have very long hind legs and tremendous tails. They scramble up low bushes with some difficulty but, in this country at least, spend the greater part of their time on the ground, over which they careen at a prodigious rate, when disturbed, by raising themselves on their hind legs and running like birds. They have baleful, staring, dark grey-blue eyes and show much fight when handled, gaping and biting with fury. The form of these creatures is æsthetically most satisfying. So many animals, like cats, are very beautiful, but the flow of their lines is spoilt by the tail being just too short.

We were armed with little air-guns and deployed through the bushes with the driver of the car, a most enthusiastic and intelligent person named Gregorio Peyrefitte; his assistant, who was, on the contrary, the least intelligent and most useless person I have ever encountered; and a small boy who had somehow become entangled in our party, acting as beaters. We put up and shot many lizards. Then I spotted a large beast, which I assumed was an iguana, making off with great stealth through the weeds towards a swamp. I crept after it, though fully aware that my puny air-gun would be useless. One always imagines that something can be done about a prize specimen once it has been spotted, even if one has only bare hands for weapons. The beast crept forward, and only now and then did I catch a glimpse of its grey back parting the herbage. I followed.

We passed through a swamp, I gaining slowly upon the quarry, and then entered a tangle of low growth with open, wet mud below. Here I had to go down upon my belly like my more distant ancestors and the beast ahead. The imitation was only fair, and I lost much ground. We ultimately emerged into an open place and, seeing the animal heading for a dense tangle, I decided to make a dash. I jumped forward into the clearing and landed with a resounding crash amid a litter of rotten wood concealed by the tall grass. Piles of stuff came tumbling down all round, and the animal I was chasing was flipped into the air some yards ahead just as if it had been shot out of a gun. It turned over as it fell to earth, and I saw that it was a small crocodile about three feet long. When I recovered from my surprise, I glanced at my right hand, which was spread flat over a rotten plank. From between my second and third fingers a three-inch rusty nail protruded; had it been another inch farther down the board it would have gone clean through my hand. I had taken a dive into a perfectly magnificent dead house, so I bawled for Fred and the others.

There is a recognized procedure in these matters. If you go at it bald-headed, turning over boards and timbers at random, the animals sleeping therein become alarmed and creep downwards to enter holes in the ground or slip away into the surrounding vegetation, which covers everything. You find nothing but lizards' eggs and ants. It is therefore advantageous to clear an area all round the periphery first, removing every vestige of grass and vegetation before so much as touching the precious pile of fallen timbers and rubbish. The central pile should then be removed piece by piece in a systematic manner, working as nearly as possible from all sides at once, and flinging the stuff out beyond the cleared circle. By this means, things that make a dash can be swatted, while the remainder are either uncovered before they know what is happening or become concentrated at the bottom centre. It is the same process as hunting rats in a corn rick.

On this occasion we laboured mightily, for the house had been a big one and must have collapsed many years before. The crocodile had made good its escape, having doubtless been thoroughly scared when the plank suddenly flipped up beneath it and shot it skywards just when it thought it was being frightfully cunning and creeping away unnoticed. The place, however, was alive with other things. The first rotten boards we lifted revealed several immense toads (*Bufo marinus*); sad, quiet, gentle creatures that I cannot bring myself to kill. They have immense eyes, with black irises crossed with iridescent, greenish-gold vermiculations, which they blink at you in a mystified and wholly trusting manner that evokes nothing but compassion. These specimens were covered with immense ticks that had plunged their cruel, pointed mouth-parts into the soft flanks and limbs of the toads. We relieved the poor animals of these parasites, whose bites we had sampled and which we knew to be most painful, and then pushed them off into the grass.

Our friend the chauffeur then cornered a small red snake with black bands and black head (*Ninia sebæ*), and while we were capturing this we found two more asleep under a near-by brick. There were many large hairy spiders that came stalking majestically out of the rubbish, and there were scorpions of more than one kind coursing about the place, brandishing their tails in the air. As we dug down deeper into the damp heart of the pile, the life changed. There were small frogs, millepedes, a nest of small rats in which we captured the mother, many snails, and some very large opilionids with peculiar spines all over their backs.

This mother rat was rich reddish-brown, while the young, which were half-grown, were clothed in dark steel-grey coats. This species is fairly rare, but is sometimes found in the thatched roofs of native houses. One would never have known that the young belonged to the mother if they had been found separately.

When we were nearing the bottom of the pile, we were suddenly brought up sharp by a most unexpected sound. We had thought that we were some distance from the road, and we had not seen or heard anybody during the whole afternoon. Now, just behind a line of bushes, somebody was hard at work with the self-starter of a car.

"Hey! Is that somebody trying to steal your car?" I asked Peyrefitte.

"No, I don't think so," he said rather testily. "Mine doesn't make so much noise."

"Have you got the ignition key?" I asked, for the starter kept on whir-whir-whirring.

"But I didn't leave the car over there," Peyrefitte insisted.

I shouted "Hi!" loudly, and the noise stopped.

"That's funny," I said.

"But the road isn't over there," the stupid assistant added. Then the small boy began to laugh.

"What are you giggling at?" I said. "Go and see who it is."

The boy giggled a lot more and I got rather peeved. Then the self-starter began whirring again, and I began to have doubts. We went to investigate, but there certainly was no car, nor even a road anywhere about; also, the starter had now stopped its whirring. The small boy continued to giggle spasmodically.

"What the devil's the matter with you?" I bawled; but the local Creoles have a maddening habit of going dumb from lack of moral courage, especially if one is so unthinking as to lose one's temper and shout. The poor lad now giggled as much out of fright as from amusement. Then the noise began again, and this time, being thoroughly puzzled, we stalked it. Dusk was closing in and it was a long time before Fred eventually uncovered its origin.

Now Fred has spent a lifetime with cars, and can spot a maladjusted tappet in a traffic block, but I honestly believe he was just as fully taken in as the rest of us—except the small boy, of course. What he found was a gentle, big-eyed tree-frog squatting guiltily in an empty oil drum. This frog periodically inflated thin sacs at the angles of its jaws, and then, by pumping its tongue up and down, produced the most prodigious volume of sound—exactly like that of a modern self-starter on any medium-priced American car. And despite this incident and the comparative commonness of this frog (*Hyla baudinii*), we continued to be taken in by this sound—on two occasions completely, once sitting in the hotel in Belize and once in the centre of the town of Merida, where there were cars starting up all around.

Belize is backed by extensive mangrove swamps. Mangroves are the first things that meet the eye in almost any tropical country; they lie like a green scum betwixt sea and land, wedding the salt waters to nearly all tropical coasts. They look verdant and peculiarly inert, and we always imagine them to be teeming with animal life. Usually we are promptly disillusioned, but in the mangroves of Belize we were not at all disappointed. They swarmed with life.

We had arrived in British Honduras in the middle of September, which, in one respect, proved to be a most auspicious time for our first investigations of the coastal areas, for at this season the crabs were on their way towards the sea. This statement needs explanation.

Crabs are a feature of all coasts. In the tropics they are also to be found all over the place, even on mountain-tops and in tall forest trees. Many are purely land animals, others dwell in fresh water, while again there are those that spend most of their time on land but trek back to the sea every year to deposit their young. Some of these inhabit mangroves and other places near the coast, while others dwell far inland. The latter have to make epic migrations each year to reach the sea. In Jamaica there is a species known locally as the black mountain crab (*Gecarcinus ruricola*) which is famed not only for its yearly migrations but also for its culinary possibilities, both

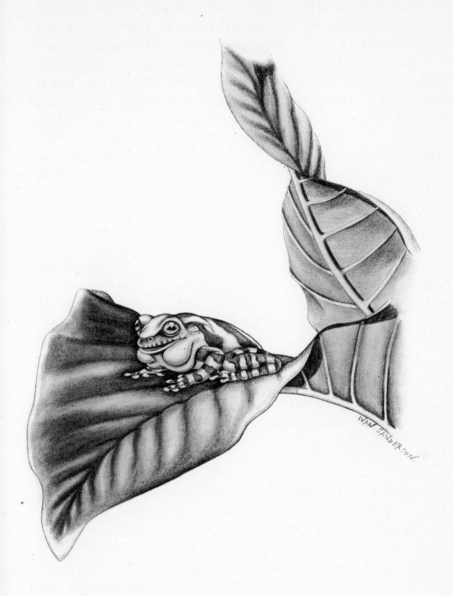

"Self-Starter" Frog (Hyla baudinii) Self-Starting

of which features warrant slight digressions. These Jamaican crabs, which are vivid red or orange, with dark red, purple, or bluish backs, grow to about the size of a small fist, being very deep-bodied and rounded.

They are gathered in the mountains, and a good Jamaican cook— of whom there are many—will perform upon them certain ministrations that are indeed almost holy. The meat is extracted from the limbs and mixed with the edible portions of the body. The whole is then highly spiced according to a recipe of which we are the proud possessors but about which we tend to be rather secretive. They are baked and served in their shells and finally eaten; but here words fail me utterly. We have a prized little book in which we have recorded details of quite a number of tropical delicacies that we have stumbled across in our peregrinations, and I can only say that Jamaican mountain crab is marked with many stars.

But this is only secondarily zoological. Of first importance are the migrations of these Jamaican crabs. When the time for this draws near, they begin to appear in the stream-beds at the tops of the mountains where they dwell. These legions, who have farthest to travel, then begin a descent to lower levels, gathering countless other cohorts as they go. Finally the whole army reaches the coastal lowlands on its way to the shallower seas to "wash their eggs," as this annual business is colloquially called. These vast hordes do not just march towards the sea at any point, which would be a comparatively simple matter on an island of this size, nor do they follow easy routes free from obstacles. They have selected stretches of coast where the beach is particularly suitable to their tastes, and to get to these they travel in a bee-line without deviation and quite regardless of the natural or unnatural obstacles that may be in their way.

Some tracts of country they thus traverse every year would, if seen in section, be much like an exaggerated cross-cut saw, multiplying many times the actual distance travelled in a straight line. Yet these crabs, despite their awkward gait and an unnecessary array of clumsy legs, tackle the proposition in a completely thoughtless and straightforward manner, just like a platoon of infantry. "Theirs not to reason why," etc., and they indeed do the thing in style, and die in the doing of it to an extent that would evoke the admiration of the most ardent imperialist. Eye-witnesses have told me of watching these Jamaican crabs fighting among themselves to reach the pinnacle of a pyramidal rock, the base of which lay athwart all their respective paths, while all around lay a perfectly smooth, open tract of country. Having once tackled the ascent, they were all determined to traverse the apex as nearly as possible in their own particular straight lines, and as the pinnacle happened to be small and the crabs rather wide, they couldn't all do it at once. It never entered their rudimentary nerve-ganglia to deviate one iota from their prescribed euclidean courses.

Since both sexes take part in this yearly trek, one would suppose that its principal object was to mate in the salt water, but this is apparently not the case, for the females stagger down carrying their eggs beneath them, and there is evidence that these eggs are already fertilized before they reach the sea. Rather, it seems that the crabs go down for the hatching of the eggs and to release the tiny pelagic larvæ, which are called zoea, into the only element that suits them. This done, the whole army starts clambering back to their mountain retreats, a distance that must to some of them be roughly equivalent to 1500 of our miles.

What we now witnessed at Belize was an equivalent though less remarkable performance. It was, nevertheless, most impressive, for the crabs indulging this seasonal whim were larger and in every way more spectacular than the Jamaican species. They were pale sky-blue, greyish-blue, or yellowish-grey and even, in some cases, bright straw-yellow. They had one claw, usually the right, which was much larger than the other, and this they carried, in that pose beloved of crabs, just as if they had one hand in a muff. These Belizarian crabs (*Cardisoma guanhumi*) are also made into a culinary delicacy, known as crab gumbo.

There happen to be long, straight roads parallel to the coast running north and south of Belize and cutting through the man-

BLUE MANGROVE CRAB (Cardisoma guanhumi)

grove swamps for some miles. Across these the crabs were trekking in countless thousands. The road was black and blue with them, the ditches on either side were alive with their pop-eyes, and the mangrove roots were crowded with their clanking bodies.

However, the main purpose of our first proper exploration of the mangroves was not crab-hunting, but the collection of a series of specimens of a certain crocodile known to inhabit these swamps. It bears the name *Crocodylus moreletii,* and is distinct from the common Central American *C. acutus.* In fact, the existence of this species was for long doubted, its identity having become confused with that of other types.

The Crocodilia are very muddling. It is the old business of the buffalo and the bison, the gnat and the mosquito, the dromedary and the camel all over again. In this case it is crocodiles, alligators, and caimans that have become jumbled up, sometimes with the gavial (which has to be spelt "garial," "gharial," or "gwarial") as a possible fourth difficulty just to complicate matters further. The trouble is that different people in different places call different animals by the same name or the same animal by different names. The result is appalling in countries where Crocodilia are found, and is most confusing anywhere. There are two kinds of camels, but which should be called dromedary, either by the layman or by the scientist, will probably never be settled to everybody's satisfaction. So it is with crocodiles and alligators, more particularly in South America, where there are no alligators despite the violent protestations of the entire resident population.

There are several genera of Crocodilia, among them the three leading ones rightfully named *Alligator, Caiman,* and *Crocodylus.* The first is exclusively confined to the United States and China. The second, *Caiman,* is represented by a number of species ranging from the Gulf Coast throughout Central and South America. The third genus comprises the true crocodiles, of which there are four species in the Americas, one confined to the Orinoco River (*Crocodylus intermedius*), one to Cuba (*Crocodylus rhombifer*), this *C. moreletii* from around Yucatan peninsula, and the widespread *Crocodylus acutus* which is found in Florida, the West Indies, Central America, and northern South America and which takes to either fresh or salt water. The important point about *moreletii* is that it links the odd Cuban species to the more general *acutus*, and is therefore a bit of supporting evidence for a connection between Yucatan and that island in earliest tertiary times.

We set out after these crocodiles (not alligators or caimans, mark you) armed with an assortment of harpoons, and instantly became involved with the afore-mentioned crabs. We have exactly the same difficulty in our work that you will perceive I encounter in attempting to record it. In the world of nature you set out to investigate some specific thing, and end up hours, days, weeks, months, or even years later amid a welter of quite other matters. On this occasion, the crabs did nothing particular to hinder our progress through the ankle-deep muddy water and its blanket of droning mosquitoes; they merely backed away from us or hurried their march. The fault was entirely ours.

Having watched with some awe their steady progress to the sea, we noticed that all those on the ground were bluish and that the bright yellow ones were, without exception, perched up on the mangrove trees busily engaged in frothing at the mouth, as crabs will. Speculation as to whether these were soft-bodied individuals that had recently shed their hard coats owing to growth led us to investigate and into trouble and some excitement.

Alma and I advanced upon the nearest yellow crab, which happened to be precariously suspended from some thin creepers that were clinging to the only tree that was not a mangrove. I made a pass at it with a hand net, reaching out over a jumble of impenetrable rubbish that blocked the way to the tree. The crab adroitly seized my net and, as the handle was covered with wet mud, it slipped out of my hand. The crab, which was manifestly not soft, held the net dangling from its great claw, meanwhile peering at me most cunningly with its periscope eyes, and then, just as I had expected, slowly and carefully backed up the tree, dragging the net between the creepers. We cut a long stick and biffed him hard, but

YUCATECAN CROCODILE (Crocodylus moreletii)

he clung to the net and went further aloft. Just before he got out of reach, I gave him a last hard clout, which unexpectedly reduced his grinning presence to a broken and revolting mess. The claw, however, retained firm possession of the net, and I had to push through the tangle and scramble up the tree to retrieve it.

In doing so, I inadvertently used a large tree-termites' nest as a hand-hold, and this came away in one piece from the tree trunk to which it was stuck. When I looked at the place where it had been, there crouched a large black scorpion. We spent some difficult moments manœuvring this menace into a suitable bottle, and then I retrieved the net. On my way down I jumped into the fallen termites' nest, which broke open and disclosed two more scorpions amid the seething mass of insects and also a short grey thing that flipped and skipped furiously about.

We both spotted this at once and recognized it to be the cast-off tail of a gecko lizard, so that a wild scramble began to find its owner. This proved fruitless, however, so, disappointed but doubly eager, we set out in search of more termites' nests in the hope of making good our partial loss. This led us into a more distant area, where the muddy floor of the mangrove brake appeared out of the flood waters. Here two other things arrested our attention.

First, the whole ground was a moving mass of scurrying crabs of another species (*Uca minax*, a name that has certainly taken our fancy), small, with brown backs and red undersides, which also carried one large claw that looked more like a muff than ever, being red with white tips to the claws, as if a pale hand protruded. These crabs retreated to leave us standing in a bare circle, and glugged down into small, water-filled holes. In capturing these, Alma and I became separated, because we wanted a few of each sex and the males—in which the abdomen, pressed flat against the underside, is narrower—were remarkably scarce, necessitating the capturing and overturning of scores of specimens. Our progress could be followed by the sound of constant slappings at the cloud of ravenous mosquitoes and sandflies that hungrily pursued us. Then all at once Alma called me over.

"What on earth's done all this?" she asked, pointing to a large area of mud from which sprouted the innumerable little finger-like, upward-growing roots of the mangroves, but which was, in addition, extensively mined.

"Are there crabs in the big holes?" I asked.

"In some of them, but not all, and how could any crab make a young mountain like that?" she asked, indicating a veritable Chichen-Itza at the base of a tree.

We went to investigate. The ground had been dug on all sides, and the mud carefully scraped into a mound. This mud had also been kneaded, and there were many small, five-toed footprints all over the place.

"Ah! Beef!" I pronounced. "Let us follow," and we did. The results were quite startling and absolutely unique in our annals, for in a short time the little tracks ended abruptly. We were brought up sharp, and looked at each other, mystified, for a definite end to any of our trackings was so novel that we were quite lost as to the next move. Then Alma showed unusual perspicacity by looking up into the foliage above.

"Whow!" she shouted, and then instantly added, "Sssh!" just as fervently. I looked up and saw them too.

Perched high on the gently swaying branches of a straggling mangrove were two large, woolly grey balls. One was firmly wedged into a triple fork, while the other sprawled across two branches. From its end drooped a short, fluffy tail. There for the asking, and almost for the taking, was a pair of raccoons (*Procyon lotor*). This presented us with a difficult problem, for we wanted these animals and we wanted them alive. Had we wanted them dead we would have been no better off, because we only had nets and a toy air-gun. Even the harpoons were with Fred at some other unidentified part of the mangrove brake, and we hadn't seen him for an hour.

Our subsequent manœuvrings were rather ridiculous, but by a fluke they produced the desired results. The mangrove on which the animals were resting was separated from the rest of the trees on three sides by an extensive open area, and the animals, very for-

RACCOONS (Procyon lotor)

tunately, were on the side of the tree facing this area. It was therefore decided that I climb the only tree that touched the one occupied by the raccoons, and by which they might escape. The plan was that, should they endeavour to retreat by this route through the branches, I would try to swat one as it passed. If they jumped to the ground, Alma was to fling a small machete at the nearest and, failing a hit, endeavour to apply the air-gun butt at short range. Our whispered council of war aroused the raccoons, who appeared to be in a post-prandial daze; they simply stuck out their eager, masked faces and peered down at us like two inquisitive arboreal dogs.

I made all possible speed up my tree, and the animals were taken by surprise, though they were, in any case, unusually irresolute. They jumped up and faced me, while the male slowly backed out along a branch to cover his mate. I was almost level with them before they came to a decision. I have seldom seen a prettier sight than these two immaculately coated creatures with their prick ears, particoloured faces, and neat little feet placed side by side on the narrow branches, watching me with their shining dark eyes.

The decision that they came to was a very animal one in its unexpectedness and obviousness. They both charged towards me, and first one and then the other leaped from the branch to the trunk of the tree and, turning three-quarters upside down in the air, struck it with all four feet, their heads pointing to the ground. Like rubber balls, they bounced off again and shot to earth. But this is where the male made his miscalculation. He seemed to have forgotten that terra firma was here represented by almost liquid mud. He went in head first with a splosh, and lost a precious second in recovering, so that his mate came on top of him. Covered with mud, he leaped round with lightning speed to snarl at her, and as he did so Alma's gun butt caught him squarely amidships. He was momentarily hurt and dazed, which allowed Alma, who can move exceedingly fast, to bang the collecting bag, loaded with bottles and other paraphernalia, over his head, jump squarely on it, and stay there yelling wildly.

The female streaked off over the mud, and as I leaped down from the tree, I had a glimpse of her scattering a shower behind her like a fast truck on a wet road. I also jumped on the bag. The big animal now came to life with a vengeance. He wriggled and scratched and growled under the bag. His powerful hind legs were free, and despite the fact that he was almost completely buried in the mud, we had to exert all our combined strength to hold him down. Getting string out of the bag was a problem, but we eventually secured his legs with this, then his fore-paws, and finally both together. We still held his head down in the mud with the bag. He objected to this most strongly and seemed almost relieved when we very gingerly manœuvred it into the empty bag, which we tied round his neck with a handkerchief. When he was thus securely trussed, we lifted our sputtering, wriggling prize and did a war dance of pure delight.

Fred took this stroke of great good fortune very hard. He rightly grumbled that he always missed being in at the kill. He glared at us and produced a somewhat bedraggled and very dejected-looking tortoise that he had spent most of the afternoon pursuing in a swamp. We set out for home well pleased, but without any crocodiles or even one of the yellow crabs.

We soon obtained some of the former. The young ones were very numerous along the roadsides in the big ditches, and were quite easily captured with light string nooses on the ends of long poles. Apparently they were so used to traffic passing along the road that they simply sat and stared at us. Later, larger ones were brought to us by men who make a trade of collecting the skins of these reptiles. These we skinned and prepared carefully, and placed in a new tank which was sealed and stored under the house. This was the last we saw of them, by the way, though the loss wasn't noticed till months later, when, of course, we had to start all over again—in the dry season, when all the crocodiles had gone off to æstivate in less get-atable abodes. Life can be very trying at times.

ERUPTION OF A WOOD VOLCANO

Night-Walkers, Billums, and Bokatoras

THREE days of hard, back-breaking work in a steady drizzle had given place, after a night in a steam-bath, to one of those vivid tropical mornings. Though we should have had to walk two miles to see the sky, we knew that it was a ceiling of soft turquoise puffed irregularly with lumps of shining white clouds. The few meandering chinks of clarity between the dense green web above us showed as much. Far below, we emerged from our tents to stretch ourselves in a shimmering pale green radiance. Occasional thimblefuls of cold water dripped from the woody giants that stood around us supporting our limited heaven.

This unusual intensity of light after three days of almost gloom, excessive even for the jungle, appears to have had the same effect upon both Fred and me. When I glanced into the mirror, I got a shock. Not only did my chin look like that of a budding Spanish grandee; there were even pieces of the jungle entangled in my person. To make a camp in the forest, one has to get very close to nature. Fred had come to the same conclusion at the same time, and was soon as busy as I with his razor in a tiny patch of sunlight outside his tent. Shaving with cold water can become not only a habit but a genuine pleasure, and I was indulging whole-heartedly when a double howl came ringing through the tree-boles.

We have recognized and very special howls in our household. A single long-drawn-out, high-pitched yell means, "Where are you?" or, conversely, "Where am I?" which is something one often does not know in the dense blanket of the jungle. Two howls of the sort that I now heard, on the other hand, mean, "Come quickly and bring a gun," which is synonymous with saying, "I have seen some valuable specimen and require immediate assistance." Such a summons is imperative and invariably sends everyone scampering to bush at top speed. This time was no exception.

Razors were dropped; nets and guns were seized; the native staff streamed—if two people can stream—from their quarters, and we charged off toward the other tent.

We came upon Fred clothed only in a pair of pyjama trousers, his face covered in glistening white lather, staring fixedly above him at the first forks of a giant tree which was clothed in a suit of tangled parasitic ferns, orchids, and creepers.

"What is it? Where is it?" we eagerly inquired, likewise peering aloft.

"It went into that hole," said my colleague, pointing upward with a soapy safety-razor.

"Yes, but what was it?" we implored.

"I don't know," he answered. "I saw its tail go in and, look, this came down while I was shaving."

He indicated the basin on a tripod of bush sticks before him. We looked. The bottom of the basin was covered with hunks of some large bright green nut with a yellow interior.

We stood about, somewhat nonplussed. We usually have to go out and look for our quarry very hard. Here was the first treasure coming into our midst before we were ready, before we had had our breakfast, even.

We got to work with a will, and soon the low growth was cleared away from the base of the great tree. Sure enough, there was a large hole in its trunk, but a hole of a very awkward shape, turning almost at right angles into the hollow interior between two of the thin buttress-roots that radiated from the bases of all the trees in that forest. After peering into this, we came to the conclusion that the introduction of a pan of sulphur and a blow-torch might be possible. This was accomplished, the idea being to smoke the animal out of the hollow interior by way of the hole far above.

After half an hour's strenuous work, however, we were reluctantly forced to give up the attempt, because no smoke appeared at the higher hole, whereas it poured out of the hole at the bottom. We came to the conclusion that the cavity did not extend up the inside of the trunk, or that it was blocked by a mass of fallen blocks and chips of rotten wood, as sometimes happens. We began debating as to what should be done.

Then I noticed that the creepers were numerous and large, and extended right to the summit of the tree. I saw also that some of them were knotted and tangled every now and then, and that there were no spine-covered rattans among them. As a result, and after due consideration, I suggested that I should go aloft.

In due course, I began the long climb, clothed in a thick shirt with sleeves to prevent arm-abrasions, trousers tucked into my stockings, and thin rubber shoes to aid foot-gripping. In my pockets were cigarettes, matches, and a long coil of strong string.

Now, husky people and athletes might shin up ninety-foot trees as they would a rope in a gymnasium, but I find it judicious to take the whole process rather seriously, very slowly and with the utmost caution. If a creeper proves to be rotten or has been half bored through by beetles or wood-peckers and gives way at a crucial moment, one requires every ounce of one's strength—and I have little—to prevent a great going down. If one has been climbing too fast, muscles are tired and breathing laboured, so that suspension by the arms alone, or bracing the whole weight with a leg, may prove the breaking point. A fall from one of these jungle trees is, moreover, deadly serious because of the buttresses of knife-edged, iron-hard wood that are raised all around below to meet one's fall.

I therefore took the climb very slowly, pausing each time I gained a safe stand or seat upon a knot of creepers. The trunk was perpendicular and devoid of branches for fifty feet. All the creepers of serviceable size were draped down one side of the tree. They were partly interwoven, and this helped me in the ascent.

After some difficulty I gained the first great fork. Up there was a space bigger than the average balcony, with a more or less level floor composed of a bed of dead leaves, creepers, fern roots, orchids, rubbish, and even some clumps of grass. Between the two great branches which rose steeply on either side was a natural latticework of entwined creepers forming the whole into a giant basket. In this I lay down for a rest after ascertaining that it did not house snakes or scorpions, and calling down to the others below that I was safe. I had a pleasant cigarette while getting my breath, and the others watched the hole to see that the animal did not escape.

I then tied one end of the string onto a creeper, the other to a piece of dead wood. Thrown out, this carried the string down to the ground, where they were ready with the lighted blow-torch, the sulphur candle, and a bottle of water. These I hauled up and, after festooning them about my person by means of short strings from my belt, I launched out over space once more.

The animal hole was on the outer underside of one of the great bifurcating limbs, about ten feet above the floor of the natural balcony. To reach it meant swarming up some creepers, swinging beneath them, and finally anchoring myself opposite the hole by twisting my legs round two separate creepers. The resultant position, though a strain, was rendered more comfortable and less strenuous by the presence of a strong though thin liane that happened to encircle the branch at this point and upon which I could partly sit.

Just inside the hole a small ledge presented itself. It was perfectly suited to hold the sulphur pan, and it was not long before I had the blow-torch arranged so that it heated but did not light the sulphur. This we find to be the best method, for burning sulphur releases so much gas that sleeping animals may become suffocated before they awake, and then roll off their ledges and tumble down into the great chimney formed by the trunk, where they cannot be reached. The heating process is slower but surer.

I was surprised, therefore, when not more than a minute after the torch was fixed, a small, clawed hand gently and cautiously ap-

KINKAJOUS (Potos flavus)

peared from the gloom above. I was doubly astonished, because I imagined the animal to be below me. Then, not two feet from my face appeared two round, soft, keen little faces with great lustrous yellow eyes, rounded ears, and a general air of ineffable gentleness. They came quietly and softly from above, head first down the farther surface of the hollow interior. They were puzzled by the smell of the smoke, but apparently little annoyed by it, for they did not sniff or even blink. I at once resolved upon a scheme; these animals could not be slaughtered; they must be taken alive.

Shooing them back with the sulphur pan, I made haste to get a noose fixed with the strong string. This I suspended from above the hole over a creeper so that the loop encircled the entrance. I then removed the blow-torch, leaned far back to one side, and grasped the free end of the string. Within a few seconds a head appeared. It peered at me but did not pause. I got ready to strike, but before I could do so the head of the second animal came out. What to do? If I waited a second longer, the first animal would be through; if I pulled, I could not have the noose for the second. And I wanted the pair. After a moment's hesitation, I pulled.

The string flew together. It caught the second individual (the female) round the neck and squeezed her head tight against the flanks of her mate, which in turn was thus encircled round the middle. With one heave and a quick jerk, both animals were yanked out of the hole before they knew what had happened, and because the hole was partly on the under surface of the branch, it required only a few feet of slack in the string before they were dangling in mid-air far out from the tree. With a rip I let the string slide through my fingers so that they whizzed groundward before their struggling freed them from the simple noose. Actually they were but a dozen feet from the ground when the female fell clear, but that is no tumble at all for this particular animal.

I looked down upon a wild scramble below as everybody fell upon the beautiful little pets. The chance of capturing a pair of full-grown, live kinkajous (*Potos flavus*) before breakfast is not a common occurrence even in a zoologist's household. These little woolly animals, related to the raccoon and built upon lines that somehow resemble a lemur, a kitten, and an animated Teddy-bear rolled into one, make the most lovable of pets—sometimes!

Naturally we were overjoyed. It was some time before they were ready below to receive the blow-torch and pan and the bottle, the water from which had been poured into the hole to make sure that none of the exceedingly dry tinder formed by the rotten interior was alight. (A hundred-foot tree falling upon a camp can do even more damage than one might imagine.) I then began to retrace my steps.

Arriving at the balcony once more, I wormed through the creepers, and reached out with my right foot to find a solid stand among the rubbish. I imagined that I had found one, and began to move my weight forward onto it.

There was but one ominous crack, sudden and sharp as a revolver shot. I instinctively gripped the creepers convulsively, while before my eyes the whole mass of rubbish lodged between the forked branches slowly subsided as if being sucked in from below. In a second there was a gaping void where I was about to step. With a roar that rose into a thundering crescendo, the whole mass crashed down the great chimney; and as if in answer there came up in its place with a full-throated hiss a great column of almost transparent flame. A jet of nearly liquid heat preceded by an arc of golden sparks rocketed up into the foliage, to sway the lesser branches like seaweed before a storm.

In a flash I realized that we had not damped the tree when we had tried to smoke it from the bottom. I had been aloft half an hour. Now beneath me was an inferno—a jungle volcano in a quite advanced stage of eruption: tons of powdery, super-dry tinder packed into a fifty-foot chimney five feet wide and supplied with a natural though forced draught more efficient than a super-charger on a racing car. I knew also that the mass at the bottom of the balcony had been the stopper that had held it down; and even now I feel slightly sick when I remember that I lay placidly upon this, smoking a cigarette, when at any moment it might have given way and dumped me into the hell below, from which I could have reached out to touch my companions between the buttresses but from which they could not have released me in less than two hours even had there been a dozen of them with axes.

At the moment, however, my predicament was too acute to allow of speculation of any kind. My first mad dash from the column of fire took me many feet up one of the great branches. Then amid the roaring of the flames, the rain of sparks, billowing smoke, and crashing of heat-agitated branches above, and the yells of those below, I did things that I could never later be persuaded to believe. It appears that I fairly skimmed up the underside of the branch to the next fork. Having gained this point, which was out of immediate danger and the range of the sparks, I regained my common sense. Around me were the branches of other neighboring trees; below me—eighty feet below me—were the blanched faces of my companions. How far away, how tiny and helpless they seemed, and how very slender the remaining branches of the tree that I was on appeared from there! I began a painfully slow but not unmethodical advance upward and outward, after selecting a road that seemed at least possible.

But spaces and gaps appeared greater and greater as one approached them, whereas the branches became proportionately slimmer and less stable. At last the one I was on began to bend. The Africans have a word, "belly-fear," and I believe I learned then what it meant.

After carefully retracing my steps—or rather, crawling tracks— and trying two other routes, I came face to face with the realization that I was trapped in mid-air just as surely as I would have been in the depths of the tree trunk. I yelled down to those below, telling them as much and expecting sympathy. Instead I got wild gesticulations.

Now the noise was terrific. Only those who have seen a full-sized tropical forest tree on fire will know just how loud the roaring can be. Up in my lofty vantage point, moreover, the crashing of the branches waving in the convection currents added to the uproar, so that I could not hear what my companions were shouting. They kept pointing to a spot below me near the fork from which the flames were coming. I remember thinking that perhaps they could see from their end that my whole branch was soon due to burn through and crash, and I had a crazy desire to bolt—if you can call it that—back along the slender branches in a last endeavour to surmount the gaping void between it and the next tree.

Luckily I didn't, for all at once I spotted the object of their excitement. It was a single great creeper that hung from beneath my branch and that did not immediately join the trunk of the tree but instead hung in a great loop and only joined it some twenty feet from the ground. As soon as I had spotted this, I saw what they expected of me and set out to do it. Those below, as soon as they saw I was on my way, sent one of their number to begin the ascent.

By the time I had reached the top they had reached the bottom and were hewing it adrift with a machete. Soon it was free below and dangling some six feet away from the smoking trunk. In the haze of smoke, I found its hard, dry surface, and in a second was over the branch and slowly descending. I passed three small holes in the main trunk belching pink flames like so many blow-torches. The heat almost scorched me, and inside I could see only shimmering white light. At last I reached the free end of the creeper, and grabbed the machete handle held out to me. I was pulled in to the trunk, and, seizing the other creepers there, we both fell rather than climbed down to earth.

Nor were we too quick, for in what seemed only a few seconds the branch below the one I had just left gave two cracks, and then sang its way to earth in one piece, landing with a thud that shook the whole forest. A column of sparks flew up, and we ran.

Luck was certainly with us that day because the branch that had fallen faced our camp; the one I had been on faced the other way. Now the weight of the tree was directed harmlessly. Not only was I safe, our camp was safe. I suddenly sat down; I couldn't help it; I felt cold despite the fire.

While breakfast was brought I resumed my shaving. My face was pure black and pure white in patches; in one of the white patches was the small perky goatee.

Breakfast over, we sat listening to the crystal stream that tinkled, gurgled, and splashed just out of sight below the tall bank on which our new home was built. The sun streamed through the huge, arching fronds of the cohune palms, bathing nature's delicate, green lace-work that was spread to catch it beneath. Above was a filigree of silvery branches patterned with bunches of orchids and ferns and many-fingered green things, stretched across an azure ceiling. Wherever you looked, humming-birds, great green flies, little blue bees, and satin-clad butterflies helicoptered silently before a fathomless mass of interwoven verdure. This was our first morning of real life; the first morning we had feasted our eyes upon a scene of such real beauty for many a month. We were utterly content and there was nothing to be said.

There had been four days of little oily boats, rickety trains, and steaming, staggering mules, terminated by a crescendo of chopping and axing in the echoing stillness of the jungle. Now all the ordered confusion of humanity had receded, leaving us at peace in this wonderful green loneliness. Our new home was no insult to nature, for the kitchen hut, the little bush house for our tiny staff, and the ends of both our own dwellings were constructed of green palm thatch, so that they blended well with the environment. Also, I had made a special point of preventing the felling or cutting of any vegetation within sight of our domain.

We have so often selected a lovely site for our temporary home in the luscious beauty of the jungle, only to have it reduced to a hideous shambles through the combined zeal and laziness of our helpers. Natives of tropical lands have no conception of any possible beauties in the jungle. Visiting foreigners are even worse. The aim of both is to clear away as much vegetation as possible on all kinds of pleas, each more ridiculous than the last. They demand the sunlight and then hide from it under hot verandas; they seek fresh air and then screen their houses and erect mosquito nets over their beds; they wish to be rid of the insects and then put gutters on their houses and water butts in the garden, and litter the place with their drains and rubbish dumps and ditches in which these same insects thrive; they want to have a view and promptly fill it up with more of their ugly dwellings, their roads and their work houses and soulless lines of miserable, cultivated plants. The local natives are the same. They want to clear everything too, and if they are building a camp and need poles and palm-leaf thatching, they just reach out and cut them down.

On this occasion, we had personally supervised the work, and prevented the cutting of anything that could be seen from the centre of the place which we had chosen for our home. When our helpers had gone we did a few hours' selective weeding with as much care as anybody would bestow upon a garden of priceless plants. We cut away the dead branches; we cleared small saplings from around the more beautiful palms so that they might stand out in all their glory and delicate beauty, and we cleaned the stream bank, leaving only the graceful balisiers, or wahas as they are called in this country, and two arching trees festooned with moss. Finally, we did a little adjusting in the boulder-strewn stream-bed, so that the waters would play a louder tune and flow into the big pool in such a way that all floating debris would be washed out of it.

This pool was something magnificent. It was seventy feet long and on an average twelve feet wide. At its deepest part the smooth rocky bottom was seven feet below the surface of the absolutely clear water. The bank on the near side was perpendicular and some ten feet high, of clean, golden clay, planted with wahas; on the other side a beach of clean boulders stretched along its length. Above there was a slight rent in the ceiling of the forest which allowed the sunlight to filter down first to one side in the morning, then into the pool at noon, and finally to the other side in the afternoon. Up and down stream stretched a dim tunnel filled with mysterious green light and butterflies. The water was cold and fresh, with a vivacity unknown anywhere but in the tropics. We had cleared the whole pool of every vestige of fallen rubbish.

As we sat gazing upon all this riot of beauty, I felt an irrepressible desire welling up inside me, a desire in no way connected with the round breakfast just completed or with the excitement of the morning's adventure. Suddenly I could bear it no longer and, jumping up, I made a dash over the bank into the pool. Almost before I had got my breath from the sudden cold immersion there were two wild whoops and Fred and Alma came sailing out into the air above to plunge in beside me and send up columns of foamless water. George and Dick, our recently acquired and as yet untested staff, stuck their faces out of the back of the kitchen, which abutted onto the far end of the pool, and we were relieved to see that they obviously did not think us mad. In fact, their expressions indicated that they approved mightily.

We began swimming around, discarding as much of our drenched clothing as decency would permit. Why can't all human beings admit that they still want to play just as they did when they were kids, instead of spending their lives in righteous pomposity? I suppose it's because there aren't enough tropical pools to go round. Anyhow, I think none of us is ashamed to remember having spent an hour of complete idiocy and fun that morning. The thing that really started us off was the "billums."

Now I can't find out whether this is a purely British Honduranean word for a special kind of fribble, but these billums are common enough in other tropical countries. In fact we have often encountered them, though I must admit that never before had they quite such an individuality. "Billums" is a general term in British Honduras for little fish in fresh water. Now little fish infest most streams in the tropics, and in many they come and tickle you if you lie quiet, but in British Honduras their activities are so single-minded and so determined that they have gained for themselves this special title. As soon as you enter the water, they dash at you and start tickling. They nibble gently at your toes and your elbows, they pull the hairs on your legs in a playful manner, and they float around in swarms with their watchful little eyes upon your every movement. You can't drive them off and yet you can't catch them even if you tempt them with bread crumbs in a net. They are frightfully cunning. They are most remarkable little people.

We once threw a piece of newspaper into the stream and they just came and looked at it. Another time Alma threw some brightly coloured pages out of a shiny magazine into their abode, and they devoured the lot in just over an hour! In fact, they eat almost anything, but when we tried to tempt them by floating bait into the mouth of a butterfly net, they steadfastly refused to follow. Yet they have their uses.

It has been suggested that Pandora opened her blasted little box on the upper Orinoco River in South America. If this is true, she must have been a British Honduranean and have collected her pests in her homeland, for the place is the very epicentre of all biting six- and eight-legged pests. Among these are small ticks, known locally as warri-ticks, which come in two sizes: adults at one and a half pin-heads and by the hundreds, and immature at a pin-point and by the thousands. These abominations lie in solid bunches on stalks, bits of grass, and so forth, awaiting the passage of some greater beast. If you touch such a congregation, they all flood onto you in what is literally the flicker of an eyelid of time. Then they spread out like a *Panzer* column and infest the whole of you, and there is only one sure cure. You undress, leave your clothes, jump into the nearest billum pool, and then try to lie quiet. The little billums get to work, and in no time divest you of every tick. The operation drives you nearly crazy, but it is better than the torture inflicted by the ticks should they get at your skin.

This morning was the first intimate contact that we had had with these little billums, and we are all ticklish at the best of times. However, our interest in them soon became somewhat more deep-seated. We noticed that they were of many kinds, though seen from above they all appeared to be simply small brown fish, rather slender in outline. We spotted some that had ruby eyes and others that, in making a quick get-away, displayed brilliant peacock-blue tails. By chasing a few into a little side pool, and locking them in with a barrier of small stones, we got a better view, and counted fourteen different kinds among them, of all shapes and colours. Most were chiclids as far as could be determined from such cursory examination, but there were also some deep-bodied, mother-of-pearl- and mauve-striped ones. These were slightly more sluggish.

When Alma and Fred had left the pool and gone to dress, I lingered quietly in the cool water, floating just under the shade of the bank. Two of these mauve-banded fish were very busy darting in and out of a small hole. I watched, and could just see their gasping little faces peering out from the gloom. One would suddenly dart out, flash hither and thither, come to rest opposite the hole, and finally back into it and disappear again. This went on for a long time, so I got a long thin twig and pushed it into the hole. Imagine my surprise when the two fish seized hold of it and pulled, while at the same time a whole multitude of tiny replicas came streaming out and went buzzing off along the bank. When the little army came to an end, the two big ones let go the twig and flashed out after them. Apparently this pair were guarding and probably feeding their brood, although the latter were themselves quite well developed and able to get about.

Arriving back at the tent, I was met by a rather worried-looking George holding a small tortoise. Now George Flowers has proved to be one of the most hard-working and serious-minded blokes that I have ever had the good fortune to employ. Perhaps this is because he could not by the wildest stretch of the imagination be classed among that assorted breed of tropical servants invariably and often quite inappropriately called "boys." Many times we have thanked the fates that George was a man, for, as is usual in our small household, he, as skinner, necessarily became its mainstay. It was doubly important on this trip, because much work fell to him that was not purely routine, but required what one might call a steady eye for reality. I had been instilling all this into him, and it was the first time that he was to show his worth.

"Where did you get that?" I asked.

"I find it on a tree, sir," he answered in his Belizarian English which, like many a patois, is impossible to translate satisfactorily.

"What?" I asked. "Now remember what I said about this sort of thing, George."

"Yes, sir. I find it on a tree fo' true, sir."

Now the obvious retort is that you don't find tortoises on trees and some years ago we would have said just that and pretty forcibly too. However, time and life in the various tropical forests of the world have engendered in us a very considerable scepticism of most accepted theories about the behaviour of animals.

"Right, George," I said. "Let's see the spot."

While I dressed I had a look at the tortoise. It was a small box-tortoise (*Kinosternon*), called by George a "bokatora." Its plastron —that is, the under-shell covering its tummy—was hinged in two places, allowing the front and rear to be closed up after the head, limbs, and tail had been drawn in. I handed it over to Alma to have its portrait taken, and then set out with George.

We went down past the kitchen and the little house that he and Dick had built themselves, and reached the banks of the stream again. We crossed this, penetrated a bit of bush, and finally came out at another bend in the stream. Here there was a wide fan of boulders, and upon this lay a number of dead trees that must have come down in a flood. George indicated a position upon one of these in the angle between the great roots that now pointed to the sky, saying that he had found the tortoise crouching there. I became very grim.

"Now listen, George," I started, "you were really quite right to tell me that you found this animal on a tree, but suppose I had not come to investigate. What do you think I would have recorded about the animal?"

"I don't quite understand," said George, and I believe that is where I first really came to like this chap immensely.

Ordinary mortals can have little idea just how profound such a simple statement can be under certain circumstances. Few will

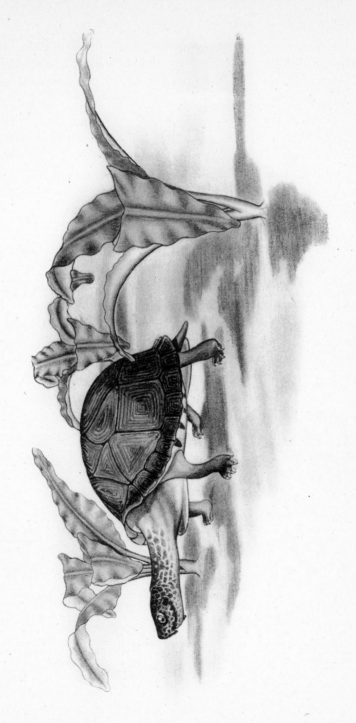

BOKATORA TORTOISE (Kinosternon creaseri)

realize the rarity, nay even the uniqueness, of such a remark in the Caribbean. The good people who inhabit these countries—and by this I don't mean only those of undoubted African ancestry—seem to be absolutely incapable of admitting that they don't know a thing. The first thing that comes out of a Central American's mouth is an excuse, the second is a lengthy statement of inaccurate facts, and the third is silence. Therefore I was now overjoyed.

"Well, George, that's perfectly splendid," I enthused. "As long as you say that, I don't mind what you do. Now listen; no harm has been done, but I want to make quite sure that you *do* know just what I want. When you find an animal, I want you to tell me exactly where you got it, not only whether it was in the water or in a tree or on the ground, but exactly where and in what kind of water or tree. In fact," I added, seeing that my employee was brightening visibly by the minute, "I want a complete picture of the whole business, even if you talk for half an hour."

"I understand, sir," he replied, and then added as he nearly always did, when he *did* understand, "Fo' true, sir."

I felt extremely good, and was immensely pleased with George. I delivered a long lecture on the "order" Chelonia, or tortoises. I explained that they were not known to live in trees, whereas a dead, fallen tree in a stream-bed was a likely place to look for them. I went further; I made the bold statement that they could not climb trees. Then I saw a new kind of lizard.

"Quick, George, quick!" I said, pointing to the quarry, which was a large kind of *Anolis* with a red stripe down its smooth, immaculate, beige back and which was sitting upside down on the bole of a tree that grew from the stream bank, and bobbing its head up and down. We began to creep forward.

The lizard saw us and stopped bobbing to watch with its sparkling golden-rimmed eyes.

"Don't try to catch it, George, just keep its attention while I get close up behind the tree," I ordered.

I manœuvred carefully, and finally, peering cautiously round the bole, made a sudden grab from both sides of the tree at once. I misjudged the girth of the bole, and my hands just failed to meet, so that the lizard jumped about and started up the tree.

"You watch it; I'm going up," I called to George, and then jumped for the first branch.

"Where is it?"

"Over this side, sir, going up slowly."

"Can I reach it now?"

"No, it's going along that branch."

"Quick, George, get up that other tree, the big one, yes."

George went up, and I advanced along the branch, the lizard ahead of me. Soon we all began to converge near a big fork in the other tree through which my branch passed.

"Now grab it, George," I called, as the reptile suddenly sprinted forward.

"Here! What are you doing, George?" I yelled, "Hi! Look out—" But the lizard shot above him and was gone.

"Why on earth didn't you catch it?" I asked.

"Sorry; oh, sorry, sir," he said, looking abject and at the same time very queer.

"What's the matter?" I asked.

"Do you want this?" he said, holding something above the leaves.

"What is it?"

"A tortoise; a bokatora, sir."

"Where did you find it?" I asked suspiciously.

"Here," said George. "Here in the tree; fo' true, sir."

And it was unquestionably so. The tortoise had been comfortably nestled among a bed of dead leaves caught in the fork of this nearly perpendicular tree, eighteen feet above the ground—which was amazing, but which clearly pointed two morals.

LESSER OCCUPATIONS

A Pygmy Marmosa, Pouched Spiny Rats, and a Yellow-Jaw

AFTER dinner, while reviewing the events of that first day, we had a conversation which brought up a rather interesting point. Fred told me that before he had met us and got to know the jungle he had supposed the great equatorial forests were like limitless zoological gardens. He said that from books and films, and more especially from reading my accounts of the jungles, he had conceived such places to be a more or less solid mass of animals, interspaced with trees. Alma seconded this statement, and they both agreed that the thing which had most impressed them about the jungle was the almost complete absence of animals, apart from birds and insects, and the scarcity of even the former of these. Alma pointed out how exceptional this day had been. It was not until I pondered these remarks that I began to perceive how true they were.

I realized then that I had got into the habit of considering each new locality we chose to visit to be merely a rather worse collecting-station than the last. I therefore mentally reviewed my notions of the jungles that I had visited in the past, and discovered that they appeared to be positively crammed with animals of all kinds. Moreover, the further back into the past I delved in my mind, the more animals the jungles seemed to have contained. I now saw clearly that this was only a trick played by time on my memory. We possess diaries of every day we have spent in the wilds, and I now distinctly

95

remembered having been much impressed, in going through these, by the frequency of days when the number of animals collected was either *nil* or very paltry.

It therefore stands to reason that this narrative gives an entirely inaccurate picture both of the jungle and of our lives in it. The whole of it could be told in a few hours, and all its incidents could be run off on a movie screen in only a little longer time. The aggregate number of hours which are specifically mentioned herein is relatively small, whereas the actual period covered is more than a year, of which all but a few weeks was spent in the jungle or at least in the field. What happens to the rest of the time?

It is simple enough to give an exhaustive account of how that time which is *not* spent in the wilds is consumed: it is, for the most part, a dry history of shipping offices and ships, good hotels and bad hotels, funny people and very dreary people, and many petty troubles and annoyances mostly accruing through one's own carelessness and inefficiency. But the time spent in the wilds between noteworthy adventures is a very different matter, and is part of the story that is customarily passed over and left unmentioned.

After mature consideration we have come to the conclusion that the greater part of this time is spent doing the following things in the following order of importance: walking, sleeping, attending to the specimens collected, mending things, writing, eating, counteracting the ministrations of insect pests, and, finally, talking. Of these, the first occupies more time than all the others put together, since it includes going to and from trap lines, hunting with guns or turning over logs or employing other methods for finding animals, mapping, examining the flora, cutting hunting trails, and exploring the bush. We estimate that our household is out in the forest, "walking," for at least twelve hours a day, if the time thus spent by the three most active members is added together.

This means that we are in the jungle actually searching for animals at least a minimum of three thousand hours a year. And yet I would not like to state that we actually see even as many as two hundred live mammals in all that time. Of course, we meet a great number of smaller creatures, lizards, frogs, arachnids, snails, and so forth, and we see countless birds and fish and insects, but for the mammals as a whole, two hundred is probably an over-estimate, while of the larger and more exciting ones I doubt if we see more than could be counted on the fingers of our hands. This is what makes these latter encounters of ours so vivid.

This would not be the state of affairs on the open plains of East Africa, where the whole landscape may be black with great game animals, or in certain exceptional places that I have visited personally, where several troops of monkeys were in sight at once. Though there *may* be places in the jungle proper where some animal is always in sight, I have yet to see such a place, and I have now visited quite a number of tropical jungles. The truth is, animal life—especially mammal life—is rather scarce in the jungle. The variety of jungle creatures is very great, and they are pretty evenly distributed through the vast areas they inhabit, but in the broader sense they are never so numerous or so obvious as the inhabitants of the open country. If anyone tells you otherwise, there is at least an even chance your leg is being pulled—and this goes for local inhabitants and natives of these countries just as much as for explorers, bug-hunters, cinematographers, and travellers.

We have recently referred to that portion of our diary covering the first week at this camp in British Honduras, and it shows that on the second day we obtained five lizards of three different species, two different frogs, a small scorpion, and one tiny, free-living red mite. On the next day we recorded nine lizards of two species, one specimen each of three kinds of frogs, and a toad, a centipede, and some small arachnids. In fact, it is not until the sixth day that anything really exceptional turned up, although we were out searching relentlessly every day. In the interim, the traps had landed two much-damaged rats, and we had accumulated a fair assortment of reptiles, frogs, and lesser life. Of large mammals we had neither seen nor heard a sign; moreover, we had seen few large birds, no parrots, and not a sign of a snake.

One of our primary tasks upon arrival at a new forest site is to cut small, clearly recognizable trails as far as possible in straight lines to north, south, east, and west of the camp. We first do this roughly, extending the paths as far as we can in a week, and working either in pairs or in relays. Subsequently we do a more accurate chain-and-compass traverse of these paths, and map them, before cutting others leading from them or directly from our camp to streams, exceptional types of vegetation, trap lines, or other particularly interesting localities.

These primary hunting trails, or "traces," as they are better called, are of the utmost importance for several reasons. First, they greatly reduce the danger of our getting lost, especially in the early days, though this is easy enough to do at any time, in the jungle. Second, it is only by means of these traces that any successful hunting can be done after dark. To take a gun and set off into the forest at night is perfectly useless, because even if you can get through the tangle, you make such a noise that any animal will run long before you can get within range. Third, these traces diminish the likelihood of twisting an ankle between unseen boulders, and the less likely mischance of stepping on a snake. Last, they are the only means of getting about quickly so that a reasonable area of the forest may be explored, examined, searched, and finally mapped in detail. The latter is a very important part of our routine work.

We had on this occasion cleared some two miles of trails, the main trace extending from a point just below the camp, at the first angle in the stream-bed, directly up and over the farther bank. This passed through a low flood plain which was overgrown with wahas and palms, thence ascended a steep bank upon which grew a forest of saplings, and stretched away through a level area that was covered first by a forest of immense, spreading fig trees and, further on, by a rather stunted growth of various species with a continuous layer of wild coffee (*Rinorea*) below them. Fred and George had been extending this trace during the afternoon, while we had been busy with the morning's catch. After dinner, Alma and I took guns and torches and set out on the first night-inspection of the new trace.

We were crossing the little flood plain bordering the stream, when there was a distinct rustle at the top of a palm. We flashed up our torches just in time to see a frond move abruptly, and then there was a startling "plop!" just behind us. We wheeled about in time to see a small sapling, some eight feet tall, sway giddily. Puzzled, we began examining it. A dozen leaves no bigger than a hand were all it could boast, and it stood isolated from all the surrounding vegetation, yet we could see nothing, and so waited, mystified, for further developments. There was another "plop!" and the sapling swayed again.

It was now obvious that something was moving on or about it, so we bent the sapling gently downwards and, sure enough, there was the cause of the plops. Clinging to the upper surface of one of the leaves was a bright yellow tree-frog, all neatly packed up with its legs tucked beneath it and its great eyes staring into the torch-light. It must have leaped down from the palm tree. This proved to be the same species (*Hyla baudinii*) that had given the imitation of a self-starter. It was pale yellow all over when we placed it in the bottle, but later it turned slowly to ochre, and then dark markings appeared on its upper side. By the time we got back to camp that night, it was variegated dark chocolate on a pale coffee ground. Next day in bright sunlight it turned to an even, dark brown above, while the limbs became vividly cross-barred with dark and light brown.

Had it not been for this chance capture, we would never have caught the real prize that night. Although we look about pretty carefully at all times, we don't normally devote special attention to low, more or less leafless saplings. We now did so with great care, and were soon rewarded.

On the bank we spotted another even smaller plant, a mere seedling, that was also swaying unnaturally and, running forward, we saw what we took to be a small brown rat clambering laboriously up the stem. We watched the little animal until it reached the summit, where it sniffed about quite undisturbed by the torch-light. It then began carefully descending the opposite side of its diminutive world. We moved forward to capture it, and only then noticed that it *grasped* the tiny twiglets with its "hands" and feet, not as a rat but as a monkey would do. Instantly we knew what had puzzled us about the gait and movements of the beast, for it was not a rat at all, but a tiny opossum only three and a half inches in length.

The little animal spotted us and became greatly agitated. He hurried down a twig, made an absurd little jump out into space, and just reached the curving leaf of a silkgrass (*Æchmea*), which is a hard, green plant like a pineapple, with curved hooks along both edges of its leaves. The opossum hustled forward, planting his little hand-like paws firmly upon the flat surfaces of the silkgrass frond. We couldn't grab him there because of the sharp hooks on the leaves, and so had to direct his advance to another slender sapling, onto which he clambered with some difficulty, panting hard. I now picked him up by the scruff of his neck as easily as I could have done a new-born kitten.

This animal became a most delightful little pet. He was a *Marmosa mexicana*, one of the small, pouchless opossums. His coat was rich reddish-brown above and pale apricot below, the fur being extremely soft and silky. Around his eyes were black spectacles, and his huge ears, his muzzle, and his tail were naked and shiny and mauvish-steel in colour. His hands and feet were pale pink, and his face was dominated by a pair of rather protuberant, lustrous, black eyes. We kept him in a small cage, because he quickly divested himself of any form of collar or harness with his efficient little monkey hands, assisted by his needle-sharp teeth and thumbed feet. He slept all day rolled up inside a ball of tow, but was very active at night, when he devoured a prodigious volume of the insects that were attracted by the light and flew into his cage.

One night a rather foul beast came zooming into the tent and landed on Alma, sending her up like a rocket. It was a water-bug (some species of *Belostoma*), an insect of the type we call "water-scorpions" in England because they are provided with front legs that look somewhat like a scorpion's pincers. This one was just three inches long, and we fell on it at once to see if it was carrying any parasites. Many big beetles and sometimes other large insects have a

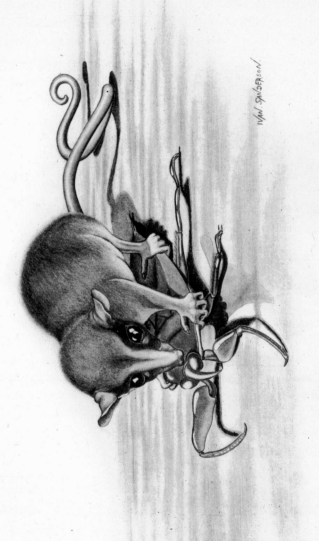

Marmosa Opossum (Marmosa mexicana) and Giant Water-Scorpion

whole host of mites running about on them, while some have small arachnids called "false scorpions," or with unwonted reasonableness *Pseudoscorpiones*, that live under their wings on the upper side of the abdomen. These remarkable parasites are just like tiny scorpions, but without tails, having small pincers which they wave before them as they run backwards.

This great insect had none, and I was just going to throw it away when Fred suggested giving it to the opossum. This idea seemed to have possibilities, so we pushed the large insect into the cage and sat down to watch.

At first, the little mammal, which was itself but little longer than the insect, backed away into the farthest upper corner of the cage, where it shook and quivered and wrinkled its ears while watching the insect's every move. We thought it was terrified, and were just about to come to its rescue when it suddenly leaped down and landed squarely upon the astonished insect's back. The little opossum clung desperately, clasping the sharp edges of the insect with its hands and feet, while it was rocked about like a rider on an aquaplane. Round and round the cage went the pair, the opossum riding the water-scorpion until we began to think that a technical impasse had been reached. Then once again the mammal made a sudden move. He unexpectedly anchored his prehensile tail to the wire of the cage side, and this manœuvre brought the insect up sharp, partly tipping him on end. In a flash the opossum jumped down, seized as many of the insect's legs as he could with his paws, and in one yawning snap of his pointed jaws lopped off his antagonist's head. He then jumped back and crouched like a dog to crack this with his molars. When he had devoured it, he advanced upon the still wildly thrashing body of the huge insect and, by judicious grabs and snaps, divested it of its prickly limbs. He then spent a happy evening leisurely taking the rest of the corpse to pieces and crunching up the hard bits. He left only the slimy mess that had served the water-scorpion as entrails.

Some nights after the capture of the opossum, it suddenly stopped raining. This was quite an event after dark at this time of the year, but it was too late to attempt any profitable hunting and I had not yet finished the evening's work. Fred took up the little collecting gun and meandered off around the camp, and when I had finished my work I took a torch and strolled out to join him.

After some time I found him standing absolutely motionless in one of the little hard-beaten paths that ran hither and thither about the camp, connecting the various houses and tents. He was quite rigid and peering steadfastly up into a prickly hone palm (*Bactris*), which was illuminated by his torch and stood not more than five yards from the path.

"Do you see something?" I whispered.

"I don't know, Ivan. D'you see something white on that palm frond?"

"Which one?"

"The one going to the left."

"Do you mean something lying along the top?"

"Yes; I've been watching that ever since I left camp, and it hasn't moved, but I can't make out whether it's a Marmosa or just a leaf. I don't want to scare it by moving."

"Why don't you shoot it?"

"I'm too close."

"Well, give me the gun. Keep your torch on it and let me try."

After this conference, I took the small gun and retreated as far as I could up the path, keeping the object in view. I took careful aim and let fly. The atmosphere was so damp in that forest that even the best powder caused a minor smoke-screen, so that we could not see what happened. When the smoke had cleared away, we examined the tree. The palm frond had been cut off clean exactly at the point where the object had rested, so we scrambled into the tangled vegetation and began grubbing around directly beneath. Alma arrived to join us, inquiring what the shooting was about.

Several minutes' careful search produced no sign of anything, and we were just about to give it up, believing the object to have been a dead leaf after all, when Alma, who had not known exactly where the thing had fallen or what it had looked like, let out a grunt and pushed her hand in front of the light. It was covered with blood.

"Here, put the light here, I've touched an animal," she said.

"Where? It couldn't possibly be so far away."

"Yes, I moved that branch. Here, look, here it is," and she picked up an animal right before our eyes.

It was a rat, coloured like the *Marmosa* but somewhat larger and with a very hairy—almost furry—tail. It also had black spectacles round the eyes and even the pink hands and feet. We have now learned that it was a *Nyctomys*, a well-known genus of tree-rat. At the time we thought it might be one of our special rats, and so carried it back to the tent in triumph and spent half the night lavishing every care upon its preparation.

The trapping had been exceptionally bad, even for a tropical forest in the wet season, which normally is very dismal. A hundred traps in three lines had produced only a few of the small reddish *Marmosa* opossums, some small birds, one or two large beetles that had inadvertently fiddled with the bait, and some young common opossums (*Didelphis marsupialis*).

The latter were, as usual, the commonest animals. Wherever you go in tropical America these creatures seem to abound. They are in the mangrove swamps pretending to be raccoons, and beating those animals at their own job; they are in the towns, competing with the ubiquitous black and brown rats; they are on the cultivated lands eating the crops and in the farms eating the chickens; they are in the forests, messing about in trees, in holes in the ground, and in caves; and you even meet them in pine trees, out on the open savannahs, or on the tops of cold and misty mountains. At this camp they became quite troublesome.

One night we were sitting waiting for dinner to be served. As usual, it had been raining hard all afternoon, but the occasion was, nevertheless, an auspicious one. Alma had prepared the fairest imitation of a full-blown curry that I have ever met, and by this I don't mean some nondescript chicken dish cooked in a thin soup containing some tinned curry powder. She had gone to much trouble to bring along certain fundamental ingredients, and had ingeniously improvised a red-hot sauce as well as all the little side dishes of chutney, prawns, cold lentils, and saffron rice. Dick was not only a good cook; he took a real interest in his cooking and in his kitchen, so that he was very gay this evening and singing loudly while serving the dinner. It was a beautiful night with a rising moon.

All of a sudden I saw something rounded and grey appear over the rim of the stream bank immediately in front of the open tent in which two three-hundred-candle-power lamps were burning. The stream was not more than twelve feet away from the already spread dinner table. This grey thing appeared and disappeared as it passed slowly along from right to left.

"Fred, what's that?" I asked, pointing.

"It's a dog, surely. It can't be, though. Is anybody coming?"

"Hardly, at this time of night."

"Hey!" I shouted, picking up a small block of wood and chucking it at the form. The round thing bobbed down, but instantly appeared again. Fred jumped up.

"I believe it's an animal, Ivan," he said, thus confirming our opinion that dogs aren't animals, but vermin.

"Get a gun, then," I suggested.

But before we could do this the small, arched back appeared in full view. It was a *Didelphis*, snuffling around with its long snout, apparently in search of the curry, the aroma of which filled the air. It advanced towards the tent, and when we made aggressive noises at it, the audacious beast merely opened its mouth and hissed at us.

Since we had many valuable things about the camp that might well appear edible to a hungry opossum, we dispatched this intruder—and when I say "we" I mean it, too, because we all had a try at shooting it before the tough beast, after leading us quite a chase through the thorny forest, finally gave up its tenacious ghost.

Apart from the afore-mentioned dismal list, the traps had produced only one species of mammal that was of interest. This was

Paul Sawtelle.

Pouched Spiny Rat (Heteromys desmarestianus)

a pouched spiny rat of the genus *Heteromys*, which is related to the pocket mice of the United States and, more distantly, to the pocket gophers.

These distinctive little creatures have rather long back legs, and lengthy tails tipped by a small brush of long hairs. Their heads are long and pointed; they have big ears, neat little forefeet, and are coloured reddish-brown above and white below. In all these respects they tally with forest-floor rats that are found in other tropical countries. Their particular claim to distinction is a pair of large pouches which have external openings on either side of the lower jaw. These extend up into the cheeks, and into them the rats crowd as much food as they possibly can. All manner of nuts and seeds—even the bitter mahogany seed—are crammed in, so that the animals sometimes appear to have heads quite two sizes too big for them. The fur of their backs is interspersed with many stiff, flattened spines.

Our primary interest in these little rodents was a study of the unusual variations that they occasionally displayed. Some were very dark, with only narrow white undersides and dark tails with a black terminal brush. Others were dark with light tails with a white brush at the tip. Still others were very light red with wide white undersides. Some even had the white extending from the chest right over the upper arm to join the pure white flanks, so that they wore dark gauntlets. We found that all this variation was purely fortuitous, but later, when we got out of the tall rain forest, it became of the utmost importance in tracing the detailed distribution of these animals and correlating it with that of the minor variations in the vegetation.

There is one night I shall always remember. Fred and I were up on a highish bank at a very late hour, engaged in a fruitless pursuit of some unseen but constantly grunting animal that was moving about the undergrowth. I was waiting in an open place under a huge nargusta tree (*Terminalia*), which was, as usual, hollow, and provided a good hiding place should the quarry come by. When a crashing finally broke out, therefore, I popped into the hollow tree and waited quietly. Then I thought I detected some movement close at hand, and flashed on the torch; but it was neither Fred nor a deer nor any other big animal. The noise was being caused by two *Heteromys* chasing each other over the floor of the forest.

The two rats were flying about the place in great, kangaroo-like leaps, whizzing between creepers, bounding over the wide-flung roots of the great nargusta, and creating a considerable disturbance. As they dashed about, they uttered continuous little low growls and high-pitched chatters. It appeared to be more of a gambol than a pursuit, for every now and then they would suddenly stop as if by mutual consent, and rest panting and quivering a couple of feet apart. Then they would be off again in headlong flight and pursuit, flashing among the roots and rubbish that littered the forest floor. They were quite undismayed by the light, and finally came right into the angle between the tree roots facing the opening of my re- treat. Here one of them cornered the other, and for a moment I thought there was going to be a fight, but instead they went into a performance that was as nearly a dance as anything I have witnessed in nature.

The ground by the tree was bare, and on this the two little rodents proceeded to execute a rhythmical series of leaps straight up into the air. First one, then the other, went up; then they would pause and with a concerted rush and a chattering, both would go up together. This continued for some time. Unfortunately, I could not see whether they were a male and a female, but if they were, this was almost certainly a form of sexual or mating play.

We once observed a pair of rat-like creatures known as *Præchi- mys* indulging in courtship antics in South America. They are also spiny-furred, live on the forest floor, and look very much like these *Heteromys,* though actually they are members of the porcupine group of rodents. These *Præchimys* dashed round in diminutive cir- cles first one way and then the other, and stood on their hind legs feigning fight. This performance given by the *Heteromys,* however, was more distinctly a regulated game. It was the regularity of the leaps, pauses, and concerted rushes, coupled with the fact that the cycle was repeated so many times, that prompts me to speculate on this being a courtship performance. Many of the female *Heteromys* that we trapped about that time were, moreover, in various stages of pregnancy.

Almost any night that one went out into the forest or even walked between the tents in the camp, one encountered these animals. Something would flash up out of the darkness into the torch-light from beneath one's feet, and go bounding away in prodigious leaps. In fact, this was about the only mammal we had seen and the only rat we had trapped.

The night is often the most profitable time to hunt, not only for game and mammals in general, but also for all smaller forms of life. Some days later Fred and I were starting on a night's search up the southern trace, as one or another of us had done almost every evening for some time. This trail crossed the creek by means of a large fallen tree, and then plunged into a thick undergrowth full of arching palms. Fred had gained time by fording the stream, and so entered this palm grove some distance ahead of me. The beam of his torch had momentarily disappeared, and I came upon him most unexpectedly as I rounded the base of a huge dead tree.

He was standing as if frozen, his torch-light concentrated on a point between two of the buttress roots at the base of the tree.

"What is it?" I whispered.

I got no reply, and he continued to stare. Then, all at once, I saw it too. Projecting through a slot-like hole in one of the rotten buttresses was a flat, evil head with a pair of obliquely set eyes that stared unflinchingly. It was the business end of a snake, but just how large a one we did not at that moment realize.

Anybody who has met a poisonous snake has had an adventure in the strict sense of the word. An adventure need not be exciting or dangerous, and the vast majority of encounters with snakes are neither of these; nor are they, as a rule, either humorous or noteworthy enough in any other respect to warrant recounting. What subsequently occurred that night may perhaps be deemed to fall into the class of recountable snake happenings by reason of the quizzical turn that events took.

We wanted this snake for our collection, whatever kind it might be, and so, though both armed with shotguns, we encountered rather a problem. How was the specimen to be captured or killed without damage? The time-honoured method with snakes is to hold them down with a stick, but although a forest is composed of sticks of all sizes, one that is both long enough yet short enough and not too rotten for holding down a large snake is a rarity at the best of times, and quite certainly not to be found at all when most urgently required. The only thing to be done was to cut a sapling.

For accomplishing this, the best instrument is a machete, but that night we had none. Our only implement was a hunting knife which Fred was carrying, and so, after a hurried and whispered conference, he put down his gun and, selecting a tough, thin bush-stick, began hacking away with the knife. The noise he made and the movement of his light apparently convinced the snake that we meant business—or, possibly, that its motionless imitation of a piece of the dead tree had been unavailing. It began to pour through the slot towards us and in the general direction of a thick pile of rubbish into which it might well disappear altogether. I called to Fred. He looked round hurriedly and uttered a loud oath, which at the time I took for an expression of annoyance at the ineffectiveness of the knife in cutting the sapling.

At this, the snake began to emerge from the hole even faster, whereupon Fred left the sapling and jumped for his gun. At the same time I stumbled around to the right to throw the beam of my torch into the angle between the next two buttresses from which the remainder of the snake was coming.

When I parted the foliage and turned the beam of light on the tree again, I was amazed to see several feet of snake of considerable girth, instead of a couple of feet of moderate dimensions. For a moment I imagined that the snake might be only a "wowla," since its back was prominently marked with a pattern not unlike that of the commonest boa found in the country. I called my doubts to Fred, and was creeping forward to try to hold the animal down with my gun barrel, when I was brought to an abrupt halt. Almost at my feet a whirring rattle began, much like a rickety dynamo getting under way. I jumped back. Could the snake be a rattler? Were rattlers inhabitants of this country? If not, what could be happening? These questions flashed through my head while I again cautiously advanced and explored the foreground with the light.

The snake's tail was slender, and extended from between the buttresses towards me among the mass of dry leaves. It was almost invisible because of the natural camouflage of its colouration, but some three inches of the tail-tip were turned upwards. This slender tip was being violently vibrated by its owner, and whirred like a machine among the dead leaves and twigs. But it was not a rattler.

All this manœuvring took but a few seconds, and as soon as I had ascertained that the snake was in all probability poisonous, and mightily so considering its length and girth, I announced to Fred that I was going to shoot it. Moving back as far as I could, I aimed well away from the head at about the centre of its length and fired. The whole charge of small shot found its mark, but was not sufficient to ruin the specimen, for it was very stout indeed.

The snake recoiled violently. The hinder portion of its body slumped down in a mass and it whipped its fore part back through the slot in the buttress. We both jumped forward, and I pushed my gun barrel over the snake's neck. Fred began tearing a long strand of liane from a neighbouring tree-trunk. He was in the process of constructing a tough noose to slip over the writhing animal's head, when I had to shout for his help because the powerful brute had begun to squirm free. The great, triangular head, which had been immediately beside my gun barrel, was now more than a foot beyond it. As Fred took up his gun, the snake rounded and struck viciously at my barrel. He opened his jaws to an angle of more than ninety degrees, bared three-quarter-inch fangs, and struck again, meeting the hard steel with a whang. As he recoiled, the other gun barrel descended on his neck, but again he squirmed ahead, aided by the soft, resilient bed of leaves below, and I had to jump to hold him down once more. This time he was held more securely, and Fred grabbed him firmly just behind the head while I seized the creeper noose.

That snake was very strong, and its lashings and writhings made it very hard to hold. I focused my torch beam on Fred's hand preparatory to slipping on the noose, and recoiled with genuine shock. It was covered with blood!

"Good heavens! Are you bitten?" I gasped.

"No; I hacked my hand instead of the sapling when you called me," he told me.

"Well, look out!" I yelled and, seizing his hand, turned it upside down so that the snake's head pointed to the ground. I had seen something that really shook me.

Fred had been holding the snake away from him, its head in the air, its body trailing on the ground. He had seized it from above, so that its throat and mouth—or, rather, the roof of its mouth—were directed away from him. The lower jaw of a snake is a loose affair constructed so that it can stretch when large prey has to be swallowed. The lower jaw was now twisted sideways out of its normal position by Fred's thumb, so that the fangs projected over its edge and onto the throat. What I had seen and Fred had not, was that each time the snake gave a convulsive jerk, a great blob of crystal-clear, yellowish poison squeezed from the tip of its fangs and gathered on his thumb. At the base of that thumb was a cut an inch long and some quarter of an inch deep which was oozing blood. The poison was already running down the thumb directly towards the cut, when I turned over his hand.

Exactly how bad this poison would be entering a deep, open wound rather than being injected under the skin by the animal's fangs, I did not then know. I later learned from the cautious medical profession that there would have been little difference, but naturally at that moment I was not greatly interested in the mere degree of the risk.

Thus began the quizzical act of this little drama. Picture to your-

self somebody holding a deadly strip of writhing animation by a
yielding, squashy and slippery extremity, in such a position that
liquid from that extremity could not run on to his hand; and another
body—somewhat agitated, though frightfully eager—skipping around
by the light of a torch trying to pop a noose of creeper over said
fast-disappearing extremity. As the snake slipped, poor Fred's hand
became ever more strained, for the harder he had to grip. The
further it went, the less chance I had of getting the noose behind its
head and the closer the naked, death-dealing fangs came to Fred's
flesh. The scene would doubtless have been quite ridiculous to a
chance onlooker, but it was grim enough to us.

Events moved far faster than they take to record. A few seconds were sufficient to show us that it was too late for the noose.
The only thing to do was to get the dreadful head onto the ground
and hold it down with the gun butt, and all this time Fred was
making furious efforts to keep his hand upside down and still retain
a grip on the snake.

Yet here again we met a ridiculous problem. The angle at which
Fred's hand had to be kept to prevent the poison from running into
the cut was so awkward that there appeared to be no way in which
he could release the snake without a possibly fatal moment during
which the animal might give a jerk backwards and drive its fangs
into his hand. We attempted all possible positions with a kind of desperation, but to no avail. And still the snake was imperceptibly slipping back, its head retreating by hair's breadth after hair's breadth
into the palm of poor Fred's hand.

Then we had a brainwave. It came tingling through my head
like a refreshing cool blast. I searched madly through my pockets
for a handkerchief, and in a second the cool blast turned to a flame.
I hadn't one!

"I've got one," said Fred, uncannily sensing my object, but I already had my shirt tail out. Stripping this off, I gathered it in
hastily at both ends and clamped it into the gaping mouth of the
reptile—and only just in time, for the snake gave a tremendous jerk
and Fred let go from pure exhaustion. For an instant I had the

animal suspended by its fangs alone from the sausage of cloth between my hands; then I dropped it and banged my boot boldly
down on its neck, ramming it into the earth with my heel.

"Keep your hand down!" I yelled, for out of the corner of my
eye I saw Fred instinctively raising it to his face.

And so we stood for quite a minute in yet another quandary.
Both the guns were now unaccountably out of my reach and I
dared not let Fred move until I could inspect his wound and ascertain to what extent the poison had flowed. This had to be examined
first, while I remained rooted to the spot covering the reptile's head.

The poison was very close indeed to the wound, so we covered
it with two thicknesses of the one precious handkerchief and Fred
retrieved a gun, which we planted on the snake's neck with perhaps
rather unnecessary force. Only then did we realize that we were still
within calling distance of camp. We let out a concerted howl for the
capable George, and as soon as he arrived and took charge of the
snake, I hurried Fred off to the stream, where we very carefully and
thoroughly washed the poison-covered thumb.

When the snake was finally brought in and we examined it by
the strong light, we discovered that it was five feet, eight inches of
Fer-de-lance (*Trimeresurus atrox*), known locally as the "Yellow-
Jawed Tommy-Goff." Its tail was terminated by a sharp, recurved,
horny spine, slender and fine and half an inch long. This was what
had caused the sharp whirring among the leaves, and probably
saved us from much direr happenings.

POMPOSITIES

Various Anolis, *Some* Fundamental Facts, *and* Dissecting a Jungle

T HE commonest animal on the floor of this British Honduras forest was a small lizard (*Anolis ruthveni*), coloured dark reddish-brown and of an average three and a quarter inches in length, including its rather blunt-tipped tail. The males of this species had deep old-rose gular fins with an indigo-blue spot in the centre. The females were without fins. This species proved to be confined exclusively to the tall southern jungles, but there it was always to be found.

In addition to this species, there were four other types of *Anolis* in this forest. There was a very large, bright green one (*Anolis biporcatus*), the males of which had gular fins of a dirty brownish-white edged with vivid orange and flame and spotted irregularly with pale powder-blue. The females had gular fins of glistening white with elongated, jet-black spots. This species averaged one foot in over-all length, lived on trees, and changed colour more rapidly than any chameleon.

Also on tree boles was to be found another large species (*Anolis capito*), which was variegated in colour like lichen, usually being mixed greys, silvers, greens, yellows, and browns. Its gular fins were dark mustard-yellow, with all the scales vivid white. This animal had a short head and large eyes. Then there was the species with a slender, elongated head, which did not change colour at all. This was the fellow George and I had chased when we found the arboreal tortoises. We captured all these during the first two or three days, but it was more than a fortnight before we came across the fifth species. Before we were through, this *Anolis* gave us several collective headaches.

This species changed colour rapidly and violently under the least provocation. The only constant features by which we could recognize it were its general form, which rather closely resembled the common fence lizard of Belize, the colour of the irises of its eyes, which were orange-gold, and its gular fins. The latter were of two kinds: the first was small and pale yellow throughout; the second was deep pinkish-orange with lines of black-bordered white scales, but when this fin was closed, the whole throat and chest was suffused with old rose. Both sexes displayed both forms. This lizard was customarily pale grey with vivid chocolate markings.

We found this species only on the fronds of palms in patches of sunlight, and they were all in the vividly marked colour phase when taken. These facts would have constituted nothing more than an isolated and rather interesting record, had it not been for a chance occurrence. Dick, our cook, caught two of these lizards when we were out hunting, and left them alive in a jar on our work table outside the tent, which was in deep shadow.

When we came back, we found what we at first thought were two of the ordinary fence lizards (*Anolis sagrei*), for both were now a uniform dark brown, just as those in Belize were on dull days. We made inquiries as to where they had been found, and when Dick showed us the palm on which he had taken them, we realized that they must be this fifth type of forest *Anolis*, which we had named Type C.A. 16 (because it was the sixteenth kind of lizard we had found in Central America). We did not then know to what extent this species could change its colour, and so we placed the jar in bright sunlight to see what would happen.

In due course the lizards changed again, but when we looked at them we were amazed to find that they had now donned another of the more common variegated colour phases of the Belize fence lizards. This brought up the question as to whether they were indeed of this species or in reality quite different, but able to don certain of the colour coats of that species, like the Jamaican *Anolis* mentioned above. In the hope of deciding this question, we experimented with them further by altering their environment in a number of ways—heating them first in dry and then in wet atmospheres, cooling them, and subjecting them to various degrees and qualities of light. They responded rapidly to all these changes, providing us with a whole series of different colour phases and patterns, each caused by a different set of conditions.

When we compared this range with that of the Belize fence lizard (which we called Type C.A. 6), we found that a certain number of the colour phases were common to both lizards, and that they were brought about by similar causes, but also that each type displayed several phases that apparently could not be produced by the other. Reviewing these *odd* phases more carefully, we then found that they were caused by environmental conditions that were customarily found only in the habitats of the lizard that displayed them, and were lacking in the habitats of the other. Here, in fact, we had a literal demonstration of the puzzling phenomenon that I have mentioned above in discussing the *Anolis* of Jamaica.

These two lizard populations—one, Type C.A. 6, from the open, brightly lighted, ozone-filled air of Belize, and the other, Type C.A. 16, from the cool, windless depths of the jungle, with its dappled sunlight—could be identical in several colour phases under several distinct sets of environmental conditions. Yet under the normal conditions in which they lived, they were quite easily distinguishable and they are recognized as distinct species, i.e., *A. sagrei* and *A. bourgaei*. In addition, there was the matter of the gular fins of the males, which in some individuals of the forest type tended towards red instead of the yellow colouring.

To explain these facts, to state them properly, or even to point out their significance, calls for an exposition of those "theories requiring factual proof and hypotheses needing theoretical exposition" which were mentioned at the outset and which form an integral part of all our work. To do this properly would entail not only a summary of the whole history of biological science, but also a great mass of intricate reasoning together with voluminous proof of a rather painfully technical nature. This would be out of place here, and yet it befits the intimacy with which I am trying to show you the life of the jungle that some brief explanation be given.

The essence of the whole matter is the study of the linkage that exists between faunas and floras through the climatology of their environment. This sounds rather like the announcement of the last lecture in an advanced biology course, but it can be put in other words though not quite so quickly or so simply. It means that groups of animals go with, or are found among, certain groupings of plants, or plants grouped in a certain manner, by reason of the particular little "climates" that those groups of plants create. For example: the birds and beasts and insects found in a pine forest are distinctive, and are there—and *always* there—owing primarily to the kind of light, the temperature range, the amount of wind and moisture and so forth that are characteristic of that forest and which suit them—and thus, indirectly, owing to the pines themselves, which bring about this particular combination of conditions.

This study is called ecology, as it is probably unnecessary to mention. To be more precise, it would be preferable to say that it is included in the science of animal ecology. The particular aspects of this science in which we are most interested, and which comprise the "theories requiring factual proof," etc., mentioned above, really lead from ecology to another branch of biological study.

This other branch is what we call systematics, or taxonomy, which means the classification of plants and animals by their appearance, their comparative measurements, and, finally, by the details of their anatomy. This study is intended to classify animals so that the forms which are truly related may be brought together. This work has been proceeding for centuries, and has now arrived at a comprehensive system of classification, covering all animal and plant life, which is, except in certain details, real, workable, and useful. It is based upon the minute study of all forms of life.

Now with but very few exceptions, taxonomy has necessarily been prosecuted through the examination of dead and preserved animals. This could not be avoided, nor was there any need for workers to do otherwise, for the results obtained were real and practical. Recently, however, it has been found that although the classification system fits the facts in all major respects, it may break down when applied to the ultimate details. When the final classification and division of animals into species and sub-species and varieties, as determined and prescribed by a study of their dead remains, is compared with nature, it is found that the two do not always fit. An example of such a discrepancy is the *Anolis* lizards C.A. 6 and C.A. 16.

When dead and preserved, these two kinds would lose their natural colouration, and would give no indication of the great range of chameleonism of which they are capable in life. Academic taxonomy might without hesitation class them together as being identical and of the same species, more especially if they both hailed from the same country; or the same science might just as readily and correctly separate them as two quite distinct species, basing the supposition on differences other than the colour in life. We have seen, however, that though they differ greatly in the colouration they *normally* display, in the precise range of changes they can undergo, and sometimes in the colour of the gular fin (and also, what is much more important, that they differ greatly in the types of habitat they occupy), they can appear at the same time identical under special circumstances. Furthermore, we collected specimens from between Belize and this jungle that took an intermediate position between the two types more especially in the range of colours and patterns that they could produce. Thus the two may actually be of the same "stock." This is quite explicable from the ecological viewpoint but most confusing from the taxonomic.

Sometimes variations in a "stock" are apparent even after death. In such a case the animals displaying them are usually described as "sub-species." But herein lies the danger. To stipulate that a certain variation is a definite sub-species, and to give it a distinct systematic name, rather implies that it constitutes a more or less stable form. It even suggests that it may have a precise geographical distribution, and that it tends to breed true to its type. This, however, is often found not to be the case in nature. The variations that may be noticed among preserved specimens may be purely fortuitous or linked with some special habit, while many that are not noticeable in this condition may be very real indeed.

Variation, moreover, may show "tendencies," so that, as one travels from one geographical point to another, the individuals of a particular species of animal that are encountered may slowly change in average appearance. After some distance, they may be almost unrecognizable from the form commonly found at the point where one started. These two forms in the dried and preserved condition, provided they had kept their true life appearance, would then be called different species, when it could be shown that they belong to one and the same stock in nature.

To obviate these difficulties, a new conception has within recent years been proposed and generally accepted. These strings of graduated variations are now called "clines," and the adoption of this concept has done much to make possible a truer correlation between the ultimate details of academic taxonomy and the reality found in nature. The reasons for clines are the same as for the differences we have noted between the two forms of *Anolis*. In fact, these differences were part of a cline, for we subsequently found intermediate types—not only types that were intermediate because of inhabiting "intermediate" geographical areas, but types that were intermediate in the ranges of colour changes they displayed. In the more pompous part of our work we are trying to show that each of these variations, however small, can be linked with some variation in the animal's environment—notably of the vegetation. We endeavour to discover and describe each of these changes and determine just how they affect the animals.

The ultimate details of systematics dealing with species and their variations must be sought in ecological studies of the animals themselves in nature, and not among collections of preserved specimens. It is only by collecting animals over a wide area in many different local environments, and recording all their variations as they really exist in life, that we can determine what truly constitutes a species. Each and all must be described separately and, if possible, the reasons for their variation discovered and recorded.

This is the work that occupies most of our time, and it is a study of the very greatest interest. We have been occupied upon the collection of these data on animal variation for a period of ten years now, in the three great equatorial forest blocks: the Orient, Africa, and Equatorial America. The paucity of the results we have obtained often rather depresses us, but certain fundamental concepts are becoming clearer every day. Among these are two outstanding principles, which are rapidly becoming united into a single underlying framework that appears to regulate the whole process of natural animal variation and distribution. There is nothing new about either of them, but stating them can do no harm.

First axiom is this: it appears that the distribution of animals is, to a greater extent than is perhaps customarily realized, regulated by the changes in climatic environment brought about by changes in the vegetation. As one examines this premiss more closely, it becomes apparent that this applies not only to clines and variations and sub-species of animals, but often to the species themselves and even to genera. Each recognizable difference in a population of animals can at least be correlated with some variation in environment, which in turn can almost always be linked with an alteration in the vegetation or with the choice by the animal of some special habitat in that vegetation.

The second principle is that the whole world is made up of an endless succession of what may be called "environmental niches." A jungle is made up of countless such niches, each slightly different from every other one in respect of its particular environmental conditions. So, for that matter, is every other type of forest or savannah or plain or desert or even ice floe, where there is no vegetation. It appears that all of these niches are filled with animals, and that each animal differs slightly in order to fit its own niche. If a new niche is created, it will immediately be filled by some animal suitable to it; if a niche is eliminated, its animal will either disappear or change to fit some other niche.

These two facts may appear to be almost too obvious to warrant mention. Indeed, once you think of nature in this light, it is difficult to think of it in any other way; and yet, until you have thought of it in this way, phenomena like the colour changes of lizards, or the sudden appearance of pests in areas where nature's niches have been destroyed wholesale, often appear obscure and puzzling.

Let us assume for a moment that all the animals we found in this jungle in British Honduras were occupying special and particular niches, and that their general form, colouration, and habits not only suited the particular environmental conditions found therein, but also had actually been bestowed upon the animals by those conditions. Would it not then be both reasonable and feasible to assume the corollary, and say that if an animal had a certain form and colouration and displayed a particular range of colour changes, it must come from a particular niche? This would seem to be at least possible, but it would call for a fairly extensive knowledge of the exact colouration and range of colour change common to animals of every possible kind of niche.

This is precisely what we are trying to find out and to tabulate, and, despite the lack of knowledge on this subject, despite the multifarious forms and colours of animals, the infinite number of natural niches, the endless variations of microclimate in the niches, and the interminable alterations in the vegetation, instances are daily becoming more frequent wherein some apparently correct predictions of this kind can be made. Let me give an example.

One day a forest ranger brought us a very beautiful lizard that none of us had previously seen. Its colouring was very remarkable, with vivid bands of black and bright green upon a broken green-and-yellow field. It was a form known as *Coryopthanes fernandezi*.

We considered this specimen upon the principles laid down above, and wrote down a description of the niche that we thought its colouration implied, stating the type of vegetation, the approximate

FOREST BASILISK (Coryopthanes fernandezi)

limits of the microclimate—temperature, humidity, exposure, etc.—
and the position in that environment that the lizard should occupy.
These notations revealed that the animal should dwell among foliage
on palms or on other leaves which gave a broad evaporating surface,
about twenty feet from the ground in a tall, cool, moist forest with
many lianes and epiphytic plants, with dappled as opposed to the
more common diffused half-light, with a certain mean temperature
and humidity range. In brief, such a niche as should occur in the surrounding tall rain forest, except for the dappled light which is not
a feature of this vegetation. Judging this lizard by our theses, however, it should indubitably inhabit *dappled* as opposed to clear or
diffused light.

We did not show these results to Señor Perara, the man who had
brought the lizard. Instead, we asked him to take us to the exact
place where he had captured the specimen. Now Señor Perara was
a responsible official who had many years' training with the Forestry
Department, so that there could be no doubt concerning his integrity. This is what made the experiment the more valuable. To
make a long story *brief*, he led us to an area several miles away,
almost at the edge of the great forest belt. Here we entered a zone
of vegetation that we had not seen before, and the existence of which
we had not suspected. In this he presently located a large monkey-
tail palm (*Synecanthus*), and pointed to one of its fronds as being
the exact spot where he had captured the lizard.

Now this palm at once fitted one of the lizard's hypothetical requirements. Also, it stood in a grove of its kind beneath many tall,
spreading fig trees. These two plants, moreover, dominated this
rather exceptional vegetational sub-zone. The fig trees bore large
but widely spaced leaves, all of which grew at the ends of the
branches so that they cast a dappled, broken light and shade upon
the palms beneath. Their trunks and main limbs were loaded with
ferns, orchids, bromeliads, and tie-ties, and there were many lianes
everywhere, just as we had predicted. Later on, we moved to a
camp nearer this locality, and took a series of accurate meteorological or rather microclimatic readings which, together with the gen-

eral ones kept throughout the year at the nearest forest stations, clearly indicated that the climatological requirements which we had deduced did indeed conform with the reality.

By coincidence and good luck, another type of the same genus of lizards (*Coryopthanes cristatus*) came to us while still in the same area but at a later date. This one was banded with irregular vertical black stripes on a pale beige, variegated ground, and had a beige-spotted white underside. Again we drew up a description of the environmental features that we surmised should be encountered in its niche, from hypothetical considerations and before seeing where it had been found. This time the requirements appeared to be even more bizarre and unlikely. In fact, by the time we had it living on the ground, in hot, dry grass but under slightly diffused light with a temperature and humidity that normally go with very tall, dense rain forests, we thought that we must at last have some definite proof *against* our theories. However, the premisses again stood the test, for this is what we found.

The lizard had been caught on the ground or only a few inches off it, in a large clump of "dumb-cane" (*Tripsacum dactyloides*), which covered the floor of a forest composed wholly of small pine trees which, with their fine needles, cut out only some of the light, and caused the rest to be somewhat diffused. The soil was sandy, bone-dry, and very hot. Lastly, this unusual area of vegetation stood at the edge of and was enveloped on three sides by tall, virgin rain forest. In fact, it was an edaphic zone, which is to say, one fortuitously brought about by the exigencies of the soil. It thus shared the general warm and very damp climate of the neighbouring tall forest, while itself having a very much drier microclimate.

Just as in the above cases, where the conditions pertaining to the habitat were predicted by analysing an animal's appearance, so also may it not be feasible to predict the animal's appearance, before it is seen, from an analysis of the relevant niches? This is fairly obvious: if you see holes in hollow trees in a tall, tropical jungle, you may assume that they may possibly contain night-prowling animals with thick woolly fur of such and such colours, and so on. The principle may, however, be taken a stage further.

Given a tall rain forest with certain known major climatic conditions, one may with permissible confidence predict therein a customary number of niches. These may be defined very narrowly. Thus we now recognize, from simple experience if from nothing else, that a forest such as we were in at this place in British Honduras has at least four niches for rats and that these niches are invariably filled by some rat or rat-like animal. These are: (a) on the ground, a long-legged species with a long head and tail, big ears, and a coat that is reddish-brown above and white below; (b) in banks, a small, dismally coloured, soft-furred mouse with small head, short limbs, slender, unhaired tail, coloured olive-brown above and grey below; (c) in trees, a medium-sized, heavy-bodied, arboreal rat with wide ears, very wide head, long whiskers, short, broad, light-coloured feet, very hairy, stout tail, and coloured red above, white below, and orange on the flanks; and (d) in low trees, a large, woolly-to-silky-furred species, usually with half-black and half-white tail, immense ears, long, stout head, and coloured mauvish-grey above and creamy-white beneath, that sometimes descends to the ground.

Having already found (a) in the guise of *Heteromys* and (c) in the form of *Nyctomys* in this forest, we postulated the existence of two other species of rats fitting (b) and (d). We explained the situation to George one day, and instructed him to lay two lines of traps by banks. The very first morning after this had been done we obtained a mouse (a species of *Peromyscus*) exactly fitting the requirements of (b). Later, as you will see, we trapped a perfect example of (d) in the form of a rat called *Tylomys*.

Investigation of these principles entails a considerable amount of study that is botanical and climatological rather than zoological. It is necessary to record everything possible about each niche from which we obtain an animal, and even about those in which we fail to find any animals, for negative evidence is of the utmost value. To this end we indulge in two routines.

The first is a daily meteorological record of the general climate and the little special climates of the niches, which is accomplished with the normal instruments. The second routine concerns the botany, wherein the principal operation is "dissection," no less detailed and often considerably more exhausting than that which is customarily performed upon an animal. Let me explain what I mean by "dissecting" a forest.

A jungle, like a body, is a complex organism constructed of many parts which interact, which can be grouped and are yet dependent upon one another just as the skeleton, the nervous system, the blood, the muscular, and other systems are in an animal. A bit of jungle breathes and grows and reproduces itself like a great animal.

The principal difficulty encountered in studying a jungle is that you can never see it. This may sound absurd. An average jungle is about one hundred feet tall, and is shaped like a much-flattened and inverted saucer, so that its edges slope down all around to meet the earth. When you enter it you become lost. You can't see the wood for the trees, and you often can't see the trees for the creepers, lianes, and epiphytic green plants that grow all over them. If you fly over a jungle in an airplane, you see even less, for nothing but a gently undulating, bumpy green mat is unfolded beneath you. If you climb a tree, you still do not gain any real conception of the jungle generally, for ants, leaves, humming-birds, and a riot of tangled vegetation obscure the view and bother you. In order, therefore, to find out just how any particular jungle or forest is constituted, it is necessary to dissect it.

Methods for doing this have been devised by forestry experts, and these methods, though laborious, are comparatively simple. We put them into practice at this camp after due time had elapsed, during which we had mapped the area in considerable detail and had roamed far and wide investigating the various included associations of plant types. The thing I like best about botanical study is that one's specimens don't run away. When you find something you've got it—as George would say, "Fo' true, sir."

We had quite a company for the first dissection. Our friend Neil Stevenson, the Conservator of Forests, had very kindly paid us a visit to act as a sort of father-professor to the proceedings. He had brought with him the forest ranger, Señor Perara, and his assistant, a quite remarkable chap called Carlos who knew local names for very nearly every tree and plant found in that part of the forest. In addition, we took along our three selves and the sturdy George, and the company was by no means too large for the job.

We set out into the jungle to a plot previously selected as being most typical of the first type of forest that we wished to examine. Here we marked out an area of 120 feet by 30 feet, the exact position of which was indicated on our detailed map, which in turn could be exactly defined on the general survey of the country. We then set to work cutting a wide trace round the outside of this plot, in order to isolate it and its vegetable contents from the surrounding growth. In doing this we all co-operated.

I distinguished myself at the outset by taking a swipe at a vine with a very sharp machete, missing it and splitting open both my trouser-leg and the skin covering my knee-cap. This rather reduced my active co-operation, but there proved to be plenty of other work to keep me busy. The plot was then divided into four blocks, each 30 feet square.

From each of these, every small plant forming the ground cover was uprooted and counted, the party working systematically from one end to the other, and each member calling out from time to time the numbers of the kind of weed, fern, seedling, or herb that he had chosen to collect. The details were entered in a book by a recorder. To each plant, the local name was given and then the total number present was worked out for each of the four plots separately. The proper scientific names which were known for all the local definitions were supplied later.

Even these first results would astonish most people. From what appeared to be a comparatively open, unencumbered bit of forest floor, no less than 2580 plants were collected, exclusive of the little green *Selaginella*, which belongs to a lowly group of plants even lower than the mosses and which here grows to about eight inches in height and spreads like a diminutive fern. These grew to the number of fifty per square yard, or 242,000 per acre! The seedlings were grouped as far as possible according to their species, as this would prove of much interest in drawing conclusions as to the future rehabilitation of such a type of forest, and also gave us valuable data on the seeds that are available as animal food on the forest floor.

This first operation cleared the ground of all small growth up to the height of a man's knee. The next thing was to do likewise with the smaller bushes and saplings—that growth which was not taller than a man. These were also listed and counted a quarter of the plot at a time. This done, a base line was drawn to scale along the bottom of a large sheet of paper to represent the long side of the plot. Vertical lines were then drawn at the equivalent of ten-foot intervals, and a series of horizontal ones representing ten feet of altitude. You probably can guess what the remaining operations were.

Every plant—bush, sapling, palm, or tree—was then sketched into this elevation, to scale and in its correct position as in nature. They were all numbered and named, and finally the parasitic plants growing upon them were also sketched in, named, and listed. The heights of the summits of the great trees had to be reckoned by primitive geometry, and sometimes necessitated cutting down much vegetation to get a view from a sufficient angle. In this last, there was something that gave us a few bad moments.

Looking up into a forest from below, it is very difficult to trace to just which trunk the billows of foliage belong. Together with the elevation, therefore, a plan of the plot was also constructed upon which the exact area covered by the head foliage of all the larger trees was drawn. From this we were able to calculate the degree of shade at any given spot, and the degree and quality of the light reaching the various strata of the vegetation and the ground below. In doing this we had completely failed to unravel a muddle at the summit of one of the giant trees. To estimate the height of this, we cleared away other vegetation to get a better view and, look-

A Dissection of a Jungle

Semi-diagrammatic representation of a plot (140 ft. x 15 ft.) of tropical rain forest in the wet sere, known locally as "mixed tall cohune."

Scale: 5/16 in. = 10 ft. Six-foot man in halo under banak tree to right.

Trees and tall shrubs: 1. (unidentified); 2. wild coffee (*Rinorea guatemalensis*); 3. white copal (*Protium sessiliflorum*); 4. cacho venado (*Eugenia capuli*); 5. waika plum (*Rheedia edulis*); 6. mammee ciruela (*Lucuma* sp.); 7. ironwood (*Dialium guianense*); 8. negrito (*Simaruba glauca*); 9. red copal (*Protium copal*); 10. mountain trumpet (*Cecropia mexicana*); 11. timber sweet (*Nectandra* sp.); 12. (unidentified); 13. maya (*Miconia* sp.); 14. banak (*Virola brachycarpa*); 15. matapalo (*Ficus* sp.); 16. kerosene wood (indet.); 17. cohune (*Orbignya cohune*); 18. monkey-tail (*Chamædora* sp. and *Synecanthus* sp.); 19. hone (*Bactris* sp.); 20. capuka (*Geonoma glauca*); 21. tree-fern (indet.).

ing upwards by the aid of a pair of field glasses, I, at least, got quite a surprise.

Growing on top of this giant tree, its roots commencing seventy-five feet above the ground and wrapping the upper branches of its host, grew a large Matapalo or strangling-fig tree (*Ficus sp.*), no less than thirty feet in height itself and with a not inconsiderable foliage spread.

That day and the following night we drew careful copies of our diagrams, and worked out the lists and counts in detail. This is one of the most fascinating occupations that we pursue in the examination of jungle life. From it emerges an exact picture of the forest—a picture, moreover, from which many further calculations can be made upon an exact statistical basis. This, combined with the maps of the local animal distribution and the sets of records of the minute variations of microclimate, gives a more or less complete picture of at least one bit of jungle and the reasons for the many odd habitats chosen and scrupulously adhered to by its animals.

"Look!" somebody will shout, pointing to some unsuspected strata of foliage slowly coming out in the drawing, "that's where the insects fly when the cool air rises at sundown. That's where all the bats fly. Now I see why they never leave that layer till later!"

And so it goes on, usually for the rest of the night.

B.-S. D.s AND THE ATTA

*Blood-Sucking Flies, the One Called "darlingi,"
and Wee-Wee Civilization*

I STOPPED collecting insects at the end of my first tropical expedition. This was not entirely due to lack of moral courage, induced by the vision of the countless myriads of these animals that swarm everywhere in the tropics, nor even to the fact that there are literally millions of carefully preserved insects in the world that have never yet been named, examined, or made use of in any way.

My first reason for abandoning the Insecta had been that I had to drop some groups of animals from my schedule, since one cannot collect everything and at the same time do useful work. Secondly, entomology has become almost a separate science from general zoology, and one, moreover, in which I was abysmally ignorant. Thirdly, the insects have had, and still are having, a good innings, since there are more entomologists than all other kinds of animal collectors put together. Of the latter, considerably more than half are ornithologists, so I stopped the collection of birds, too, but that is irrelevant.

Recently, however, through an ever-increasing interest in the diseases and pathology of animals themselves, we have found ourselves more and more drawn towards the medical world. For reasons which will be explained later, we have had to commence the serious collection of diseased organs and other evidence taken from wild animals. Moreover, our normal studies of internal parasites have led us in the same direction. Finally, we were persuaded to take up the collection of the blood-sucking Diptera, an investigation in which Alma is particularly interested.

Before we embarked upon this new group, Alma and I talked matters over and concluded that there was no reason why the distribution and incidence of flies should not be governed by the same laws as apply to other animals. We therefore decided to do the collecting along the same lines and with the same technique that we employ for all other groups. Thus no fly was to be acceptable unless full data relative to its particular natural environment were available. This proved later to be a thoroughly worth-while decision.

It seems necessary to digress for a moment, and offer an apology for the rather unnecessarily sanguinary mouthful, blood-sucking Diptera. In point of fact, I am at a loss for any simpler comprehensive title, because the group thus designated is a purely arbitrary one, and comprises an assemblage of two-winged flies hailing from several different families, all with quite outrageous names. The mosquitoes belong to the *Culicidæ;* sandflies to three families, the *Chironomidæ, Simuliidæ,* and the *Psychodidæ;* the horseflies, gadflies, and so forth belong to the *Tabanidæ,* and the tsetse flies to the *Muscidæ.* In addition to these are less well-known flies belonging to the families *Blepharoceridæ* and *Leptidæ* for which there are no English names. Finally there are the *Hippoboscidæ,* which we shall meet again later. The only things they all have in common are that they are two-winged flies of the order Diptera, and that they either habitually or occasionally suck blood. We personally call them collectively, B.-S. D.s, and leave it at that.

Alma duly set to work collecting these things, and in no time at all Fred and I were undergoing dire trials and tribulations as a result. She collected mosquitoes most systematically from all the possible niches that could be defined in the surrounding forest. Among these were several stands of balisiers, which are called wahas in this part of the world. These plants fascinated her not only because of their inherent beauty of form and their weird flowers, but because one species (*Heliconia champneiana*) proved to be one of her happiest hunting grounds for B.-S. D.s.

She found two species of mosquitoes and another B.-S. D. breeding in the water held by the sauce-boat-shaped sepals of its flowers. This flower, unlike those of the other Heliconias in this area, stands erect, is bright yellow, and holds a considerable amount of water which fairly swarms with small animal life, mostly eggs, larvæ, and pupæ of various small insects. These she transferred, complete with water, to jars, and it was here that life became rather difficult for Fred and me.

Alma got extremely enthusiastic about this mosquitarium of hers. The first we knew of it was one morning when the marmalade appeared at breakfast sprawled dejectedly over a plate, and we demanded to know what had happened. Dick grinned, as usual, and informed us that Mrs. Sanderson had emptied all the available jars. Mrs. Sanderson was, moreover, absent at the moment, so we ate our breakfast in comparative silence. Later Fred was summoned to the other tent. He soon returned looking rather purple.

"Listen, Ivan," he said, "Alma wants a box like this."

He produced a very complex plan and elevation, and spread it out before me. One look explained the matter of the marmalade. There were spaces for eight jam jars.

We conferred together and decided that the wisest course would be to try to talk her out of it. We tried this, and thought we had been successful, but that proved to be a complete misapprehension. Later in the day, sounds of hammering, off-key singing, and some rather dubious language floated to the skinning tables from Alma's domain. With evil intent, I refrained from going to ascertain the cause for as long as possible, but finally I could bear it no longer and went to investigate. Imagine my horror when the first things that met my eyes were several pieces of badly planed wood lying about— pieces that could have come only from our one empty case, which I had been treasuring for a very special purpose. A little bit farther on was Alma, wielding a hammer most ineffectually amid a welter of straw, nails, jam jars, and what-not. I was too late to prevent the obvious culmination of such activities. She had hammered a thumbnail and broken the best piece of wood.

"What are you doing?" I inquired rather morosely.

"Well, you wouldn't make me a mosquito box," she began, in a most feminine strain.

"I never said that. I told you we would make you one when we could do it properly," I retorted.

"But my mosquitoes keep on hatching out and pupating and I must have some place to put them."

"Leave them on the table, then."

"They might get knocked over."

"All right," I said, "as you have ruined the only good case we have, I'll make you a box. Now what exactly do you want?"

This produced a string of requirements which, when boiled down, was found to omit about seventy-five per cent of the paraphernalia called for by this particular work.

"Wouldn't it be better to have a case like this?" And I drew a rough sketch. "Then you would have all the things you want all together."

To my surprise, this struck a responsive chord. There were signs of wild delight, and so I started on the rather complicated task with the few rough tools that we carry to the bush with us. The process was slow and inefficient, because Fred, who is official carpenter, was away attending to the traps. I got tired, bad-tempered, and very touchy as time wore on. Then the final straw came in the form of Fred, who stalked into camp also hot, tired, and hungry. He asked what I was doing, and when I told him he growled at me.

"What the devil's the matter with you?" I barked.

"You can't make it that way. It'll never be any good."

"Listen," I said, now thoroughly peeved, "suppose you come and make the blasted thing yourself!"

"I can't do that," he said.

"Why not?" I demanded, and we glared at each other over the admittedly hopeless effort of wood and rusty nails.

"Because it will look terrible."

Then, on the heels of an answer like that, Alma must needs turn up and demonstrate that without a shadow of doubt the jars would not fit into the compartments which I had specially constructed for them.

After that there was a protracted period of wrangling during which we all changed sides. Fred now wanted to make the box just to show my inefficiency, I wanted to make it in the form of a simple tray because I had been unable to do the complicated bits, and Alma now didn't want it at all because we were being so difficult. It was a very trying time, but the mosquitoes eventually got housed and we still have the box.

These mosquitoes used to pupate and metamorphose into their final form at all odd hours of the day and night. It became quite a game getting the large, dark-coloured pupæ, which were ready to release the fully formed mosquitoes, into separate little bottles. There was then another hysterical period, when the insects ulti- mately did come out, getting them away from the water onto a matchstick so that they might dry off, before they should be killed and put away in the collection.

On one occasion a jarful of larvæ steadfastly refused to pupate. After some weeks they had grown prodigiously, and, as we were about to move, something had to be done. Alma therefore divided them among three jars and started experimenting. The first lot were warmed by placing the jar in hot water; these all died at once. The next lot got the same treatment, but the temperature must have been just right, for they all pupated in absolutely record time.

The remaining lot, however, refused to be hustled. On the last day before we moved, Alma got desperate. She emptied a pipette of neat whisky into their water, and I have never seen animals imbibe new life as they did. They skipped and wiggled around the jar till it made you dizzy to watch them, but they neither died nor pupated. In desperation, Alma gave them another "double" the next morning, but this seemed to improve their health still further. Finally we had to leave, and they were transferred to strong preservative al- cohol in which they succumbed, though I must admit to having passed a few ghastly moments of fantasy before they did so, imag- ining them living and thriving in pure alcohol.

Even with the primitive tools then at her disposal for this work, Alma was able to identify her catches as belonging to several different types. We were of course unable to define these species, knowing nothing about the systematics of mosquitoes, which is a most specialized job, but it soon became fairly obvious that these animals were indeed governed by the same laws of vegetation and environment that circumscribe all the other groups of animals that we were investigating. This became even more apparent some time later.

In due course, the flies were packed up—the wrong way, we later were informed, but then, one must learn by experience, I suppose!— and went off to Dr. Komp, medical entomologist to the United States Public Health Service at Panama, who had sought specimens for examination from British Honduras. They were gone some time.

In the interim we had many long talks with our friends in the Medical Department at Belize, and among the matters discussed were the local incidence of malaria, and its varieties. We had heard that the type of malaria around the district where we had been working was extremely virulent. The doctors confirmed this, and stated that the reason was at present unknown. They also told us that this same type appeared at certain other places, the exact positions of which were presently seen to bear considerable significance.

Then a telegram arrived from Dr. Komp, asking whether there was any possibility that some of the mosquitoes which we had sent down to him had come from some other country. Replying in the negative, we received further communications from him saying that some mosquitoes of a species known as *Anopheles darlingi* had been found in our collections. This, we were told, had not previously been recorded from north of Venezuela, and was of particular importance as a very dangerous malarial vector. Dr. Komp wanted to find out as quickly as possible just where this little brute was, and what it was doing so far north as British Honduras. He subsequently came up personally and found out plenty, which he has since recorded in appropriate places.

All this was very stimulating, and of some practical value to public health as well as to the mere study of mosquitoes. To us, however, it was more than gratifying for a particular reason.

Had we not collected our B.-S. D.s along the lines which we employ for other groups, and had Alma not paid attention to the detailed subdivision of the forest vegetation into a pattern of specialized niches and then carefully collected her mosquitoes from each, we would never have obtained a single specimen of these *Anopheles darlingi*. These insects, though numerous enough, were, at that particular season, found only in one very minor sub-zone. They were all caught on small flood plains, either by the streams or in old stream-beds now left high and dry in the forest, both of which supported a specialized flora and had a unique microclimate. Such detailed records and methods thus demonstrated their worth, but there proved to be an even bigger aspect of this affair.

In our work upon the flora of the country, we had the good fortune to have the help of the very active and highly scientific Forestry Department, which has the vegetation of the country well mapped. From this map, combined with observations which we have subsequently made in more northern territories, it has come to light that the incidence of this very virulent and often fatal type of malaria appears to coincide with the distribution of a certain type of vegetation or floral zone in which alone the very special sub-zone preferred by this mosquito can exist. The total extent of the major zone is great, extending far beyond the confines of British Honduras. We have now learned from quite other sources that this type of malaria is also found throughout the range of this particular type of forest.

If, therefore, it should turn out that this virulent malaria is carried by this particular mosquito—which of course had not previously been suspected of dwelling so far north—it would explain why the distribution of the two is coincident throughout the whole area. And this is just what is suspected. Our contention is that if you know the distribution of either the forest, the malaria, or the mosquito alone, you will be able to predict the range and incidence of the other two. In fact, this applies not only to these animals; the same methods can be adopted anywhere and with regard to any animals, plants, diseases, and so forth, the exact distribution of which it may be desirable to ascertain.

It so happened that on this occasion we also devoted some of our time to another group of insects. Our interests in this case were purely economic in that our principal object was the testing of methods of exterminating them, for they happen to be one of the worst insect pests in tropical America. These were a genus of ants known to science as *Atta* and to laymen as cutter-ants, parasol ants, or wee-wee ants.

These wonderful creatures are widely known, not only to the inhabitants of the countries in which they are found, but also to many people in other parts of the world who have taken an interest in natural history. They are also a favourite example to theoretical communists and other wholesale schemers in search of plans, who positively dote upon their socialistic organization. Like most other ants, they live in large, organized communities, dividing their labour and thereby getting much more done. They may indeed be called civilized, moreover, for they are in the agricultural stage of development but at the same time appear to be ethically much in advance of industrial communities.

The great strength of the wee-wee ants lies in their numbers and in their organization, for individually they are puny creatures. The smallest sterile workers are less than a fifth of an inch long; the largest of the big-headed, fighter-organizers hardly exceeds three-quarters of an inch in total length, and an average cutter carries his body but a quarter of an inch from the ground. To make up for their size and consequent lack of individual strength, however, they systematically increase their numbers and then maintain them instinctively—or intelligently, if you will—in proportion to the tasks that the community has to undertake.

The *Atta* live in subterranean cities or interconnected groups of cities which are sometimes of startling dimensions. Various experts have attempted to estimate the number of individual insects that inhabit the larger of these cities. The estimates vary between a few hundreds of thousands and several millions. We attempted various estimates ourselves, and, having discovered that two hundred of the ants could be placed in a tube an inch in diameter and one and a half inches in height, and having gathered spadefuls of the ants from an average nest, we were led to conclude that the higher estimate was nearer the truth. Let us, nevertheless, place the estimate at one million per fully established city, and ignore the small daughter cities, the newly established colonies, and the immense but rarer super-metropolises.

This number is nothing very astonishing in the insect world, especially when the teeming termite skyscrapers are considered. It is rather the number and wide distribution of these cities that make us pause and consider further.

We counted the cities and found that in the undisturbed virgin jungle in this country they existed to the average of sixteen per square mile, but that in the less tall, fringing forest, which surrounds the true jungle, their numbers had risen to thirty-six per square mile.

There are many parts of the world where termites' nests are more numerous, and there are pine woods at home where seething ant-hills are more frequent, but later we found that upon land which had been cleared there were no less than eighty-one to the square mile, while the introduction of cultivation upon such land resulted in the cities' increasing in number to the appalling figure of two hundred per square mile.

There are many animals that store their collected food, and there are a few that actually keep domestic animals of another species, but with the exception of a few insects which accidentally plant spores in a purely mechanical and very primitive way, the *Atta* is the only animal, apart from man, that has developed and perfected the practice of agriculture. This unique accomplishment is the essence of their success, and through this alone they have been able to advance many other of their activities to a degree of efficiency that sometimes surpasses our own. The time-labour released and made available to the *Atta* through this means has, moreover, made it possible for them to surmount obstacles which we humans are at this very moment struggling to overcome.

Two years previously, we had built our camp on top of one of these *Atta* cities in the jungles of Dutch Guiana. The ants were apparently not inconvenienced by our presence, and carried on their nightly activities throughout the period of our sojourn. Their main highways ran between our tents, and one of the principal gates to their city was immediately beside the cleared area where we took our meals in fine weather. We had ample opportunity to study their habits at that place, and became deeply interested in them.

Later we met an investigator who was making a special study of these insects, and we assisted him in digging up some cities. We were surprised then to find that there is still a great deal to be learned about the actual organization of these cities and even about the insects themselves. This is the more peculiar since the *Atta* are such a prominent feature of the American tropics and have drawn the attention of naturalists and laymen alike since earliest times.

As these insects are very serious pests in many localities, destroying crops wholesale, many methods have been suggested and tried for exterminating them. It may be safely said that none has proved completely successful, and that even those which are partly so do not seem to have the same effects in all localities. The famous naturalist Belt long ago recorded that corrosive sublimate was very efficacious in discouraging the *Atta*, and we were present at some preliminary experiments with this method in South America.

This substance has a most unusual effect upon the ants. As soon as they touch it they seem to go mad and start biting their brethren and fighting madly. This madness is, moreover, cumulative, so to speak, so that the more ants that participate in the fight, the more furious they become and the more ants they both attract and kill. The result is a seething ball of madly fighting ants.

These fights were started on the main highways and at the entrances to the cities. Many ants were killed, but after their remains had been cleared away by rain and decomposition and other forces, the normal activities of the community recommenced. We were therefore asked to ascertain whether there was any way in which internecine wars could be started such as would completely exterminate the whole colony, and if so, to devise methods for doing this simply. After much deliberation, we decided that before these questions could be answered we must excavate a number of nests to determine their exact layout, and ascertain whether they were all built to a common plan in any one country. If the battles could be started in some key position in the cities themselves, complete extermination might be possible. We had to find these key positions and, by mapping many nests, determine how they could be found quickly and simply with a minimum of digging.

We therefore first selected a large nest near the end of our eastern trace, and as soon as opportunity arose, we all set out to start work upon it. The nest was a large one, forty feet in diameter, and proved to be twelve feet deep at the centre. The digging was a tremendous job, and took us many days, for we were very short-handed. From time to time throughout the following year we opened more cities of all sizes and in many types of country. We also made other observations upon the *Atta*, and what we have now seen, combined with the known facts about these insects, has answered most of our questions concerning them—including proving the efficacy of the corrosive sublimate method of extermination. Our observations also revealed that the nests follow a single plan in a given area.

Since insect engineering is in no way so precise as our own, and always leaves such a tremendous margin of safety, there may be great irregularity in the details of the construction of the *Atta* cities. The city usually appears above ground as a roughly circular, low dome of naked earth, rising, in some cases, to a height of six feet at the centre. The whole of this dome is composed of tiny pellets of earth, excavated by the ants and carried in their jaws to the surface, where they are systematically dumped over the steeply sloping sides of the ramps that rise from sundry exits. After this mound has been beaten down and washed by the tropic rains many times, and constantly added to by the tireless insects, it becomes hardened. The ants then re-excavate it from beneath, and construct in it certain chambers, the purpose of which we will see later.

Below the dome, the city forms a rough hemisphere. At the very bottom, sometimes as far as fifteen feet below the ground surface, lies an immense chamber. This takes various forms, but is usually sink-shaped with a low roof. It is a drainage sump, into which rain water collects, after coursing down the great covered roadways and endless tiny passages. This water eventually sinks into the earth below. The city is customarily built about the roots of one or more stout trees. The roots not only brace the ceilings of chambers, but also deter or altogether prevent the digging operations of large, insectivorous animals in search of food.

A plan common to all the cities is followed with regard to the arrangement of certain salient features. To leeward of the nest from the prevailing wind, several holes often as large as rabbit burrows are always to be found. These are kept free of debris, and occasionally small parties of ants are seen here engaged in clearing their floors, repairing their walls, or enlarging them. These are air-conditioning vents, designed to draw foul air from the nest rather than to let fresh air be blown in. This foul air contains poisonous gases to which the ants are highly susceptible and which originate from their specialized agricultural activities. Should fresh air be blown in rather than the foul air drawn off, these very agricultural processes would become impossible.

The city is a complex of chambers, cross-roads, passages, and deep galleries. In addition, there are invariably two types of structure, or rather excavation, that are of particular importance. It is these and the uses to which they are put that render the *Atta* so resistant to all aggression, even the attacks of man.

After a city has been dug out, the scurrying blanket of insects that has been covering the whole ground surface will be seen to have almost entirely withdrawn. Further digging into the solid soil beyond the true periphery of the city will presently disclose large, deep, kit-bag-shaped chambers with smoothly plastered walls, choked to their limits with a solid mass of more or less immobile ants. Leading from the summits of these deep shelters, curving passages can be traced upwards to within a few inches of the surface of the soil, and thence downwards again almost to the base of the city. These passages will be crowded from the uppermost point of their curve to the entrances of the plastered shelters with a solid mass of the enormous-headed giant organizers, ants that do no work, but merely supervise and, in crises, fight.

At times of extreme danger—under natural conditions, occasioned mostly by floods—the organizers herd the whole community of ants into these deep shelters, where they fall into a comatose condition. The organizers then take up their positions in the approach. Should the danger be animate, there is practically no animal that could get by this phalanx. If, on the other hand, floods are invading the city, the waters will find great difficulty in rising over this upwardly curved passageway, owing to the air pressure retained by the carefully plastered and almost impermeable walls of the shelter. When the danger has passed, the organizers come to the ground surface via the empty city, and enter small, vertical shafts descending from holes in the natural surface of the ground to a point only a few centimetres from the base of these plastered chambers. From the bottom of these, they open tunnels into the bottom of the shelters, thus allowing cool air to filter into the mass of comatose insects from below. This soon revives the workers, who then swarm back into the city to resume their normal activities.

The ants make use of these deep shelters when the cities are fumigated with cyanide gas, and the air-conditioning vents and all other entrances are firmly sealed down. Small wonder, therefore, that attempts to eradicate this pest are usually doomed to failure. Instead of exterminating the population, moreover, cities thus treated are often induced to found daughter communities.

The most important public utility of an *Atta* city requires special mention, as it underlies all their potent vitality. As has been mentioned, the great upper dome is re-excavated. In it, many vaulted, hemispherical chambers are constructed. These are hotbeds, in which the food of the community is grown. They are carefully air-

PARASOL ANTS (Atta) ON THEIR HIGHWAY

conditioned, being ringed by many small, pore-like openings which can be closed or opened according to the requirements of the crops.

The sole crop is a species of fungus (*Rhözites gonglyophora*) found nowhere else in nature. The spores of this fungus are carried by the "queens," or fertile females, in special pouches under their heads when going out to found daughter cities. The hotbeds in which this unique plant food is grown are made of cut portions of specially selected leaves and flower petals, which are gathered by the ants and dried or moistened to exactly the correct degree before being laid down. The spores are sown in this mass, and as the fungus develops it feeds upon the hotbeds and reduces them to a bun-shaped, mauvish-white, porous mass of a fluffy consistency. When it is correctly matured, the ants seal down the chambers and arrest the growth.

In some cases the chambers appear to be kept as stores; in others they are partly cleared and dried for the production and eventual collection of spores, or again they may immediately be employed as nurseries for the hatching and rearing of the young, or as mammoth quick-lunch counters. When the leaf portions of which the hotbeds are made are brought in by the large cutters, small assistants, which are also sterile females, take charge. They carve up and masticate the leaf, fashion it into small pellets, and pack it into the mass just as we would do with special manure or leaf mould in a flower pot.

The fungus grows in the form of long tendrils, which envelop and penetrate these pellets. At the end of the tendrils, small, globular, false-fruits are produced, and it is upon the viscous liquid with which these tiny spheres are filled that the insects feed. The small assistants collect this substance and feed it to the larvæ, which are housed in these hotbeds. They also feed the few egg-laying fertile females and the great sterile females, or organizers. The cutters apparently feed themselves during the daytime, when they may be found crowded into some of the food cellars feasting in serried ranks.

When the nutriment in the leaf pellets has been used up, or when a whole cellar is cleared, the small assistants roll all the garbage into large pellets and carry it away. The extraordinary fact is, however, that instead of simply taking it out of the nest and dumping it like the excavated soil, they carefully pack it into one of the deep, kit-bag-shaped shelters that lie outside the nest. They continue dumping into one of these until it is full, but they leave a clear space all round between this manure heap and the wall of the chamber. It seems that this mass then serves some other important function, but what this may be has apparently not so far been determined.

The hotbeds for this fungus food require very particular vegetable manure. Just any leaf will not suffice. The treasured fungus, and therefore the ant-horticulturists, have special preferences. The extraordinary perspicacity of the ants in selecting the very best material available has to be witnessed to be credited. Most unfortunately for our human agriculture, the requirements of the *Atta* seem always to coincide with our own. Not only are our young, healthy, and most profitable crops most suitable to them, but in forests where planted crops do not exist, the *Atta* unfailingly select the fresh shoots of the most valuable timber trees!

The ants' methods of collecting material for their hotbeds are not only remarkable and highly destructive to our economy, but they also give rise to some of the most astonishing activities in the animal world, and are perhaps more fascinating and awe-inspiring to watch than anything else in the jungle. The collection of the leaves for the hotbeds occupies much of the working time of the community.

Leading from the outer edge of the cities are, on the average, eight main roads. These are eight to ten inches wide, and immaculately bare. Their surfaces are of flat, hard-beaten earth. Where they cross open areas or beneath low trees where heavy rain may fall upon them, they are often cambered or even partly covered, being sunk between overhanging walls. Sometimes, at real danger points, they plunge down into tunnels.

The main arterial roads customarily begin to branch some thirty feet from the cities, either bifurcating or giving off small side roads. At the main bifurcations there are often shuttle crossings that form triangles or even traffic "circles." The ants adhere to these roads, and if they happen to stray from them they are utterly lost, wandering around apparently with the sole idea of finding them again. They travel along them rapidly and surely. Traffic at difficult junctions is sometimes directed by one or two organizers, but for the most part the workers travel without aid. Should the traffic be disorganized by outside agents, the large cutters line the roadsides, but if they in turn are dispersed, word is carried back to the nest by relays of ants dashing up to and touching the nearest of their colleagues with their antennæ. The message finally enters the nest, and the organizers then hurry out and take control.

The roads eventually lead to the bases of trees from the crowns of which the leaves are to be cut. The times for work above ground vary in different parts of the world, according to the degree of development of the city, the weather, the season, or even, after the city has been well founded, the special preferences of the community. Most parasol ants work only at night, and by day the roads are deserted but for occasional lone, big-headed organizers on a tour of inspection. At night they are teeming highways of activity.

The cutters go out at sundown, and running along between them are many very much smaller individuals less than a quarter their bulk. It is the business of the latter to assist the cutter at the top of the tree. When a large segment of leaf is nearly cut through, one or two of the small assistants seize hold of it to prevent it from falling when the last cut is made. We have sat for hours under a tree where work was going on, and have never seen a single piece of leaf fall in the torch-light.

When the leaf is cut, the little assistant often climbs up on it and so rides back to the city. The large carriers seize the load with their jaws, which operate horizontally, and thus hold the leaf portion vertically above their heads so that a line of ants looks like a fleet of tiny ships with large green sails.

The weight of these loads is very great. We collected several hundreds of the ants with their loads. They were weighed in groups of a hundred, and an average of the results arrived at. From this, the weight of an ant and of its average load were calculated. An ant was found to weigh .0175 gramme, and an average load .035 gramme,

so that the ants carry exactly twice their own weight. Further calculation showed that whatever the size or shape of the portion of
leaf, it always bore the relation of 2 : 1 to the weight of the ant.

Taking the average weight of a man to be 165 lbs., he would have
to carry 330 lbs. to equal the task of the ant. Incidentally, a man is
some 4,000,000 times heavier than one of these ants!

The great loads carried by these "superhuman" little creatures
are by no means the most astonishing part of their activities. We
measured a large number of roads from the points where they issued
from the cities to the bases of the trees. They proved to be on an
average three hundred feet in length, though exceptional ones half
a mile long are recorded. By dipping the ants in a shallow pool of
ink and then allowing them to run over sheets of paper, we were
able to collect a number of measurements of their strides or paces.
These averaged roughly a quarter of an inch. The stride of a man is
approximately three feet. Simple calculation then showed that an
ant walks the equivalent of eight and a quarter miles from the city to
the base of the tree, and another eight and a quarter back again,
carrying the equivalent of two men. Nor is that all.

The *Atta* also most conveniently happened to be on an average a
quarter of an inch tall. Now, many of the trees that they were
scaling were more than a hundred feet high to the topmost leafy
branches, and by perching on the highest branch that we could reach
and using field glasses, we saw that cutting operations were taking
place upon the very summit. In proportion to the height of an ant,
therefore, these trees were approximately 28,000 feet high, or proportionately equivalent to Mount Everest, the highest mountain in
the world. Furthermore, the trees are perpendicular for the greater
part of the ascent and descent. Thus, in distance alone, the ants walk
the equivalent of twenty-one and a half miles, and climb the equivalent of the highest mountain in the world of man, on each trip, on
every working day of their lives. Their capabilities almost stagger
one.

We naturally became eager to see how long it took an ant to ac-
complish this Gargantuan task. The rate of progress of a great num-

ber of empty-handed—or empty-jawed—and of loaded ants was timed over ten feet of roadway. It was found that, allowing for traffic jams, occasional loss of direction, stopping to assist friends, and even retracing of steps, the average unladen ant covered ten feet in one minute and forty-six seconds, whereas a laden individual took two minutes and twenty-nine seconds. Thus the combined average is approximately two minutes and seven seconds to cover ten feet, or an eighteenth of a mile an hour. Since a man's pace is 144 times greater than an ant's, and he travels at an average of three miles per hour, the average *Atta* may be said to travel at the equivalent of eight M.P.H.

We then tied tiny loops of white thread to several cutters as they left the city. Their progress was followed to the base of the tree, and their return from aloft was awaited there. When they eventually reappeared, they were again followed back to the city. The time that they were occupied up the tree varied greatly, some being down again in half an hour whereas others were gone over three hours. The average time taken for the whole of a journey to and from the city proved to be on the average three and a quarter hours— three and a quarter hours to walk over eight miles, climb Mount Everest, pick up two men, and carry them home again!

Marked individuals were often found to make two trips during the course of the night, and they may make more, though they always spend about three hours in the city between excursions. The cutters are apparently allotted a definite task, and if they are late to work they must carry on until they have completed it. Marked ants found leaving the cities at dawn were to be seen struggling bravely back hours later in the glaring morning sunlight along quite deserted highways.

Leaf loads are never abandoned. They may be dropped through collisions with other ants, or apparently from fatigue, in which case the ants rest with their heads upon them by the roadside. In the former case, either the little assistants or other empty-handed cutters travelling in the opposite direction give a hand and hoist them into the vertical carrying position again.

Sometimes the bases of the trees, the roads, or the city gates may be strewn with apparently abandoned green loads. These have not been cast away, only laid down temporarily. This mostly occurs after sudden rain, and is due to the fact that the leaves must not be placed in the hotbeds when either too wet or too dry, lest the fungus not grow properly. These are therefore laid down either to dry off or to be dampened by dew or rain.

Should they be too dry and no dew or rain fall for some time, so that they dry up, they, together with any dead leaves that fall upon the nest, are carefully cut up by the small assistants, who operate in large parties and are apparently specialists in this work. The remnants are then carted away and dumped off the edge of the mound. Any herbs or bushes that may grow upon or over the city are likewise attacked and denuded of all leaves. Even the tough silkgrass and other hard plants are thus cleared away, but the resultant leaf portions are never carried down to the hotbeds for agricultural purposes.

Parasol ants are not mere regimented automatons. In all their ceaseless, regulated activity they seem to find a place for individual initiative, intelligence, and, perhaps, even compassion. If you gently place some heavy object over one of them, or persuade one to walk on a sticky surface to which he adheres, and then make this known to the others, the newcomers will run up and interlock antennæ with their entrapped mate. Then they will run around pulling first at this leg, then that, and when they discover that they cannot give adequate assistance, they will get into a great state, running about constantly crossing antennæ as if to convey to the entrapped individual that he is not to despair. Finally, they dash off to the nearest road and rush among the busy throng, touching antennæ right and left. The ants will swarm round these couriers, some even putting down their loads, and all hurry off, guided by the original finders, and set to work systematically releasing the prisoner. The harder the task, the more ants are fetched, and we have even witnessed occasions upon which organizers were called from the city, the equivalent of five and a half miles away. These latter did no actual labour themselves, but in each case when they appeared the victims were quickly freed, and often took up their loads again before rejoining the throng on the road.

With their ceaseless ordered activity, their devotion to duty, and their complex economy, it is small wonder that the *Atta*, labouring under their little green parasols, are almost a match for man. Despite their devastation of our crops, they challenge our intellect and command our utmost admiration.

It is perhaps permissible to say that these animals are really civilized. They certainly undergo a constant drudgery befitting this estate, though what we see among them at the same time possibly holds out just about the only promise for our own future. The *Atta* undeniably retain some element of personal initiative and perhaps even individual compassion for their fellows, which is woven into the fabric of their over-organized lives yet does not seem to detract from its general and all-pervading efficiency.

A FEW MILES'
DIFFERENCE

A Jungle Feast, Urodeles, Geckos, and a Cacomistle

OUR next home was only a few miles away. Our only reason for moving at all was to place the workings of our organization in the midst of the next type of vegetation that had to be examined. Here we fully expected to encounter a new congregation of animals, and in this we were not disappointed.

On the first day after our establishment was in running order, Alma and I set out upon a preliminary tour of inspection; at least that is what it was to have been. There was a small path running through the forest by our camp, and from it branched a small trace that was almost overgrown. We went along this very quietly, for there were squirrels about, and we wanted a chance to shoot one or two. The afternoon was well advanced, and was overcast as far as we could determine from within the depths of the mammoth green quilt. It had been raining fitfully all day, and there had been a distant thunderstorm meandering around.

As we entered the natural archway of the tall forest, we were arrested by movements in the undergrowth far away to the left, and after a hurried council, we set off in that direction, creeping forward bent almost double beneath the undergrowth. It was a long way, but as we drew closer to the noises, it was borne in upon us that the disturbance was both continuous and widespread. Since there was a definite set of noises, and since these were irregular, we judged that they must be caused by animals. We became doubly wary, for we had seen the spoor of tapir and of a very large sounder of peccaries, both of which we would have liked to observe. We also needed some specimens of the latter. They are both very wary creatures, and peccaries of one particular species, if cornered, have been known to become more than troublesome. As we went forward, the noises did not increase in volume, but they spread across an ever-wider front.

Then I nearly put my hand on a great bird that was squatting among the dead leaves on the ground. I verily believe it had been asleep, for it got up in an uncertain manner, peered at us first with one eye and then with the other, and leisurely hopped up onto a branch. It was a very beautiful creature clothed in uniformly russet-brown plumage, and as it was a game bird, we were half inclined to shoot it for our pot, but decided against this in view of the noises ahead. This decision was fortunate indeed, for had we caused a disturbance we should have missed seeing one of the most exquisite sights that the jungle could offer.

After some further scrambling, we came upon the source of the sounds, and discovered that they were caused by a veritable cascade of small fruits falling onto the taut drumheads of the palm fronds that grew below in the belly of the forest. Towering above were enormous, wide-spreading tamarind trees, interspersed with some other acacias and giant mammee apples. Pressing forward very quietly, we presently came out from under the palm grove into full view of the trees, and at the same moment one of those intense, rather acid-yellow, after-rain suns came out below the dark pall of the sky. Its hard yellow rays floodlighted a scene that was almost unearthly in its beauty. We positively gasped as we looked up.

The sky was leaden, with blue-black clouds beneath which the yellow light rushed from a cleft which we could not see, low on the western horizon. Against this angry backdrop, the feathery tama-rinds with their smooth, twisting, silver branches and the bunchy, heavy-leafed mammees stood out clear as metal-work. The foliage of the tamarinds was the most delicate and ethereal duck's egg blue; that of the mammees was dark, heavy green interspersed with the vivid chartreuse of the young leaves. Only here and there did its rough chocolate limbs and trunk appear from the mass. Dotted about these two trees, in the satisfying poses that only wild things can assume, were a dozen huge, jet-black howler monkeys, two dozen or so large, flaming red macaws, and about two hundred vivid green-and-yellow parrots. On the tips of the tamarind branches were clusters of bright, cherry-coloured pods like large string beans. The whole scene was illuminated by the biting intensity of the cold yellow sunlight, which picked out every feature and every colour, bathed every surface, and rimmed every edge.

Slowly we sank down upon the bank under cover of the arching palms that framed that picture, and put down our guns. We couldn't have said a word had we wanted to; we were as utterly speechless as if our mouths had been gagged, instead of hanging open as they were. We sat there in a veritable trance until dusk, never moving except to avoid an occasional red bean or piece of a great mammee apple as it came hurtling down from the feast above. Marriage is a wonderful institution, but I don't think I ever appreciated it so wholly as I did that evening. To see such a sight alone would have been something to carry with one for ever, but to see it and feel it in company with one's most loved companion was a supreme experience.

The fruit was ripe, and the animals had gathered to partake of the feast. We had seen parrots, but no macaws or howler monkeys, in the forests that we had until recently inhabited. We were greatly interested in these black howlers (*Alouatta villosa*), or baboons, as they are locally and quite incorrectly called, for it was they, and not the gorgeous red-blue-and-yellow macaws with all their squawking and clattering, that added the touch of jungle mysticism to the scene.

There is no animal, not even the mighty elephant or the lion himself, that carries such an air of regality as does the howler monkey. A lover of great heights, he ascends the tallest trees and there roars and growls and bellows and coughs his defiance of everybody and everything at whatever time of day or at whatever season he desires.

BLACK HOWLERS (Alouatta villosa)

Once you have lived under the sound of the howler's roar, the echoes of the slumbering, silent jungle will have entered your soul. You will wake up on a quiet night in some horrible northern place with a ghostly echo of it in your ears; when you are tired and lonely and sick of the world, it will suddenly come flooding into your mind, a forerunner of visions of long, still rivers winding between towering walls of greenery, of stately palm groves breathing in the platinum light of the moon, of inky pools of shadow moving silently on a leaf-strewn floor.

This troop was very busily employed cramming as much of the bright pink mammee apple flesh into their mouths as they could hold. They had no time for roaring. Only occasionally did one pause to grunt belligerently at a macaw that approached too near, or growl as it shook a branch to rid it of the fluttering, chattering, gossiping parrots. Once again I ask what it is about parrots that makes them seem so friendly. Perhaps because they live so long, they come to take on the character of a lot of old, green, jungle club-women; their unceasing conversation is devoid of malice, and they are exceedingly busy at all times, just like a knitting circle.

The howlers appeared to pay little attention to the parrots, though they kept an eye on the macaws. They were big, black crea-tures with powerful arms, heavy shoulders, deep-scowling faces, and long, prehensile tails, which they kept securely anchored to a handy branch. They were all adults, and we suspected some moping females of being imminently expectant mothers. In this part of the country these creatures stay up in the hills until the mammees ripen; then they move down to the plains by easy stages.

There was one big male whose antics were most amusing. He took a great deal of time selecting fruits to suit his apparently rather fastidious taste. On one occasion, after trying many and finding none to his satisfaction, he lost his temper, and, seizing first one and then another, sniffed them perfunctorily and then hurled them to the ground. Finally he jumped up in an obvious rage, and went trundling off to the top of the mammee tree, where he squatted glaring out at the evening world, coughing occasionally and grumbling continuously to himself. It was all we could do to avoid bursting into laughter, because his behaviour was so like that of one of our older and much respected relatives.

We left this beautiful scene at sundown. We wanted a howler monkey for our collections and we wanted some parrots for food—and excellent eating they are—but somehow a gunshot would have been sacrilege that day. We often went back to this place, but though there were always many parrots and macaws about, the monkeys had moved on after finishing the mammees.

These were not the only new animals that we immediately encountered in this latest locality. There were many signs of larger mammals, in the form of tracks and so forth, but what was of more interest to us were some very small beasts that we stumbled across in a variety of ways.

The commonest palm and also in some places one of the commonest trees in this jungle is the cohune (*Orbignya cohune*), the hard stony nuts of which are crushed and burned to make a charcoal of great purity that is an even better filter for gas-masks than that made from coconut shells. This plant starts life as a one-leafed affair which then grows to the dimensions of an oil palm with a fleur-de-lis of beautiful great fronds that sprout from just above the ground. To look at it in this stage, one would imagine that it had reached the fullness of its glory, but in reality it has hardly started upon life.

Poking about the forest, you tend to hack at trees with your machete in an aimless fashion. Every now and then you get a surprise when the machete blade gives a whang, flies back, and almost jumps out of your hand. It has then hit a full-grown cohune. These plants don't flower and fructify until their heads reach the sunlight —which is to say, not until they have grown up to the canopy of the forest. Their trunks become more or less smooth and unringed, and look just like those of hardwood trees. Often you realize they are palms only by looking up at their heads, which are of titanic dimensions.

Palms die eventually, like other plants, but the manner of their death is different. Whereas an ordinary hardwood grows hollow and tired and rotten and ever more bald, finally crashing to earth during a high wind, a palm simply stops producing new fronds. The dead, dangling fronds rot and ultimately fall off, so that the tree dies standing up, and a great shaft with a rounded point is left projecting up into the forest foliage. This may stand for years, so that a dead and fallen palm, and especially a dead cohune, is a rarity in the jungle. When one does fall, or when a whole head comes off for some reason and crashes to earth, it creates an exceptional little environment. We chanced upon one or two of these fallen cohune heads in the area of our first jungle home, and in them we found some curious little creatures.

A palm is a fibrous thing, and when it dies and rots, the outer skins of the frond bases become hard and brittle shells, while inside they are reduced to sodden, spongy masses full of tough strings. The trunks likewise develop a hard outer husk, while internally they are also reduced to a mass of loose fibres.

We spend a lot of time breaking up and turning over any fallen trees and logs. They are the retreats of many small animals that are not met with elsewhere, so we went to work on the first dead cohune that we found. Having turned it right over and found nothing but a toad underneath, we set to work pulling it to pieces. Between the bases of the rotting fronds we found one or two tiny snails, but nothing else. Then we started splitting open the fronds and the trunk, and this was where the unique environment was disclosed. Inside, among the sodden fibres, was an assemblage of small creatures. There were small red crabs, various insects, an odd lizard (*Lepidophyma flavimaculatum*) with its head covered with armour plating and its back with hard studs and bosses, a new kind of scorpion, a distinct type of *amblypygi* or whip-scorpion, and a rather large-bodied, short-legged opilionid or "harvestman."

This last carried its eggs, which were bright orange, lozenge-shaped capsules with translucent shells, in a neat row arranged round the periphery of the upper side of the abdomen. Sometimes we came across what appeared to be perfect specimens that were in reality the dried husks of these arachnids. When opened, these husks were found to contain a perfect and well-developed young one only about a third the size of the husk and completely imprisoned within it. How these immature animals get inside the husks of what are presumably their mothers I cannot explain. The eggs are manifestly hatched externally, and the animals are without biting mouth parts.

These were intriguing finds, but in capturing them we had caught occasional glimpses of some black and shiny things that shot across our field of vision and then disappeared once more into the stringy mass of the rotten palm trunk. When we had all seen these, we conferred and decided to capture one by working from both ends of the palm at once. This had the desired effect, and when we reached the centre we had cornered three of these things, so that they flashed back and forth in a confined space. George eventually pounced on one, and when we had bottled it, we found that we had a kind of newt (*Œdipus elongatus*).

Newts and salamanders constitute the order Urodela, or tailed amphibians; their relatives are the frogs and toads and the worm-like cœcilians. They look like lizards, but can readily be distinguished from reptiles by their smooth skins devoid of scales. It so happens that during the past few years we have not worked in any country in which these animals are found, so that the advent of these specimens was of particular interest to us.

They were only about four and a half inches (110 mm.) in length, the tail being as long as the head and body. In form they were like worms, being about seven millimetres in diameter throughout, with the tail as fat as the body. The head was small and blunt, with small eyes and two reduced tentacles under the slightly overhanging snout. The flanks were constricted by about fifteen vertical strictures, as if minute rubber bands were pinching the skin. The limbs were Lilliputian, with four tiny fingers and five equally small toes, all fully webbed. The limbs were not used except for the push-off, the animal progressing by a furious serpentine wiggle. Their colour was bluish-black above, with widely separated and irregular white flecks, and dark steel-grey below. Under a lens, this colouration

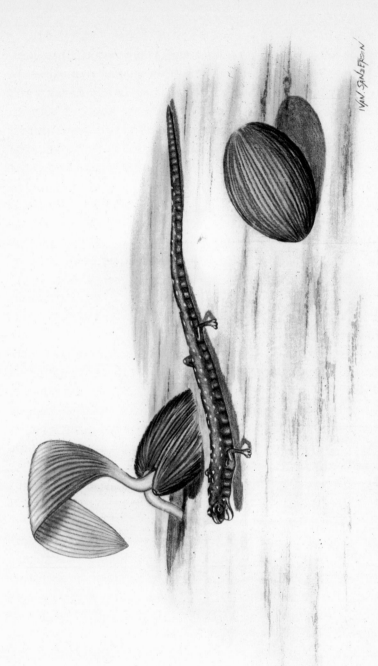

CANNIBAL SALAMANDER (Œdipus elongatus)

appeared granular, being made up of tiny groups of dark speckles on a light ground.

On one occasion, George went out hunting for small fry, and found one of these urodeles, which he put in a bottle. When he got back to camp, he gave me the bottle and I was dismayed to see in it what I took to be the aftermath of some internecine struggle. The bottom of the bottle contained a mess of fragments of these urodeles. I admonished George for putting more than one of these specimens into one bottle. George looked at me wide-eyed. He very rightly resented any questioning of his veracity, and told me quite simply that he had collected only one. We therefore extracted the mess and spread it out in a dish.

There was one live and perfect specimen measuring 113 mm. with a girth of 7 mm. Then there were two heads and bodies, both approximately 50 mm. in length, one 5 mm. in girth, the other much digested and reduced to a mere skull and backbone. Also there were two tails both 55 mm. in length, and with girths of approximately 3 mm. From one, the skin had been almost entirely digested away. From this it appeared that the live animal had disgorged the remains of two of its own kind both only 8 mm. shorter than itself. George confirmed that it had looked very fat when captured, but that it was not at all sluggish.

At first we puzzled as to how all this could have gone into the cannibal, but when you come to consider a cross-section something like the accompanying sketch, you will see that the two heads and bodies and the two tails could be neatly packed in without unduly stretching the animal.

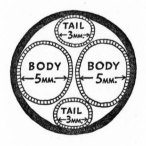

When we got to this new type of vegetation, almost the first thing which we caught was a specimen of another species of urodele (*Œdipus mexicanus*). This was much larger and bulkier than the little cannibal, with an exceedingly short, broad head and quite prominent eyes that had horizontal pupils set in an orange-gold iris. Its limbs were better proportioned, but the digits were even more reduced. It was bright salmon-pink above, with two longitudinal lines of dark brown, irregular blobs. The limbs, underside, and flanks were an even brown. Specimens were taken from among wet grasses growing in damp depressions or by streams. We encountered none in dead cohune heads and logs, but in their place, two new types of lizard turned up.

We had thought it strange that no lizards of the gecko family were encountered in the first type of forest that we had examined. They are a ubiquitous group in tropical lands, and usually rather common in hollow trees in the tall jungles, but we had seen none, though we had looked carefully. Now we struck two species almost at once in cohune logs and stumps. The first was a tiny animal (*Sphærodactylus glaucus*) of a dull colouration, with disk-like terminations to its fingers and toes. The second put our staff in a great ferment.

When they first saw this beautiful grey-and-black-banded lizard, with its evil, pointed, flat head and baleful, pale blue popping eyes, they shouted "Scorpion!" and backed away. When laughed at and pressed for an explanation, they said it was a "galliwasp," and poisonous, though at the same time they admitted that it was not quite so bad as the other "black galliwasp." Now this presented several distinct problems.

First of all, we had to contend with this ever-present native belief, common to nearly all tropical countries, that certain lizards are deadly poisonous. In Africa it may be some common chameleon, in the East Indies an ordinary lacertid; in Haiti it is an *Anolis*, in Guiana an iguana, and in Spain a gecko. In British Honduras it is the "galliwasp" (*Coleonyx elegans*), which is also a gecko and brings us to a second problem.

In Jamaica they call a certain lizard a "galliwasp," but there it is a burrowing lizard (*Celestus*) belonging to quite a different family, whereas they call geckos "wood-slaves." This is very muddling. At first one feels that it is all of little consequence, since none of them are poisonous in any case, but here comes the next problem.

As it is so constantly declared in the country that these geckos are poisonous, Mr. Anderson, the curator of the Belize Museum, became interested, and sent some specimens back to England for identification and with a request for a definite ruling as to whether they were venomous. He tells me that the collection included specimens of what the natives regarded as the two types: the bad and the very bad ones. In due course the answer came back that they were not poisonous, that they were such and such lizards, and that natives often attributed deadly qualities to such harmless animals. Some time later, however, Mr. Anderson told me he received a further communication from the expert, stating that he had had cause to make a more detailed examination of these specimens, and that he had been surprised to discover that their teeth were grooved and perforated, and that there might therefore, after all, be something in the local belief.

It is difficult to pin natives down about the finer points of natural history, but as far as I can find out, we have not yet obtained any of the "very bad" galliwasps. I am therefore at present unable to add to this observation, but should it be established that these geckos are poisonous, they will take their place with the gila monster, as the only other known lizard that is thus equipped. It was the great naturalist Alfred Russel Wallace who said that almost every native record about animals, however fantastic it may sound, usually proves to have some foundation of truth, and we personally would rather second this statement than deplore it.

It was at this second jungle home also that we got the grey-and-white rat, *Tylomys*. We suspected this animal of being at least a partly arboreal species by reason of its broad, short feet, although the first few specimens were trapped on the ground. It was a very handsome rodent, with thick, fluffy fur that had that strange, almost mauvish tinge that silver-tipped maroon hairs interspersed with a

French grey undercoat produce. Its ears were large, its underside pure white, and its tail dark grey with large, rectangular, plate-like scales.

Rats are the most difficult animals to define. Their numbers and species are legion, and most of them vary greatly. We normally collect about a dozen rats to every other mammal, and sometimes have as many as thirty distinct species by the end of a trip, so that they present us with many problems. While in the field, we do not attempt to assign the proper scientific names to the animals we collect. Indeed, such a course would be impossible in the absence of a mountain of literature and study collections for comparison, and also it would be a dangerous practice, because all the more interesting observations upon the animals' variations and minor points of form might be overlooked if a proper name could be stuck on a specimen directly it came from the trap.

For this reason, we devote much time to each animal, and the first specimen of any new kind that appears is examined very closely and meticulously described. These grey-and-white rats put in an appearance one morning and then we saw no more of them for two weeks, the reason, I believe, being that because of heavy rain the ground was too moist throughout this period to permit them to descend from their normal arboreal habitat. Then once again they began to come in from the traps.

We had our detailed descriptions of male and female adults and of the immature females from the first batch. When, therefore, a male came along that was nearly twice the size of any that we had seen, we went to work upon it at once to determine whether by any chance the drawings and photographs that we had of a supposed adult male might in reality pertain to an immature specimen. Almost immediately, however, we saw that certain features of this specimen did not conform with our records. It is quite remarkable how constant these lesser features are in any species of rat, and yet how much they can differ even between supposedly closely related species.

In this case, this discovery prompted us to examine the rat in more detail, and finally we spotted quite a number of other things that might otherwise have passed unnoticed as being due merely to its greater size. The fur was coarser, being woolly rather than silky; the pads of the feet were cleft; the scales of the tail were smaller in proportion. Lastly, when we washed the tail, which was covered in mud, we found that it was black for the basal half and pure white throughout the terminal half. In fact, we had an entirely different and new type of rat on our hands, in general appearance identical to the other, but in details very different. We later learned that this species was more truly arboreal. We found this out through the discovery of another new animal.

Surely there is no such thing as a rare animal in the world. Some creature which you treasure in one place becomes a positive pest in another locality. In Surinam we were extremely pleased to see a kinkajou; after a few weeks in British Honduras we would have been quite delighted not to have seen one. They literally swarmed in all types of country, inhabiting the mountain forest, the tall lowland forest, the secondary vegetation, and even the taller growth on the swampy northern plains.

They became a pest to us in our night hunting. We would go out with lights, searching for eyes in the trees. There would be a crash and a swaying branch, a cascade of falling twigs and fruits, then some eerie squeals, and we would fire. In answer the foliage above would toss as if struck by a hurricane, and pairs of burning golden orbs would appear all over the place. These lovable little animals travel about in large parties of as many as fifty individuals, and there may be ten such parties within the area covered by a night's hunting. To make matters worse, they also live singly or in couples, and, as one never knows what a pair of eyes in the torch-light may be, they became a constant distraction. Besides this, we hated shooting them, for we quickly collected a sufficient series of specimens, and they are one of the most attractive and inoffensive of tropical mammals. They make delightful pets, too, having all the ingenuity of the pleasanter monkeys without their mischievousness, and being spotlessly clean, adorably pretty, easy to keep, and most affectionate. They can at the same time be extremely savage and inflict a very bad bite, but on the whole, house-trained kinkajous are better behaved and more reliable than almost any other animal.

A few nights after we had got settled in our new home, Fred and I went out along a main bridle path because it was very wet and we had no need to go pounding through the infinite at that stage in our examination of the area. We got interested in a stream full of tortoises, saw a deer, shot an owl in the hope that it might have swallowed some rats' skulls whole, as these birds often do, and spent a lot of time examining spiders. When we cast the torch beams down the path, which was covered with low herbs, the whole place sprang into life like a fairy street. Myriads of tiny cold, silver lights sparkled everywhere, not only on the leaves of trees, palms, and bushes, but also all over the floor of the path. At first, we took these to be droplets of water, but closer inspection disclosed the fact that they were all the eyes of spiders. The entire forest was sprinkled with them.

This made shooting very difficult, for we could not be certain whether we were looking at a pair of spiders close at hand or at a pair of mammalian eyes far away. Then all at once a very decided pair of brilliant golden orbs flashed out in the head of a dense, creeper-covered tree.

Fred fired quickly, and something fell into the bushes. Then a second pair flashed out on the same tree. He fired again, but missed completely, and the eyes went tearing away up a branch and disappeared into another tree at great speed. We ran forward and started searching for our prize, fully expecting that it would be just another "night-walker," as the kinkajous are called locally. Our delight was therefore unbounded when we finally spotted a long, black-and-white, ringed tail sticking out from a mass of rubbish. When we extricated the owner, we got a further pleasant surprise. It was a cacomistle, though it almost stumped us for a bit and had Carlos, the man who knew all the animals as well as all the trees in the country, completely beaten.

This animal (*Bassaris sumichrasti*) is the southern form of the

SOUTHERN CACOMISTLE (Bassaris sumichrasti)

pretty little sharp-faced animal known as the "Ring-tailed Cat" in the south and west of the United States. Unlike the northern species, this animal is comparatively large, and a dull olive grey-brown in colour. It belongs to the raccoon family, and looks like a mixture of coati, kinkajou, and raccoon. The face is sharp and rather foxy, but lacks the black mask of the raccoon. The body is like that of the kinkajou, but lighter in build and more attenuated; the tail is extremely long, and non-prehensile; it is carried straight out behind the animal and is seldom more than but slightly curled.

Fred was sure that the other eyes belonged to its mate, and he located a large hole at the top of a neighbouring tree from which he thought the pair might recently have issued and which would be their permanent daytime retreat. We returned the next day and made a thorough search, and, as so very often occurs, we stumbled across something quite different. But we never saw another cacomistle in that place.

Having laboriously climbed to the big hole with the aid of ropes and a pulley, we found that it was even bigger than we thought. Fred descended into it with a torch, and had plenty of room to spare on all sides. I waited below with a ready-cocked gun in case something should squeeze past him and make a dash for the open. After some minutes, a great rumbling broke out in the bowels of the tree, and shortly afterwards Fred's head appeared.

"Hey!" he shouted. "For the love of Mike don't shoot. There's a mass of big rats in here. I'm going down to the bottom to shoo them out. Wait till they're well away before you shoot."

"Okay," I called, and he retired below again.

Three big rats duly appeared and started hurrying up the outside of the tree. I waited as long as I dared, and then with surprising originality bagged two of them. When these were retrieved, they turned out to be a pair of the larger and more special grey-and-white ones with half-white tails.

IN A BOTTOM ON TOP

*Tapirs and Mountain Cabbages, a Jumping
Tommy-Goff and a Boulder Trap*

EXTREMELY cold water dripping on my left shoulder
with the relentlessness of the Chinese "water cure" woke
me up. One side of the tent was open, and as I peered out
into the unearthly blue light of dawn, nothing was to be seen but
a solid-looking curtain of mist. Except for the splashing murmur
of the mountain river and a slow, incessant dripping, there was a
great silence. Shivering with the chilling dampness, I pulled the
pile of thick camel-hair blankets more closely round my neck, and
inspected the roof of the mosquito net. It bellied menacingly downwards immediately above my head. Forming on the bottom-most
bulge of the belly was a large globule of viscous-looking yellow
liquid. I watched this, fascinated, as it gathered weight, and then
involuntarily ducked when it fell.

I was still deliberating whether I should continue to get wet or
climb out into the cold, dress, and go aloft to repair the tent roof
when there came a resounding twang and the whole structure
lurched drunkenly to starboard. "Curse!" I thought to myself.
"There goes one of the guy ropes," for I knew they were pulled too
tight for this climate. There were signs of imminent collapse at one
corner of our abode, and water slopped about on the roof of the
mosquito net, which was fortunately made of almost impervious
material. I started to get up.

Then there came some further twangs, and the whole place rocked again so that I expected it to come down and envelop me at any moment. I pulled on some clothes and stumbled out into the blue mists to see what was happening. And that was where I got a first-class surprise.

Our third jungle home was on the banks of a small river some thousand feet up in the Maya Mountains above a group of magnificent falls and just at the edge of the great *terra incognita* that stretches thence almost to the Guatemaltecan border. The main structure, which Alma and I occupied and where eating and much of the work went on during the day and the first half of the night, faced a level area that we had cleared. Almost immediately behind the back wall the ground rose at an angle of about forty-five degrees for some miles into the region of mountain cabbages and the unknown. At the far side of the little clearing was a six-foot perpendicular bank, beyond which a wide, very shallow, crystal stream splashed and murmured along over a level bed of pebbles and boulders. Beyond this was another small, level plain about a hundred feet wide, and then the land again rose precipitously.

We were camped in a bottom, with a four-hundred-foot series of waterfalls about a mile downstream and a forty-foot fall a quarter of a mile upstream. As a result, the vegetation around was more than lush. The trees were loaded to breaking point with ferns, orchids, bromeliads, tie-ties, and other epiphytes, and every twig was festooned with streamers of pale green moss and dull-coloured lichens. The little flood plain that made the floor of the bottom was covered with a forest of many beautiful, slender, feathery palms: cohune, hone, a monkey-tail (*Chamædora*), two kinds of *Geonoma* called the capuka and the pacaya, and a few mountain cabbages (*Euterpe macrospadix*), interspersed with four species of waha, the whole making an impenetrable grove of juicy, wet greenery. To add to the solidity, immense clambering rattans (*Desmoncus*), known locally as "basket tie-ties," the most infernal of all plants, sprawled everywhere, their spine-covered strands and bamboo-like leafage lying in ambush with the evil cunning that only this plant can achieve.

We were as yet hardly settled, after some extremely strenuous path-cutting and innumerable troubles with a lot of mules and horses, several of which, while fully loaded with our possessions, had gone clear over the edge of the precipitous mountainside up which we had had to scramble to attain this high position. We had not yet cleared our primary traces or adequately explored the terrain. Apparently the wild life of the place, which had never come in contact with man before, had likewise not yet completed its preliminary reconnoitring. The animals had their traces and high-roads well laid out, and we must have planted our dwelling athwart one of these.

As I rounded the tent, I came face to face with two prodigiously ugly beasts considerably more bulky and just as surprised as myself. Between them stood a diminutive and inquisitive-looking parody of them. For a few seconds we all stopped and stared at one another, twitching our respective long noses in the inquiring manner of all startled mammals.

Here, amid the morning mists and the guy ropes, stood a family party of tapirs (*Tapirella bairdi*), mystified and confused by this incomprehensible obstacle that had suddenly appeared in the middle of their principal highway. Here was I, a half-awake naturalist, also amid the morning mists and the guy ropes, no less confused and only a little less mystified. My only immediate advantage was that I could put a name to the animals at which I was staring. Having stared long and searchingly at each other with our respective bloodshot eyes, both parties then retreated precipitately.

What I should have done, I suppose, was to launch myself upon the spotted and inquisitive youngster, and chance the possible though most unlikely wrath of the oldsters. Failing this, I should have remained rooted to the spot, for, by so doing, I might have learned something thoroughly worth-while. Instead, I was obsessed with the idea of getting a gun, and that, of course, spoilt every-thing. At my first move, the tapirs wheeled about like startled cows, and went lumbering off down the neatly cleared path leading to Fred's tent.

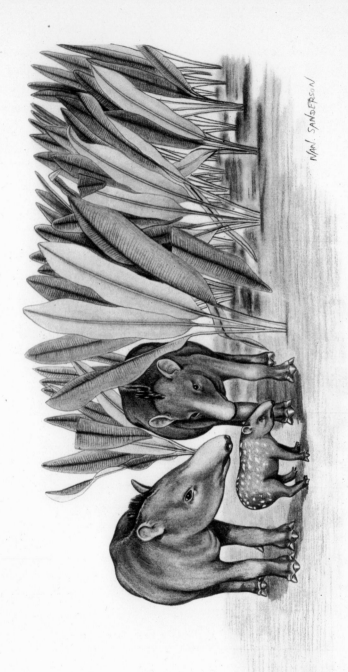

IVAN SANDERSON

TAPIRS (Tapirella bairdi)

I yelled for George, grabbed the shotgun, which always stood loaded and ready, and some extra-heavily charged cartridges, and bolted back onto the path. At that moment there was a tremendous crash in the distance, yells from George, and a formidable volley. I charged along, panting, rounded the last corner, dived through Fred's tent, and almost collided with George, who was heading up from the kitchen at equal speed. We dashed back through the tent and crashed into the wahas beyond, whence came sounds of head-long flight.

"Did you get one, George?"

"No, sir," he panted, "I've only got small shot."

"Did you aim for the little one?"

"I only saw one."

"Was it a baby or a big one?"

"I don't know, sir, but it had horns, fo' true, sir."

"Horns!" I said, coming to an abrupt halt. "What on earth do you mean? Mountain-cows don't have horns."

"Oh! No, sir; not mountain-cow, sir."

"What did you shoot at, then?"

"A deer, sir; a deer, fo' true, sir."

"Good Lord! Where did it go?"

"It was in the kitchen and went through Mr. Fred's tent."

We pounded on through the wahas, and came out upon the river bank again. Far to the left there were sounds resembling the charge of a cavalry unit over a cobbled street, so we leaped into the river and ran forward. The mist was less thick here, and we just caught a glimpse of one small and two big, fat forms cantering over the boulder-strewn river bed and heading for the falls, but before we could take aim they swerved to the right, plunged into a stand of wahas, and were lost in the mist.

"They're gone, George, but where's the deer?" I said gloomily.

We looked around for some minutes, but saw no sign of this either, so we regretfully retraced our steps to the camp, arriving at Fred's back door.

My assistant takes any morning very hard. Being awakened so

early as this had brought him up gasping like a rodent disturbed in its winter hibernation. He stuck his blinking face out at us from a small hole in the mosquito net, and groaned.

"What on earth's going on?"

"Nothing much, dear boy. Only three tapirs and a deer went through your tent."

"Ugh," he growled, "don't talk rubbish." Then he withdrew and went back to sleep.

It was some hours before Fred appeared again. By this time George and I were high up on the mountains behind our abode.

The summits of tropical mountains are always mysteriously intriguing places. There is about them a quietness and purity occasioned by the rarefied air. There is also an aloofness that is accentuated by the occasional bell-like call of some queer bird, by the gentle sighing of light breezes in the foliage, or by the wheeling of an eagle far below instead of above you. The vegetation is often odd, with a certain elfin quality. As much light sometimes comes from below as from above, which produces queer shadows and a subtle beauty that is not met with in low places. You almost expect to see little gnome-like faces peering at you from behind the boles of the trees. Sometimes you do see them.

Our objects on this morning's exploration were twofold. First, we wanted to see the unusual kind of mountain forest that was reported from the top of this range; second, we had a very special table delicacy in mind. In addition, of course, we intended to collect what wild life we encountered, for the usual reasons.

After leaving the misty, sodden bottom of the gorge, we entered a zone of immense hardwoods containing positively giant mahoganies and a huge variety of other trees with curiously attractive local names: timber sweet, silly young, prickly yellow, pigeon plum, waka-chewstick, and others. Here the forest floor was tilted at a sharp angle, and was comparatively clear. A mile farther up, the growth changed to rather stunted timber with a lot of vines and lianes and without any of the cohune palms which are such a constant feature of the same forests at lower levels. It was here that we entered another zone of animal life.

The animal assemblage in the bottom, up the side valleys, over the lower shoulders, and thence on into the depths of the mountains proved to be different from that of the lowland plains more in degree than in actual make-up. It was distinguished by the presence of nearly all the animals from all the sub-zones of the lowland vegetation, though it had in addition a few species not met with there. This fauna continued up the mountains to the twelve-hundred-foot level, where the next change took place—the one which we noticed first this morning.

Here we almost trod on a bright green snake with a yellow underside, to which George promptly put the local name, "thunder-and-lightning snake." This species (*Dryadophis boddaerti*) is not uncommon, but is rather local in its incidence, being very decidedly circumscribed in its distribution by certain features of environment. The next creature that we saw was a very beautifully coloured lizard. It had the form and general appearance of the variegated green *Anolis capito* from the plains, but its colouration, composed of green, grey, brown, and yellow jagged-edged mottlings, with vivid black lateral stripes and other odd-shaped markings on a pale green ground, was altogether novel. Besides, it lacked the brilliant gular fin of that species and seemed incapable of any colour change.

Somewhat farther on we encountered another area of tall forest that was open beneath, and under which the ground was covered with crisp dry leaves. Upon these was a great hopping of small frogs, which proved to be the species *Eleutherodactylus rhodopis* that we knew well from lower levels, but which were here all in a novel colour phase. We carried some of these back home with us alive, but nothing we could do would persuade them to change to coats of the colours and patterns worn by their lowland brethren. Only after their death and two days' submergence in preservatives did they slowly come to resemble them, as a result of a gradual loss of all their life colouration.

We also collected some new snails, arachnida, and other lesser forms of life, and saw a brightly coloured small squirrel which we could not take because we had no guns with us. For this I will never forgive myself, for we never saw the species again, and it was most distinctive, with a bright golden stripe along its flanks and a banded tail. We continued upwards, and finally passed the three-thousand-foot level into the region of the mountain forest.

The term "mountain forest" is really a very misleading one, for there are at least five distinct types, which fall into an equal number of well-defined zones and which may be met with at altitudes of 3000 feet to 13,500 feet, according to the latitude in which they are encountered. Only upon very high mountains standing on the Equator itself will all these zones be encountered in a single ascent. The term is usually reserved for a gnarled growth of stunted, moss-festooned trees found above the upper mountain grass-fields, which is the highest-altitude type. That which we now entered was the lowest, and here consisted of plants that are for the most part found in swampy places at sea level in this country.

The ground was covered with a thick layer of armadillo grass (*Rynchospora cephaloides*), and the principal trees were pole-wood (*Xylopia frutescens*), mountain mangroves, and the mountain cabbage palm. The trees were low and widely spaced, so that the whole place was flooded with the brilliant mountain sunlight. A gentle breeze ruffled the head foliage; there were many delicate flowers among the grass; strange birds with plaintive calls flitted between the tall, slender palm trunks. It was a very fair and gentle world, quite unlike the bustling, struggling, deeply breathing jungles below.

Here again we collected all the small animals we could find. We also set about getting our dinner. The mountain cabbage palm has a straight, annulated trunk of no great girth, bearing aloft a long, shiny, green cylinder, from which the frond bases spring. The head is in fact like that of a royal palm, only on a smaller scale. If this head is split open lengthwise and the harder outer leaf bases peeled off, a long, soft, central core will be disclosed. This, the "heart," is actually the apical growing point of the plant, together with the embryo leaves.

Hearts of palms of various kinds are a common dish on tropical lunch tables, but the mountain cabbage of British Honduras is in a class by itself. Not only is the flexible cylinder of exactly the correct diameter for inserting into the mouth—which is an important consideration when eating the thing like celery after dipping it in a French dressing—but also the flavour is of a delicacy that cannot be described in words. We cut and opened quite a number of palms and extracted the "cabbage," which we rolled in a clean cloth and put away in the bag. We then returned to camp.

We found our work harder at this home in the mountains than at any other place we had ever visited. Many factors contributed to this. First, the rainfall was very high and sporadic because of the surrounding mountains. Second, the temperature varied greatly between night and day, from day to day, and even from hour to hour; we recorded differences of thirty-two degrees within seven hours. Third, the jungle was for the most part very tangled and dense, and the ground surface so precipitous that it made movement, except along our traces, almost impossible. Finally, the whole forest comprising the zone in which we actually lived—that is to say, the six-hundred-to-twelve-hundred-foot belt, which is at the best of times a transition zone—was split up into a number of exceptionally clear-cut sub-zones, most of which were occupied by distinctive plant associations. Several of these, moreover, were almost completely sterile as regards the groups of animals we sought, though often enough full of birds, insects, and the other groups that we do not collect.

These factors, combined with many petty annoyances occasioned by the excessive damp, which made even waterproof cartridges swell up, caused mould to grow on everything, and prevented specimens from drying, gave us endless trouble. We cut our primary traces, only to discover that they all ran through the most sterile sub-zones. We cut new ones into the areas that we had found to be more prolific of specimens, and only succeeded in scaring the animals. In fact, I don't think we have ever struck a place where the animals knew so little about men and yet were so very easily disturbed, shy, and "touchy." At first they had blundered right into the camp, but when they found out about us, they seemed to pass the word around. At any rate, they all vanished completely.

Animals are very susceptible to changes in climate. Here, a small shower that only dampened the forest prompted all the animals to retire, while an hour's hot sunshine brought out a galaxy of creatures never seen before and which again disappeared with the sun, never to return until it again shone with exactly the same degree of intensity and warmth. All this was very mysterious and confusing, and it kept us on the run day and night. It also accounted for the very patchy and scrappy collections that we made, by which I mean that we obtained a large variety of animals, but seldom more than one or two specimens of each. Every day and every hour of the day would be different in each of the many distinct sub-zones, so that, although at least one of us was out on the prowl at almost any time, we seldom if ever met the same conditions twice and therefore seldom encountered the same animals.

For instance, one evening Fred went out along the northern trace between sundown and dinner time. When I finished the work on hand, I picked up the little collecting gun and a torch, and strolled out to see what he was doing. I found him some way from the camp, once again standing stock-still in the path, with his light beam focused on a tangle of creepers clothing a small tree. It seems that I was always coming across him thus occupied. We went through the set formula:

"What is it, Fred?"

"I don't know. It may be an animal, but it hasn't moved and I can't make out."

"Where is it?"

"Do you see that creeper under that branch? Well, it's on that."

"Which creeper? I can't see anything."

"The one on the left, down by those leaves," and so on and so on.

It was always the same. Fred would spot something with his un-canny eyesight, and I would peer at it and go through a course of minor botanical geography, using branches and leaves as salient points, and yet never see the animal. Finally I would give the gun to Fred, and he would fire and apparently nothing would happen. Then we would both spend a happy half-hour searching below the tree, arguing as to where the animal had been and where it should have fallen, until finally I would find it by peering myopically among the rubbish and feeling around with my fingers like a great whip-scorpion.

On this occasion there was no deviation from the set formula. Fred shot, and nothing but leaves fell as far as I could see; we searched, and I eventually found a small mammal. It turned out to be a species of opossum (*Marmosa alstoni alstoni*) that was new to us. In form it was much like the little lowland *Marmosa*, but was many times larger. The head was broad, with a very short, sharp muzzle and small ears. The tail was long and naked, brown at the base but pale pink throughout the terminal half. It was clothed in long, woolly, and yet silky fur coloured olive-brown, with silver flecks on the back and flanks. The underside was apricot-yellow, which extended up onto the cheeks. The muzzle was yellow, and the eyes were surrounded by black "spectacles." A prettier little mammal I have seldom seen.

We had been collecting along that path almost every night, as it was one of our main traces and we had to pass along it both to get to and return from hunting and work in the whole of the northern, eastern, and western areas, and we never failed to examine the trees as we went along. This was the first and the last we saw of this beautiful species. The reason for this, in all probability, was that a thick fog was gathering when we shot it, a thing that did not occur at other times until about three-thirty in the morning.

An almost exact repetition of this incident occurred a few nights later. This time I picked up a large specimen of the grey-and-white tree-rat. On a third occasion it was Alma who did the shooting, and the incident occurred in daylight.

We were marking out a plot of the forest to be dissected. The place we had selected was the level floor of the bottom, about a quarter of a mile up our main west trace. On this grew a type of forest composed of very tall hardwoods, with a veritable mosaic of great trees below and, beneath these, an almost continuous stratum of low palms. The floor was covered with a carpet of small lilies and ferns, while the trunks of the big trees were clothed in capes of weird parasitic plants—or rather, in the strict sense, epiphytic plants, for the majority of them merely dwell upon their hosts, and do not live upon the latters' life blood, as true parasites would. We had cleared out the lower strata, including the medium saplings, when all of a sudden George shouted, "Look!"

We did so just in time to see something fly from one tree and disappear into the foliage on the trunk of another. Alma raised her gun and let fly. It was one of the snipiest shots I have ever seen, and a gasp of admiration went up from the assembled company as something small and brown came spinning down to fall among the dead leaves. Of course we all ran forward and started looking about, but although five people had seen the thing fall within a half-dozen square yards of more or less clean ground, nobody could find it. In the end I once more came across it by a combined sense of touch and second sight. It was an extremely rare bat (*Centronycteris maxi-miliani centralis*), chestnut-brown in colour, very small and with the oddest twisted ears, the tips of which turned right round to face backwards. Again this was a unique specimen in our collections, though we passed that way every day and were constantly watch-ing the trees and disturbing their coverings of creepers and other places of concealment suitable to bats.

The effects of climatic changes upon the incidence of the fauna at this place were so marked that they would indeed have been ob-vious to anyone. For instance, during two weeks we saw no sign of a snake, and then one morning half a dozen turned up in a few hours. This might have been coincidence, but was very probably not so, for most of the specimens were caught at places which we had constantly searched and over which we passed every day.

I caught the first one on the river bank when going to get water. It was a little thin brown animal (*Coniophanes fissidens*) with a white line on the side of the head and many small, pin-point spots along the outer edges of its beige underside. The second was a coral snake (*Pliocercus elapoides*), which Fred trod on in the main western trace. It was simply pottering about the forest floor. This species is vividly banded yellow, red, and black, and is harmless. The third, another of the little thin brown ones, was caught by Dick in his kitchen in the act of swallowing a small scincoid lizard (*Leiolopisma assatum*).

While we were examining this specimen and the lizard taken with it, George, who had been out extending the northern trace up the mountain behind the camp, came running with a long sapling. At its far end, entangled in its forking branches, was a knot of shiny scales. George dumped this on the ground before the tent, and held it down with the sapling. He was panting and extremely rattled.

"Good Lord, what's the matter with you?" I asked, jumping up.

"Look you, sir, it's a Jumping Tommy-Goff, a bad snake, fo' true, sir. Phew!" he panted.

"What happened, George?"

I often found George's talk rather difficult to follow; Belizarian lingo is so full of odd expressions, side kicks, old-fashioned English, and abstruse double meanings of its own, that it is very difficult to understand at best. But when George was excited it became quite impossible, and he was now more disturbed than I have ever seen him either before or since. I am afraid he must have thought me very stupid for not understanding my own language, and most annoying for making him repeat everything a dozen times, but I finally got his story.

It appeared that he had been trace-cutting at a fair rate, bending the saplings and small bushes down with his right hand and cutting them off close to the ground with his left, for he is left-handed. He had come to a steep bank and had taken hold of a small, low capuka palm, and, after cutting through its base, had lifted it bodily to throw it away over the surrounding tangle. As he did so, something fell on his hat, which was a strange, battered affair with a not inconsiderable saucepan-shaped depression in the top. Thinking that it was a bit of dead stick, he had put up his right hand, removed his hat, and shaken out the contents. Imagine his feelings when eighteen inches of extremely thick snake poured out and remained suspended by its fangs, which were firmly anchored in the rim of the felt hat immediately beside his fingers. No description of his ensuing moves is necessary. In fact, George quite rejoiced my heart with an almost truly African pantomime of events, which culminated in the gathering up of the deadly snake on the sapling head and running with it to camp.

This "Jumping Tommy-Goff" (*Trimeresurus mummifer*) is quite the most evil-looking brute I have seen. As a snake it is a washout, being so short and having such a tremendous girth in proportion that the tiny tail doesn't reach the ground and the animal is a hopeless wriggler. To make up for such shortcomings, it has some dubious habits. As its name implies, it is credited with great powers of locomotion. If you get some locals really going about this snake, you will have visions of it flying through the air like an arrow, bounding over streams, and bouncing along through the jungle after you. In reality, the most it can do is suddenly to straighten itself out frightfully quickly, which action, it has been estimated, can project it for some two or three feet down an incline. It can also travel in a straight line very quickly with a minimum of "snaking," so that it does indeed appear to shoot along and hop over low obstacles. This it manages by its strong, band-like ventral scales.

Its reputation as a jumper, however, probably originates from quite another habit. This is its predilection for resting in the heads of small palm trees. In these it lies neatly coiled, with its great weight supported by the radially arranged frond bases. If you pass close by and disturb it, it goes through its little act of getting as straight as possible as quickly as possible, and as a result is often projected right out of the palm. Apparently this is what had happened to

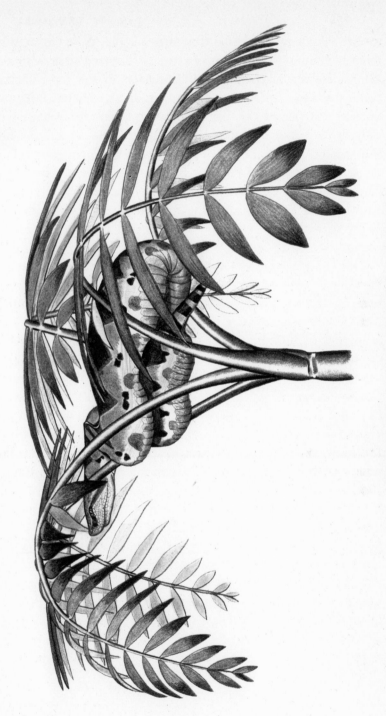

"Jumping Tommy-Goff" (*Trimeresurus mummifer*)

George, and it is understandable why people should have come to regard it as capable of making prodigious leaps.

Like all other snakes, this species varies somewhat in colour and pattern. This specimen was pinkish-beige, with brown diamonds along the back and a double series of black spots on the flanks. The lower jaw is yellow like that of its relative, the Yellow-Jawed Tommy-Goff; the underside of the body proper is dirty pinkish-white with dusky spots, while under the tail it is dull brown with white spots. It is, as a Scotch friend of ours said, "that poisonous!"

There was a great goo-goo-eyed frog (*Rana palmipes*), with tremendously muscled legs and a bright green snout, which we had collected at our first home on the plains and which we now met in the stream bed opposite our mountain camp. Here it was even bigger, but its head was not green. If a torch was flashed into the river bed at night, myriads of small, baleful, reddish eyes would shine out, and as your eyesight became accustomed to things, you would perceive that these were owned by frogs perched rather regally upon the clean, rounded boulders. We collected a lot, and used them for some experiments to determine the degree and speed of their colour changes.

Then we obtained a single individual the front of whose head was bright green, as in the lowland form. This stimulated me so much that I asked everybody to go to the stream straightway and collect as many more as possible, and they all went off with great willingness, so that I sat down after dinner looking forward to a very happy evening. The captures consisted of what at first appeared to be only two species of frog—the goo-goo-eyed one, of which there were no more green-headed individuals, and another known as *Eleutherodactylus ranoides*, for which mouthful I am afraid there is no English name. After a time, however, I realized that *E. ranoides* also consisted of two quite distinct species, which were so extraordinarily alike *in life* as to be almost indistinguishable. In fact, it was only after they had been measured and pickled that any real differences between the two became apparent. They were really quite different frogs, and the new one was forthwith christened Frog C.A. 11. Naturally, I had all our previously collected *E. ranoides* fished out and re-examined, but there were none of the new type among them.

This, being a species new to our collections and, incidentally, new to science, called for further collecting at once, since we had learned that promptness was everything in this forest if one needed more specimens of a certain animal. By this time, however, everybody was otherwise occupied, so I took a torch and a big bag and set off for the stream. The night was filled with frog talk and glowing eyes.

It was presumably once again some vagary of the climate that had prompted this new kind of frog suddenly to put in an appearance in great numbers, for we had seen none before that night, and saw none afterwards. The presence of the enormous numbers of other frogs that were also about that night was doubtless occasioned by the same causes.

Leaving the camp, I moved slowly up the river bed, and, as so often happens when out searching at night, one interesting sight and then another led me on and on, until I finally approached the boulder-strewn gorge at the foot of the forty-foot falls. This was a very odd place. The river shot out from an overhanging cliff, and thundered down into a welter of tumbled blocks of rock and great tree trunks piled at the bottom of a small gorge with precipitous, smooth rock walls. There were very deep pools and gushing sluices between the great slabs of rock. A giant tree lay across the gorge like a flying buttress, and formed a natural bridge with its ends jammed against the rock face some thirty feet up.

There were frogs here too, and I advanced from one capture to another until I was almost within the flying spray from the falls. The noise here was deafening, for the towering walls of the gorge, which were more than a hundred feet high but not more than fifty feet apart, magnified the roaring of the waters many-fold. The rocks below were slimy and extremely slippery. Between them were deep, dark cavelets into which I thrust my torch.

Then I saw a tree-frog floating with its snout out of water in a tiny pool far down between two great boulders, and, being eager to get this, I lay over a rock and reached down into the hole. I could not quite reach the frog, and in manœuvring to increase my reach, my feet slipped on the rocks behind and I slithered backwards and downwards. My left foot went down farthest, and I grabbed wildly for a hand-hold. My left hand went round the end of a log, and I gripped it frenziedly. The log gave an ominous crack somewhere down below, and before I knew what was happening I felt my left leg gripped around the ankle as if by a powerful vice. I let go and came to rest in a very cramped position.

When I had put down the collecting bag and screwed myself around as far as I could without further hurting my imprisoned left ankle, I discovered that a huge boulder had moved down towards two others, and anchored me. The boulder must have been supported by the log, which had rotted. The log had broken below when I grabbed it, and allowed the boulder to shift. I was securely held, and although there was little actual weight on my foot and ankle, it was just tight enough to be painful and to prevent me from turning about freely.

I had long been wondering what would happen to me next. The jungle seems to delight in setting traps that are more ingenious than even man himself could devise. It is a harmless enough place to live and move about in, provided one behaves properly. The dangers that one might expect are hardly ever encountered, and yet a string of quite improbable things happen to us in never-ending procession. I smoked a cigarette and took stock of my position.

At first I tried pulling, but soon gave that up. Then I tried to turn my foot around, but the space into which it was jammed was too small, and the attempt proved extremely painful. I began to wonder about my predicament, and the more I thought about it, the more disturbed I became. The worst trouble was not that I was caught and held fast. More disturbing was that it had started to rain torrentially, and I had no idea how long it might continue or how much the river might rise as a result. The water was still some feet below me, but we had witnessed prodigious floods before, and these sometimes bore along with them great bumping logs and wildly thrashing branches.

A far greater danger was the tremendous noise made by the falls. Although I knew the household would be out to look for me in due course, I realized they would be guided in this search almost solely by shouting and awaiting answering calls from myself. Only by the merest chance would they think of penetrating so far into this gorge, for it was a difficult place to get into, and was easily inspected from outside during the daytime. I could not, moreover, be seen, as I was now wedged down at the bottom of a deep pit between towering rocks.

I tried to move the boulder, but its whole weight had descended upon its neighbours and it was a great deal larger than I had at first suspected. I then tried cutting the laces of my boot, to see if I could pull my foot out, but my ankles happen to be very slim and my ankle bones very large, so that I was, in effect, most firmly held. After these efforts I attempted another cigarette in the downpour, while I further racked my brains for some way out of my predicament. Then I noticed the shaft of a small dead tree sticking up among the boulders a little way distant. It was smooth and shiny, and looked comparatively new and strong. Of course it was just out of reach.

First, I got a small stick and tried to pull the little tree toward me, but the stick was rotten and broke, and there were no others within reach. Next I tried with a piece of the rotten and accursed log that had broken and released the boulder, but it was also too soft and broke, and I began to despair. It was raining a deluge by now, and I was soaked to the skin and very cold. The best course on such occasions is to undress, and this I started to do. When I came to my trousers and realized they could not be removed, I suddenly had a brainwave.

With my knife I quickly slit up my trouser leg, and then stretched this garment to its fullest length, joined it to my shirt, added to this my handkerchief, the strap from the collecting bag, and one small piece of string that I happened to have in my pocket. I now had an extremely crude lasso. With this I made many passes at the top of the small tree, and finally had it securely hooked. Then followed some very tense moments while the tough wood, and the not-so-tough materials of which my clothes were made, vied with each other in what might be called a life-and-death struggle—until there came a sudden jolt and the tree moved. As I released the strain, moreover, it remained in its new position, and when I shook the rope of clothes, it wobbled about drunkenly. It was free.

It now had only to be lifted out of its seating, and by good fortune there was the broken end of a small branch just showing above the boulders. After some manœuvring with another piece of rotten log, I got the lasso under this and gave a great heave. On the fourth or fifth attempt, it came free, and almost knocked me out as it came.

Now began what was to be the longest job of all. I was greatly disheartened by this, for I had thought that my troubles were nearly over. My intention was to use this small tree shaft as a lever to move the boulder, but I soon found that neither it nor I, nor both of us combined, on the principles laid down by Archimedes, were anything like horsepowerful enough even to budge it. I tried this way and that, but to no avail. Looking round to see if anything else could be done, I came to the conclusion that there was only one chance left. The other two boulders that held my leg were somewhat below the chief offender, and were held in position by still another big one, beyond which there was a large pool. If I could move this other boulder, the little ones might shift enough for me to get out.

The job was complicated by my being screwed round with my back to the task, but after much straining I got a good fulcrum selected and managed to bring the great lever into play. Almost immediately the big rock shifted a little, followed by one of the smaller ones. I felt the pressure suddenly leave my ankle, and with a jolt of thankfulness I turned my foot round preparatory to pulling it out, but as I did so there was an ominous crack, and intense pain shot up my leg. The original big boulder had shifted again on its rotten log base, and once more imprisoned me, this time more uncomfortably.

However, I was now facing the scene of operations. I rammed in the tree-lever, and as soon as it was firmly wedged, gave it a tremendous wrench. It snapped off clean with a report that echoed even above the roaring of the falls. I got a tremendous shock, and was thrown backwards violently.

I know it will sound rather silly when I say that I looked down and saw my left foot squarely planted upon the rock alongside my right one, and that I could hardly believe my eyes. In fact, I remember looking steadfastly at it for some time, and then at the hole where it had been imprisoned, before I realized that something had happened and that I was free. It appeared that the final effort, which broke the lever's tip, had also shifted the rock sufficiently to allow me to withdraw my foot at the instant I was flung back. If this was not the answer, then I must have made some other involuntary and superhuman effort, for there was no denying the fact that I was free and in full possession of both of my feet, while the boulder was again firmly planted athwart the hole in which my ankle was so recently locked.

Since my trousers were beyond much hope, I donned my shirt in the form of the "sham-pants" of our Hindu brethren, and then retrieved the rest of my belongings. Chancing to look down into the original hole, I was amazed to see the tree-frog still floating aimlessly in the small pool. This time I reached down head-first, with my feet in the air, and made a quick capture. Then I gathered up my things and beat a cautious retreat over the boulders to the nearest point where the bank was climbable. In due course I arrived home, limping and extremely cold.

As usual, nobody seemed to have noticed my long absence, though it was nearly two o'clock in the morning. Fred had shot a fat paca, and they were all skinning it and discussing which bits they were going to eat on the morrow.

OVER THE DIVIDE

Boa and Beef-Worms; Parrots, Squirrels, and Deer

THE change occasioned in animal life by a change of locale from one vegetational zone to another became especially obvious when we left our mountain abode and travelled down onto the plains and out beyond the limits of the great forests to establish our next home in the pine belt. It was quite plain that there was a radical change where the lowland pines meet the tall jungles, but there are just as perceptible breaks between the former and other types of growth—even other hardwood forests—farther to the north. It was by an examination of the animals that the fundamental importance of this particular "divide" became apparent.

There are many animals that are indigenous to both sides of this divide, but there is a fair list of those that are not. Moreover, among the animals there is the notable difference that, as soon as one crosses this line, going north, one meets a new assemblage which goes on increasing in numbers and in variety until it merges into the fauna of North America. Although some southern forest types of animals extend their range to the north, all the northern types appear to end their range abruptly at this "divide," and we have yet to find one that enters the southern jungles.

Fred and I arrived hot and perspiring under a scorching morning sun among the first pine trees. We selected a suitable spot not too far from running water, and set to work upon the most hateful tangle of vegetation that I have ever encountered. The pines were of all sizes and fairly well spaced, and the locale could by no means be called a forest. Beneath the pines was a ten-foot tangle of very thin-stemmed, hard, dry, scraggly bushes with small, hard leaves, bound together into a close-woven mat by many extremely thin, tough lianes and masses of cutting-grass (*Scleria secans*).

Words to describe this latter plant are unprintable, so it must suffice to explain that it is a climbing grass with leaves and stems all of which have edges constructed like the better types of safety-razor blade. If you look at one of these under a microscope—the razor blades, I mean—you will see that their pretty, glistening edges are in reality a ragged row of minute, irregular, chipped, and broken teeth. You don't cut with a razor blade. If you use it lengthwise, you saw with it, and if you employ it in the normal fashion, you presumably raze with it. With the cutting-grass, however, your own part is mostly passive. Its cutting edges may be drawn over your skin in either of the above ways, and, either way, produce an equally unpleasant effect. If they slash you lengthwise, you get a very fine, clean cut that smarts painfully; if they scrape across upon a wide front like a razor, you receive a series of parallel striations. These are not so noticeable at first, but as your perspiration filters into them they smart even more furiously than the cuts, and by the evening arise red and swollen upon your skin.

Cutting a forest sapling or even a large tree with a sharp machete can be a pleasure. The keen blade bites into the wood with a pleasant and reassuring ring, if one has learnt the art of wielding the thing. Clearing a path through wahas is a pleasure, because the pithy stems hop off with a satisfying plock. Work on this tangle below the pines, however, was something quite the contrary and altogether soul-destroying. We finally discovered that the only effective method was to wrap our arms in rags, hack out a channel around the sides of a large piece of the tangled growth, and then back into it, cutting each strand that joined a root as it was disclosed between our retreating feet. Thus a great mass was slowly severed both from the ground and from its surroundings, and could be pitchforked out of the clearing. Space had to be cleared for three tents and the kitchen, and paths cut to connect them. There was no way in which we could lay out the plots; we just had to cut our way to some point where the ground appeared suitable, and then start to work and keep cutting until a large enough area was cleared. The work progressed slowly, but was not without comic relief. The first incident occurred after we had been at work for an hour. Fred called out from the heart of the tangle:

"Hi, Ivan! Come and look at this."

"Coming!" I shouted, for he was some way off, and I set out along the newly cut trace.

Rounding a corner, I saw Fred crouching on the ground holding something that heaved beneath a tent bag.

"What've you got?" I asked.

"A present for you."

"Does it bite?"

"You've had a college education, find out for yourself," he rejoined with an irritatingly British lack of originality.

"No, I won't play," I said.

"Won't bite, eh?" he came back, his appalling punning increasing my peevishness.

"No, I won't," I said, putting a large foot down rather firmly upon the heaving bag.

"Look out! Don't hurt the poor thing," Fred said, raising the bag and disclosing a very great deal of madly heaving snake.

"Good Lord!" I shouted, jumping back with the greatest alacrity.

"It's all right," he almost purred, "it's only a wowla."

"Listen, dear boy," I said, now being thoroughly roused, "how the devil can you tell one snake from another? Don't be such an ass; nobody can be sure of what a snake is simply by looking at it."

I must admit that he did look a bit contrite at this. He pulled back the bag, which, as a matter of fact, was made of extremely tough canvas and would have prevented any snake from striking, more especially if it were held down tightly, as this one was. At the same time he held something out in his hand.

When I took time off from goggling at the snake to look at this, I saw it was the head of a large boa or wowla. I then looked at the heaving body on the ground again, and perceived that it was headless and therefore quite harmless. My relief gave way to much laughter at the time, but I continued to grumble about Fred's rather peculiar sense of humour for some days afterwards.

It appears that he had been pushing his way backwards into the tangle, and hacking at the roots, when he had seen blood on his machete. Having made an examination of himself and found no signs of damage, he extended his search into the ground cover, and there had found the snake's head. A further search had disclosed the body neatly packed up in a shallow hole. The brute must have put its head out in an inquiring kind of way, and got it cut off for its trouble.

This snake was nine feet nine inches long, nothing very remarkable in itself, but nevertheless a decent-sized specimen. We didn't want it particularly, since we already had sufficient of this common species, but we noticed a large swelling about its middle which instantly excited the hope that this would prove to be some valuable mammal that the snake had swallowed whole. We immediately slit it open with our knives and dumped out the contents with bated breath. It was a complete *Didelphis* opossum—the omnipresent, the unwanted, the perpetual nuisance.

Behind this, however, at the pit of the snake's stomach, we found something very curious. This was a ball of dark brown, coarse mammalian fur, along with a few of the tougher and less digestible portions of the long limb bones of the victim. Such hair balls are common in some snakes. These animals have a cunning method of digesting and absorbing everything possible from a meal, and neatly collecting the hopeless parts into a ball which is then vomited up. The curious part about this ball, however, was its contents.

When we broke it up we found inside three large, somewhat flattened, but otherwise quite undamaged, maggot-like bodies. These were very large so-called "beef-worms" or "mosquito-worms," which parasitize various mammals.

These horrible beasts, of which we had already collected four different species, are very widely distributed in the tropics. They are the larvæ of certain two-winged flies (*Dermatobia hominis* and other flies of the sub-families *Hypodermatinæ* and *Sarcophaginæ*, though I doubt if this means much to anybody but a two-winged fly expert) that have a life history that is surely among the strangest and most complex in the animal kingdom. This history is said to be as follows.

The adult female fly, wishing to lay some eggs, hangs about suitable places until she spots a mosquito hatching from its pupa case. The fly seizes the newly emerged insect, and lays its small eggs upon it. The hapless mosquito is unable to refuse, still being soft and doubtless unable to cope with its new aerial world in many other respects. In due course, the mosquito hardens up and then goes forth in search of nourishment. If it finds an animal and starts a meal, the beef-worm eggs are brushed off by and become entangled in the mammal's fur. In time, they hatch, and the small larvæ therefrom instantly burrow into the new host's skin, making therein small flask-like chambers in which they live. In other cases the eggs are laid on plants near water. They are encased in a cement that softens and becomes sticky with moisture. These eggs may then adhere to mosquitoes or other insects or even directly to the final host.

The larvæ leave a small opening in the "flask" at the skin surface, for, it is said, breathing purposes. One species which grows very large, and keeps a wide opening of this sort, appears not to be a true parasite. This form lies with its head projecting from the flask, and appears to feed upon animal or vegetable matter against which it is brought in contact by its host.

These loathsome maggots grow to startling dimensions, some being one and one-half inches long. They are annulated, can squeeze in and out in peristaltic waves, and are often provided with rings of backwardly directed, spiny bristles. They have sharp, rapacious-looking jaws, and fill their flasks with a clear, messy liquid. They raise huge, volcano-shaped swellings on their hosts, which include human beings. In fact, they are very prevalent human pests in British Honduras, as are the related forms in other parts of tropical America and the similar tumbu fly of Africa. For some reason no one in our household contracted any, but we saw many on other people. They look like small boils at first, and the uninitiated mistake them for such. If they are squeezed, however, the insects have a nasty way of bursting inside, and setting up serious infection, which in turn often leads to blood poisoning. These beef-worm "boils" should be plastered with gum or a wad of chewed tobacco, which stifles the insects, whereupon they can be squeezed out harmlessly. Failing this, the neck of the "flask" should be stretched with forceps and the larvæ squeezed out.

The larvæ finally leave the "flasks" and drop out to harden and pupate on the ground. We have often found the pupæ in birds' nests and the retreats of rats and other animals.

This hair ball from the snake's stomach looked like the remains of a coati, an animal which is very prone to act as host to beef-worms. In any case, it could not be supposed that the great snake had deliberately picked three beef-worms off some animal by choice, more particularly in view of the clearly demonstrated fact that they were less digestible than the most solid bone. This is the strangest fact about this chance discovery. What is it that beef-worms, which are not internal parasites, have that absolutely prevents them from being digested or even vaguely harmed by the exceptionally powerful digestive juices of a large snake—juices which had eaten away solid bones and reduced the hair in the ball to a soft, spongy mass? Here is something in animal chemistry that would repay analysis, for these three beef-worms were quite unaffected, and still perfect in every detail.

Neither the wowla (*Constrictor constrictor*—though I am personally very uncertain how much constricting they really do in the wild state) nor the beef-worms were new to our collections. In fact, both were very common in the high forest. By clearing this animal's hide-away, however, we found something we had not seen before. Not more than a foot away from where this large and voracious beast had dwelt, we caught a rat in its nest along with seven young ones. Apparently there is no limit to the unexpected in nature!

One would certainly have supposed that the snake would have scared the underfur off any rat, especially such a snake as this, which had obviously been out hunting quite recently and killed a large opossum. Moreover, one would have been none the less sure that all our shouting, talking, hacking, and, particularly, the spattering of the snake's blood about the place, would have warned such a keenly sensitive creature as a nursing rat that the time to quit had come. Finally, the capture of a rat by putting a machete across its back is in any case exceptional.

This rat (*Sigmodon hispidus*) was just the type one would expect to find in a pine zone. It had hard short fur, small feet with sharp claws, a short tail, small rounded ears, and was brindled brown on the back with a greyish-yellow underside. There seems always to be a rat something like this in the open country adjoining a tropical forest, just as there are always, *in* the forest, at least the four types described earlier. This animal became our spot-type for the northern vegetation, and it has never let us down. It was trapped up to the very edge of this growth, but three yards farther on into the southern vegetation over the "divide," it was never taken.

The mother rat had constructed a neat nest inside a large clump of grass. This had two entrances, and was lined with finely chopped grass chaff and many small pieces of beetles' elytra, presumably the remains of meals.

We have established, as I said earlier, that the degree and quality of the light in different types of forest affect the animals greatly. We have now decided that we ourselves are exceedingly prone to be affected by the same factors. Looking back upon our many jungle homes that now lie scattered about the world in their quiet, overgrown forgottenness, we perceive that we retain a distinct impression of each that is pervaded by a unique atmosphere; and the atmosphere of a natural place, just as much as that of a restaurant, seems to depend upon its lighting. There was something about the mountain forest above our recent camp that impressed us with a queer sense of gentle aloofness, so that, standing in it, you felt as if you were among the gods of very olden days who dwelt upon

Elysian heights. It was delicate and fresh and so very far above the wrangling world, and yet it was only half as high as a very similar-looking place that I once climbed to in Sumatra, where I had half expected to be struck by lightning all the time, and which I had hated and feared. I believe it is the quality of the light that so affects one, just as it was when we lived beside the lapping, muddy waters of the Dutch Guiana coast on a sand spit, among crabs and red ibises, and all the time had the sensation of being on another planet.

We love the great equatorial jungle, and the taller and denser it is, the better we like it. There is a closed and friendly feeling about its endless roof; it is a place—or, rather, a thing—into which one can dive for protection; once inside, it is rather pleasant never to have to see the sky for weeks, even months, on end. Coming out of it, we always feel naked, rather scared, and with such sensations as might be attributed to a hermit crab that has been pulled out of its shell. The jungle vacated is to us a paradise lost. On this occasion, however, our regrets were softened by the very mysterious new beauty and atmosphere of the locale into which we finally squeezed ourselves.

Perhaps it is the memory of the birds that prompts me to stress the strange beauty of this place, for when we had finished our clearings and erected the tents, they came in their hundreds and were bolder than we had ever known them elsewhere. Lovely, smoky-blue individuals about the size of a thrush would come hopping into the tents, exploring the table legs for insects. Smaller olive-green ones with neatly spotted waistcoats were for ever fluttering around our feet, dipping their fan tails and peering inquiringly up into our faces. Large, screeching things with red wattles and crests used to come sailing in from nowhere and land, wobbling, on the guy ropes.

Nevertheless, this place was by no means a paradise. Its purely local climate was only a little less annoying than that of the mountains. Starting the day at dawn, we awoke, shivering in a thick mist, to find everything quite drenched. The soil was jet-black, and oozed water. By seven o'clock, the mist had cleared and the sun had come out, but everything continued damp. The morning was then idyllic until about ten o'clock, with a crystal clarity and a wonderful freshness to the air, many birds in the bushes, and a smell of resin everywhere. The next period was hot and got hotter. Everything dried up, paper curled into tubes, tops of boxes cracked and gaped; we stifled, and drank gallons of water, and the earth turned pale grey. By noon we retired under a net to get away from the bottlas flies.

These, together with doctor flies, contribute much to the character of British Honduras. The former are sundry small black sand-flies of the genus Simulium. They settle on you in clouds, and inflict bites that leave a red area centred by a small blood blister, which finally turns black. While doing the recording when we dissected a plot in this pine zone, my hands were so excessively bitten by these flies that I could not write next day because of the swelling. Their abdomens fill with your blood as they take their meals. The doctor fly (*Chrysops costatus*), of the Tabanid family of B.-S. D.s, is an ordinary yellowish fly that also bites hard and long and leaves a large red blot.

These creatures made the dry heat of the day terrible, but at about two o'clock it got too hot even for them, and they cleared off, making way for other, even smaller sandflies of the genus Culicoides, though it made little difference to our tempers! These got through the net and drove us out. In the late afternoon a refreshing wind began to sigh through the pines. We took tea, and entered the finest phase of the day. As the sun and the wind dropped, the whole earth assumed a soft and ethereal loveliness. We had time to turn our attention to the birds and the flowers and the painted evening skies. Then, sharp at six-thirty, the mosquitoes arrived and drove us back under the net, where we remained, becoming increasingly cold and damp, until we were forced to climb between sodden sheets amid a cloud of stray members of all the pestilential winged hosts enumerated above that were invariably trapped within our mosquito nets.

On the whole we were not unduly worried, because we were
kept very busy with the work. We were still hard by the edge of
the real jungle, which here took the form of low tangled intermediate or fringing forest, but we were also within reach of a
troublesome growth known locally as *akalche*, which is a Mayan
word meaning "a low place of trees," i.e., an overgrown swamp.
This growth belongs to the northern group of vegetational zones,
and consists of a mass of straggling, oversize shrubs through which
the vicious cutting-grass climbs and beneath which the ground is
often covered with tufts of armadillo grass. We hunted in both of
these growths, as well as out upon the main stretch of the pine
zone.

The only animals of note that we took from the intermediate
forest were lesser anteaters (*Tamandua*), which were rather plentiful. They were all of one variety, with pronounced and clearly
defined black and yellow areas of pelage, and they were all completely diurnal. We met them clambering about trees in the heat
of the day, and hauled one from a shallow hole in a bank in the
early morning. It was curled up asleep, and we were assured by
locals that in this country at least they always live in holes in the
ground, where they make rough nests from some grass and leaves,
and whence they emerge to forage only during the day.

The other animals from this intermediate forest were but replicas
of those which we already knew well from our previous collecting.
From the *akalche* came a new tortoise, some of the scorpions common to the pine zone, the ubiquitous nine-banded armadillo (*Ta-
tusia novemcincta*), and some other oddments. We did not, however, investigate this growth with any thoroughness at this time,
but devoted all our energies to the pine zone. This repaid us well.

It is unwise to make generalizations about nature, but it is perhaps permissible to say that the best time to hunt for mammals in
the tropics is at dawn. In certain kinds of country it is worth
while to go out again at sundown, and open low growth at low
altitudes, such as this pine zone, is one of these. An old trace led
from our camp eastward towards the sea. This led from the area of

almost pure pine, in which we were living, through a narrow tongue of *akalche*, and then entered a large tract of the fringing forest upon which the pines were encroaching. The trace continued through this vegetation for some two miles, and then unexpectedly came out upon a level plain covered with long grasses, dotted with small clumps of palmetto palms, and shaded by many tall pines.

Because we had seen no sign of a living creature, not even a bird, we had decided to turn back, when we stumbled upon this palm-dotted plain. It was late afternoon, and Alma and I had been out since lunch time on a cruise of exploration to see what the country was really like around our new home and to decide, if possible, where it would be most profitable to cut our principal traces.

We had not suspected the existence of such country anywhere in the neighbourhood, and, as it was a completely uninhabited and undisturbed area, and was our first view of such a scene, it made an ineradicable impression upon us.

Here was a little world apart—one of those natural stage sets that are somehow pervaded by an atmosphere of unreality, as if more suited to another planet very similar to but still not quite identical with our own. It was locked away in the depths of otherwise quite ordinary and altogether dissimilar country. It was an open growth in contradistinction to the surrounding forests, and yet its trees were taller.

Standing hidden just inside the tangled growth, we looked out on this quiet scene. It was fortunate that we waited some time before stepping forth, because there proved to be many treasures lurking there which would have vanished had we betrayed our presence too precipitately. We first noticed a flock of large green parrots with blue heads, which appeared to be busily employed tearing the pine cones to pieces. Parrots somehow don't look right on pine trees, so we watched curiously.

The parrots' activities resulted in a continuous rain of debris falling to the ground, but from where we stood we could not see where this landed. Each time something particularly large fell, a

peculiar chattering noise would break out, apparently from the
ground below. We discussed the probable cause of this sound, and
came to the conclusion that there must be some small birds feeding
there. The air was very still, and sounds carried with great clarity,
so that when the gabbling of the parrots suddenly ceased altogether
we heard a continuous commotion which had previously been in-
audible. Then all of a sudden there was a great outcry, and two
somethings flashed momentarily up a tree bole. As these were quite
plainly not birds, we decided to investigate.

Getting down as flat as possible, we wormed our way quietly
forward, watching the parrots closely to see whether we made any
noise that their sharp ears could detect. It took us a long time to
reach the near edge of the long grass, and when we did so, we still
had to find some channel by which we could get through it without making a commotion, or some hole through which we could
catch a glimpse of the activities beyond. The noise made by the
dry grass and our dragging our guns along with us rendered the
process rather difficult, but we found a small gap far to the right
which was carpeted with clear short grass and pine needles and
which led through this miniature jungle that confronted us. Into
this we crawled.

It first turned to the right, away from the point we wished to
approach, but then forked, and the left channel ran back towards
the centre of the clump. We followed this and slowly approached
the trees from which the chattering now came ever more distinctly.
The natural pathway entered a small clear arena surrounded on
all sides by the tall grass and having no other outlet. As we cautiously crawled into this, we thought our efforts had probably
been in vain, but we were just in time to see an animal leave the
opposite end by way of a low archway or tunnel. We saw only
the creature's tail, but judging by the slow rate at which this disappeared, the owner did not seem aware of our presence. We advanced even more cautiously, and, lying flat on the ground, peered
into the tunnel.

We had expected to see a dark passageway leading into the grass,

IVAN SANDERSON

YUCATECAN GREY SQUIRREL (Sciurus yucatanensis)

but instead we found ourselves looking through a small window directly at the base of the cluster of pines in which the parrots were feeding. What we saw was a rather perfect natural idyll.

There were about half a dozen large, greyish squirrels (*Sciurus yucatanensis*) feeding and gambolling about. They were larger animals than the little close-furred species that we had collected in the tall forests, and they had fluffier tails and lighter, thicker coats.

These squirrels were very busy. Their principal occupation appeared to be the collection and removal of small, hard, shiny, green fruits which we now saw were being shaken by the parrots from a mistletoe-like epiphytic plant that was growing on the pines.

The squirrels were gathering these fruits in their mouths, four or five at a time, and then running off with them into tunnels in the grass beyond. We did not realize what was taking place at first, because there seemed to be an endless army of the busy little animals appearing out of the grass, picking up the booty, and then running off again, but when we recognized an individual with a very tattered tail as having made three distinct and separate appearances, we saw that the same animals were going round and round. They were taking away the fruits, caching them somewhere, and then returning for more. It is difficult to hazard a guess as to why they didn't go up the trees and get them for themselves, but there was doubtless some good reason. We lay for some time watching all this activity with the greatest interest, for it is seldom that one has the chance of observing animals carrying on their normal activities at such close range.

Then one of the green fruits fell right in front of the window through which we were peering. This soon caught the sharp eye of one of the little labourers. He had just been chased up and round the bole of one of the trees by a rival claimant to another nut and, having lost the fracas owing to the advent of a third individual, he was looking round disconsolately. He came hopping forward with his tail curled up, and paused about three feet before the tall grass front. Then he advanced again and was just about to seize the nut when he looked up and stared directly at us.

A squirrel's face normally wears an utterly blank expression, so that I would not have believed one capable of registering so plainly the various emotions that now flashed across his countenance in rapid succession. First it was alarm, but this quickly gave place to unutterable amazement. The little animal obviously didn't believe its eyes. Perhaps it was the very one that had previously been through this archway to fetch a fruit that had fallen in the arena in which we lay. Finally, its amazement gave way to frank incredulity. The little creature became most comical. It suddenly turned its head away and pretended not to look, all the time watching carefully out of the corner of its eye. Then it suddenly looked round again, as if to catch us out, but we kept as still as possible. Next, the animal squatted down as a dog would, with its forelegs stretched out before it, and put its chin on its forepaws. But that, was when it really sensed danger. It must have caught some scent that had previously escaped its hyper-sensitive little nostrils. It sniffed wildly, uttered a loud chatter, leaped in the air, and, throwing a final terror-stricken glance in our direction, flashed out of our field of vision. The other squirrels immediately paused in their labours and sat up on their haunches, quivering and sniffing. Then they too bolted in all directions, some taking to the trees and others disappearing into the tunnels beneath the grass.

Something of their alarm must have been transmitted to the parrots, for they all fell silent. Then by twos they launched off the trees above and beat away towards the setting sun. The whole place had suddenly gone dead.

We were just going to get up and leave when a slight movement in the grass beyond the pine trees made me pull Alma down again. Something had stirred the grass blades along a considerable front in such a way that I knew a big animal was hidden there. We waited, almost holding our breath lest we further disclose our presence.

Slowly and unconcernedly a beautiful greyish-brown deer rose up from behind the grass and stood turning its delicate head from side to side and listening intently. Satisfied that it was unobserved,

SAVANNAH DEER (Odocoileus truei)

it bent its head down behind the grass and kept it there for a long time, so that we thought it must be grazing. It was, however, quite otherwise occupied, for it presently raised its head again, and immediately afterwards a second even more gentle and delicate face appeared beside it. Slowly, as if arising from a restful sleep, a little fawn appeared in view. It stretched its limbs one after another, and then laid its pretty head gently against its mother's flank and rested there gazing out at the quiet evening.

This was the third time that we had witnessed an almost identical scene, each time in a different country. On both previous occasions, however, it had been but a fleeting glimpse, and then the lovely animals had taken fright and bounded away. This time we were vastly more fortunate, for the animals walked slowly through the grass to the right, and finally, just when I became convinced that they must be down wind from us, they turned and walked right out into the open space before us. We were so pleased with this turn of events that we did not notice for some moments that two more deer had risen up from the grass beyond and were now staring quietly in our direction with their funnel ears held wide. When Alma spotted them she gave a little gasp, which I am sure the animals heard, for they suddenly paused and listened intently. Yet they did not take fright and, indeed, the two new ones also came walking into the clearing.

The deer then started eating the fallen fruits. The dusk was closing in, and the whole world was flooded by that intense pinkish-amber light that the setting tropical sun often casts upon the face of the earth, bringing its every tint into unusual brilliance. The dull grey pine trunks now glowed with a reddish light; the vivid green grasses leaped into iridescence, and the beautiful animals assumed an unreal painted appearance. When this brief period of ethereal loveliness faded, we deemed it time to withdraw, and so moved back as silently as possible. I do not know whether the deer were disturbed, but we caught no sound of them beating a hasty retreat.

Stretching our cramped muscles, we regained the trace and set out for home.

ON A PINE LAKE

Fox and Puma; One Crocodile; Peccaries, Coatis, the Eyra, and a Tailless Skunk

OUR discovery of this place of pines had proved so enchanting that we returned the next day. It now became clear why the term "ridge" has been adopted for this very distinctive type of country. It could by no means be called a forest, a grove, or a belt—nor even a zone or region. Had I, personally, been required to choose a suitable word, I believe I should have taken "lake" as being the most appropriate. Its open character and abrupt edge, coupled with its contrast to the region that surrounded it, gave it many of the qualities of a large, isolated body of water. Animals came into it from outside to feed and gambol, while at the same time it had a fauna all its own. What is more, it was ringed around by a distinct belt of vegetation composed of plants that often do cover the shores of lakes in this country.

We arrived at its edge shortly after dawn. We had left the patch of smaller pines where we were living shrouded in a thick mist, which also extended over the _akalche_ and the mixed growth through which we had passed. At the edge of the "lake" or "ridge," however, it ended abruptly, and although the ground here was just as sodden with dew as elsewhere, even the tree tops stood out in vivid clarity. We had approached very cautiously this time, and stood for some minutes in the obscurity of the last bushes scanning the open country ahead. Again our care was rewarded, but this time by something quite new.

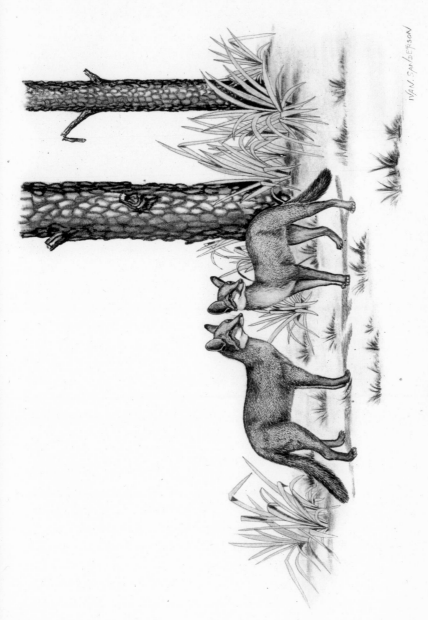

IVAN. SANDERSON

SAVANNAH FOXES (Urocyon cinereoargenteus)

The trace emerged upon the narrow end of a long tongue of the pine ridge which widened beyond into a huge level stretch that extended for miles. Down the centre of the tongue ran a natural pathway, clear of tall grass and trees. Just when we were about to step out into the open, two small, alert forms suddenly materialized in the middle of this path. Neither of us saw them arrive; they seemed to appear without sound or movement. They stood motionless, but full of pent-up energy, peering intently in our direction not only with their gimlet eyes but also with their sharp noses and pricked ears. They were a pair of slender grey foxes (*Urocyon cinereoargenteus*), with reddish-brown ears and necks, and fine brushes. They stood quite still while I cautiously raised my gun.

Then I stupidly glanced at Alma. She never moved an eyelid, but I read her mind as clearly as if she had spoken. She later told me that my surmise had been quite correct: she *had* been mentally murmuring, "Damn it, sir, *shoot a fox!*"

The result, of course, was that the two animals had time to sense their danger. They wheeled sideways and paused for a second with their faces turned over their shoulders. Then they streaked off at a fast and effortless lope between the pine trunks. I never had time to fire. I burst into uncontrolled laughter, and turned to Alma, but she was staring past me with a ludicrously startled expression, to a point far to the left. I instinctively followed her gaze, and what I saw made me forget my mirth altogether, for there, standing quietly between two pine boles, with its clumpy forefeet placed neatly together, was another animal.

It was a magnificent, red-coated puma, and the tip of its tail was curling slowly about, like some oddly animated appendage to a terra-cotta statue.

That was a very difficult moment, because (you must understand) in reality one simply doesn't see the great cats. In twelve years of wanderings in the wild I can count on the fingers of one hand the examples I have seen; actually, they have been four in number, plus one pair of eyes. The residents of tropical countries who have seen wild examples are very few indeed, and we have one friend who has spent the best part of fifteen years in the forests of British Honduras in places where jaguar and puma spoor is often thick on the paths in the morning, and he has never yet seen one. Of course, East Africa is verminous with lion and there are startling individuals, like "Tigerman," who make a profession of jaguars in South America, but those are different matters. What I wish to convey is that, despite all you may have heard to the contrary, meeting one of the large cats is more than exceptional in most tropical forest countries which are known to be infested with these creatures.

I had often wondered how it would feel to meet such a beast face to face, although I had already done just this on the first occasion that I saw a really wild tiger. That meeting, however, was so unexpected, and was over so quickly, that I had had no time to take stock of the situation. On other occasions the animal has been going away from me at high speed, or vice versa. This was something different; we now met face to face and eyed each other, simply as two mammals with inflated egos. The situation was also complicated by Alma's presence, which made the immediate future definitely unpredictable.

A sidelong glance at her told me nothing. She was standing perfectly still, just looking, and had she possessed a tail, I verily believe its tip would also have been twitching. My own feelings were dominated by a most regrettable and all-pervading lack of decision. I had two barrels loaded with very heavy charge and shot, but, unfortunately, I had not yet put on my glasses, as there had been nothing special to peer at. I would have liked a fine mountain lion for the skinning table, and for my vanity, but I was far from confident of my marksmanship without my eyeglasses, particularly if things began to happen too quickly. Lastly, I have a great respect for the greater cats, and a considerable distrust of widely held beliefs upon their habits and behaviour. It is often stated that the puma is a coward, but it is also held that Alsatian dogs are suitable playfellows for children. I therefore got my fowling piece in readiness, but continued to stare.

I suppose the period of inaction lasted but a few seconds, but it seemed much longer. Then both the puma and Alma began to move ever so slowly. I knew a crisis was coming, and, gripping the gun with my now rather hot little hands, I wished fervently that my glasses might by some miracle be perched on my long nose. The crisis passed swiftly and almost unnoticed, for Alma slowly subsided so that I thought she was being purely Victorian. Glancing down, however, I found that her small weapon had come up level under my right arm. I was just starting a fervent plea to her not to shoot, knowing that the cartridge in her collecting gun contained a meagre half-dozen small pellets, when the cat took a step backwards and turned its head to the left. Even less decided now, I also started to raise my gun slowly, but the animal moved once more and so placed itself behind one of the two big pine trunks. It was then almost entirely shielded, and took good advantage of the fact, for it began to retreat, very slowly at first, but soon quickened its pace to a trot which rapidly gathered momentum and ended in a spurt of speed that almost confounded the laws of possibility. Before we realized what had happened, the puma had vanished silently, in one great loping rush, into the tangled undergrowth beyond the pines.

Thus went our first and only great feline, true to form and the dictates of convention. We were left in the first rays of the morning sun and the aroma of resin with guns at Position Two, and very mixed feelings. But the day had only begun, for of all the places that we have visited, this pine ridge presented us with animal life in a more concentrated form than any other.

We had spied a small pond at the junction of the side inlet by which we had entered the main body of the pines; this we decided to investigate. As we pushed towards it through a tall growth of sedges, we feared that it might, after all, be merely a swamp, since the water was at first only ankle-deep; but when we reached the edge of the reeds it deepened abruptly. The surface of the pond appeared jet-black, though the water, upon closer inspection, proved to be transparent and bright yellow in colour. The pond itself was almost exactly circular and about two hundred feet in diameter, and was littered with fallen tree skeletons.

These hard, white, dry forms were not just dead trees; they had the staring bleached appearance of desiccated bones lying out in the open. These were the ligneous skeletons of tall, slender hardwoods, and yet there was not a sign of any tree other than pines and a few overgrown bushes anywhere else in the neighbourhood, either living or dead, standing or fallen. To attempt an explanation of this phenomenon would necessitate too much conjecture, but the result of whatever had taken place was a small pond covered with a mammoth lattice-work of hard and peculiarly well-preserved, interwoven wood girders.

With the aid of long, slender, dead-white sticks, which were lying about in great profusion and which made excellent balancing rods, we found that we could not only cross the pond, but walk all over it by traversing the criss-cross network of fallen trees. A certain agility was necessary, for some of the logs formed natural see-saws, but none of them was rotten or friable.

We saw some basilisks, which promptly took to the water and, wishing to collect a few from this rather singular environment, we put down our guns and ventured out over the pond with fine string nooses suspended from the ends of the longest sticks we could carry. We had captured one or two, and were both perched precariously on the upturned, rooty end of a large tree skeleton, when a sort of aqueous volcano began to erupt just beneath us, and shook us to the core, both metaphorically and literally. This was very fortunate indeed, for had we not as a result grabbed each other in a loving embrace, we might well have fallen off our exalted perch straight into the jaws of quite the biggest crocodile that we have ever had the misfortune to encounter. We looked straight down upon this loathsome monster as one would in a well-regulated zoo, while he, having caused this warning commotion, slowly sank down into the yellow waters, displaying his pale, slimy back, which was covered with algal growth and looked pallid and rather dead like the tree skeletons.

This terrifying creature was not very long as crocodiles go, probably not more than about ten or twelve feet, but his girth, which was also magnified by the water, was fantastic. Neither of us has ever seen a crocodile shaped like that. The nearest approach to it is a great, lumbering monster that is kept behind a quite inadequately fragile fence in the Centenario Zoo at Merida in Yucatan.

When the brute had subsided almost out of sight, and we had somewhat recovered, he suddenly came charging up out of the depths and burst out of the water for half his length, coming to rest with his fore-body over a submerged log, and his head sticking up into the air at a sharp angle, but pointing away from us. There he paused, with one cruel, greenish-yellow eye fixed upon us, and as the hinder part of his body began to sink, he gave a mighty wriggle with his lumbering tail which projected him to a position athwart the log. We could have reached out and poked our sticks into his half-open mouth.

"Quick, Alma!" I squawked, recovering from my paralysis and stuffing our loose impedimenta into my pockets. "Leave your stick; come on, hurry!"

Very fortunately, we happened to be perched some seven feet above water, and were not in the centre of the pool. Lying across our root were several trees, all leading by devious routes to the sedges and, eventually, to dry land. One of these trees was very large and broad, but it was half submerged in the water. Along it we could make a dash, but we had no idea just how fast the crocodile could travel across the litter of intertwined trunks that filled the distance between his present position and this log, nor were we by any means sure that his present performance was merely early-morning play-fulness. Along that route, one slip might well bring disaster. There was, however, a very long, though slender, tree trunk that stretched from the other side of our root to a point far away into the sedges, and nowhere descended to less than six feet from the water. This seemed to be the surer road to safety.

We set out along this perilous natural bridge on hands and knees, holding the slender trunk with our hands like lemurs, and gripping it with our shanks by putting our knees on one side and curling the upper sides of our feet round the other side. We went slowly, as we could not know whether the tree was rotten, and in any case we doubted its ability to support us both at once. When we got to the middle, it began to sag and wobble ominously.

"Go back, Alma, quick!" I called.

"Look, he's moving, Ivan."

"The croc?"

"Yes."

"Never mind. Go back, carefully."

Somehow we got back to our root again.

The crocodile was indeed moving, but very slowly. He was obese and probably unused to much activity at this season. It was also probable that his small brain could make little sense of our behaviour. He was slowly crawling over the submerged tree, but still pointing away from us.

"Now," I said, "you go first, and hurry."

Alma fairly buzzed off along the slender, swaying bridge. I held my breath during the whole time that she was on it, and closed my eyes and prayed while she navigated the second and much slenderer part. When she was over the sedges, I called out to her to jump and run and, as soon as she had done so, I breathed a sigh of thankfulness and scrambled aboard myself.

As I did so, I perceived the crocodile some way off to the left, swimming gently in clear water. He was still going away, but was still watching me with his cold right eye. Just after I passed the half-way mark, my heart lost a beat when I again glanced in his direction and saw that he had rounded a mass of fallen logs and was coming straight up the fairway towards me, full steam ahead. A crocodile advancing with his forehead and snout cutting the water, no matter what his intentions, is a very evil sight quite unsuited to the tenser moments of unprofessional tight-rope walking. Half-hypnotized by this demoralizing approach, I blundered ahead, though I don't believe I need have been quite so scared, for I was still about seven feet above the water and could have remained there or on the tree root for longer than it would have taken Alma to fetch help from camp; in fact, I feel sure that under the circumstances I could have clung there until rigor mortis itself set in. Many things might have happened in the interval, but short of shaking me into the water by rocking a great mass of solid timbers, the croc could not well have got at me. However, when but twenty feet of limpid water separated the crocodile from a point immediately below me, the creature glided to a standstill and, after interestedly observing my lemurine progress, slowly submerged. As I came over the first reeds, I glanced back at the now ominous stillness, fully expecting to see him making for the point where my bridge came ashore. Instead, I was much heartened to see him swimming along towards the other side of the pond, having already passed under my tree.

I reached the end of the tree and, taking a flying leap into the reeds, raced for the firmer ground. Alma came running up with the guns.

"Phew, what next?" I said, rather feebly, adding, "*Jamais deux sans trois.*"

"You're right," said Alma, "come on, hurry!"

She bustled me off round the outer edge of the reed bed. Passing between some bushes opposite the place where we had gone in towards the pond, she cautioned me to be quiet and beckoned me forward. We crept on in silence, gradually reducing our pace. I gripped my gun very hard, not knowing in the least what to expect next. We came to a halt and listened; there were gentle murmurings ahead.

"What is it?" I whispered in Alma's ear. "Have you seen it?"

"No, but I think it's peccaries. Look," and she pointed to a number of double tracks in the mud.

"Well, be careful; we've been lucky so far."

"Don't you leave me!"

"Don't worry, I won't."

And so we went forward again until we saw the reeds by the pond moving at several different points. We advanced very cautiously, but I inadvertently trod on a dead branch concealed in the thick sedges, and its cracking made a noise like a pistol shot.

For answer there was an immediate stampede ahead, and some dozen peccaries of all ages and sizes went tearing off out of the reeds onto the clear pine ridge. We both fired, and a small one fell while the others careered off into the mixed forest beyond. We retrieved our trophy, which was a half-grown male, and decided that we had had enough. We shouldered the pig and went home.

This peccary was small and very muddy. We wanted its flesh for purely gastronomic purposes, so I didn't pay much attention to it beyond noting that it was one of the ordinary *Dicotyles tajaçu*. I subsequently kicked myself for this lapse from duty.

There are two well-recognized and clearly definable types of peccary, namely, the collared (*D. tajaçu*) and the white-lipped (*D. labiatus*), both of which are found throughout tropical Central and South America. The former is the more common. There are many tales about the habits of both species, but most of these directly contradict one another. It is probable that the habits of both species vary greatly from country to country, as well as between groups and individuals and at different times of the year. Their behaviour seems also to vary with the conditions of the animals' livers or whatever it is that most affects the emotional outlook of the Ungulata.

In all the countries that we have visited, there are constant reports of three species of peccary to each of which very definite sets of habits are attributed. We believed we had tracked down the third species in Dutch Guiana, when we learned that a Chinese had imported pigs and subsequently let them go in the forest when he went bankrupt some thirty years ago. In British Honduras, however, the reports centre upon three very distinct animals. One, heavy-limbed, small-headed, and travelling in large droves or sounders, is manifestly the white-lipped peccary, while another, with a white collar, is just as surely the collared species; but the third had been described to us as shaped like the latter but larger, grey as opposed to dark brindled greenish-brown in colour, without a collar, and with very black limbs in marked contrast to the rest of its pelage. This last form was said to travel only in small family parties, headed by an old male with rather prominent tushes.

Judging by past experience, and knowing the very considerable variation displayed by the collared peccary, especially with regard to the development of the pale collar, we took this story rather lightly. As the months went by and we saw only typical collared peccaries, we almost forgot the matter until we came to investigate the pine ridges. Among the collections accumulated from this type of vegetation were more peccaries.

The next that we obtained was an ordinary enough collared specimen with a very pronounced collar, but the following two, a pair, were so different in appearance that when I first saw them lying dead on the ground I never for a moment thought that they were peccaries at all. These animals were pale grey, the hairs being banded black and white with the white greatly predominating. In life they had no collars at all, but after dressing the skins and brushing the sparse fur around the neck, the arrangement of the pale bands on the hairs made it just possible to imagine that they wore such marks. There was a slight fawn wash on the cheeks and flanks, and the feet and "stockings" were jet-black in great contrast to the rest of the colouration.

We then discovered that these grey animals came only from among the pines and that they would not enter the other types of growth even under the strongest provocation. The true *tajaçu* sometimes ventured out onto the pine at night, and often entered clearings in the forest to feed, but they adhered to other vegetation as much as possible. From this, it appeared that there were two quite distinct forms in this country, either races of *Dicotyles tajaçu* (which I hear has been rechristened *Tayassu angulatus!*) occasioned by these animals being curbed in their range by differences of vegetation, or representing two distinct species.

At this camp we got specimens of another animal over which there are likewise many elements of doubt, again occasioned by native assertions as to their habits. These are the coatis.

There is supposed to be a "kind" of coati in Central America—
that is to say a group of closely related forms which may be
looked upon either as a single variable species (*Nasua narica*), or as
comprising several closely related species. South of Panama, other
distinct species are recognized. All are remarkably variable, not so
much as between individual members of any one population, but
more particularly from place to place. Yet there is one native observation upon all coatis that is as widespread as the animals themselves.
This is to the effect that there are two kinds having very different
habits. The first is said to be gregarious and to travel always in large
troops often on the ground; the second, to be a solitary animal more
prone to ascend and often travel by trees in tall forest. This rumour
is just as persistent in British Honduras as it is in South America.

The difficulty is that there are undoubtedly the two sets of coatis,
those that go about in large troops and those that wander singly. In
some countries, however, where two quite distinct species are found,
both of them are split into solitary and gregarious parties. It is manifestly, moreover, neither a seasonal variation of behaviour nor a
sexual one, for we ourselves have shot both solitary males and females on several occasions. It has also often been reported that the
large groups do not contain any adult males, but are entirely composed of females and young. Many troops, however, consist of animals of both sexes and all ages, many of the males being fully mature
sexually. Perhaps it is possible that the older individuals of all kinds
of coatis have to leave society when they become too decrepit to
hold their own among their aggressive progeny.

What we saw in the pine zones—or rather, what Fred saw—added
nothing towards any elucidation of the habits of these animals in
this particular locality. The first one he encountered was strolling
down the main path at sundown, with its tail stuck up in the air and
its short little back legs working overtime trundling its low sturdy
body over the soft, sandy ground. I can picture the scene well
enough, though Fred was characteristically uncommunicative about
the details. They appear to have approached each other with some

Honduranean Coati (Nasua narica)

solemnity. Then the coati stopped dead, and rose on its hind legs, sniffing the air with its long, rubbery proboscis. Fred raised his gun and pulled the trigger. Nothing happened because the safety catch was not released; whereupon the coati sniffed disdainfully, got down on all fours, and trundled off into a bed of long grass beside the path. By this time Fred had got straightened out with his weapon, and went in pursuit.

Entering the low, tangled forest, the coati got behind the bole of a tree and grunted. Fred struggled into the liane-filled mass, doubt-less breathing hard, and, having carefully adjusted his safety catch, inadvertently let off both barrels. This was the signal for the coati to make off at high speed.

Much disgruntled, Fred returned home and said not a word of all this to us at the time. Instead he ate a hasty dinner, and then set out with a head-torch. He arrived back at midnight, and during the interval there had been much shooting at various points in the far distance. He carried a bundle over his shoulder, and looked very pleased with himself. We got the full facts about both sallies about half an hour later.

On his second outing he had devoted some time to investigating the area where he had seen the coati, but, finding nothing, he had continued up a small trace to the west. The path was filled with clumps of tall grass. He saw nothing throughout a stretch of about two miles, until he turned into a small animal track to the right. This led to a more open place filled with large clumps of small trees sur-rounded by bushes, and filled in between with grass of medium height. Here he saw eyes and fired, but failed to kill a paca that made off into the bush.

Imagining that it might be wounded, he went in pursuit. He told us how he got lost in the tangle, and how, in searching for the open place again, he stumbled upon a number of large birds that, from his description, must have been wild turkeys. These didn't exactly gobble at him, but behaved in such a barnyard manner and looked so like domesticated turkeys that he held his fire, being undecided whether he had got into the back end of some isolated native farm-stead. The birds made off at a gallop, and, coming to a decision too late, Fred loosed two parting shots without effect.

He eventually found the open place again, and thought he saw a large tree-rat, which he shot after three attempts. It was, of course, a young *Didelphis* opossum, which made him pretty angry. Dis-gustedly he decided to return.

He had regained the trace and was pounding along thinking angry thoughts when he came face to face with an absolutely prize speci-men. It was a beautifully proportioned, red-coated cat, with arched back and long, slender tail. He told us that it looked like molten gold in the torch-light, and that it stood motionless in the centre of the trace while he raised his gun, took careful aim, and neatly dis-patched it.

We were just as delighted as he at this fine bit of hunting, for the animal was an eyra (*Felis fossata*), a species that we most particularly wished to inspect closely for several reasons. There is nothing very special about this cat's appearance except its wonderful coat, which in this individual—for they vary considerably—was composed of that exquisite type of reddish hair that is really metallic golden-copper in colour. This, combined with the usual feline cleanliness and immaculate perfection of the animal, which extended even to its glistening white teeth, made it an unmatched natural exhibit.

Besides the great cats—the jaguar, ocelot, and puma—there are in tropical America several smaller species over which there is constant technical wrangling. There are spotted ones, plain-coloured ones, and others with extraordinary markings composed of irregular light strokes on a dark ground, as if someone had with chalk attempted a game of ticktacktoe on their pelts. To these smaller cats, a variety of names have been given. It has, however, been noted that most locales support one small spotted species and one or two greyish or reddish ones. This was the first of the smaller cats that we had ob-tained, so we pored over it long and rather lovingly.

We immediately noted that it had retractile claws, a fact to which Fred drew our attention. This appears to be a good feature for dis-

EYRA (Felis fossata)

tinguishing this species from the jaguarondi (*Herpailurus yagua-rondi*), which is often similarly coloured but which has absolutely unretractile, fixed claws like those of a dog. If it is true, as some people assert, that intermediate types between these two animals exist, there are some very interesting discoveries coming which may help materially in clearing up the muddle regarding these rather obscure and less commonly collected carnivores.

We were out hunting busily every night after that in the hope of getting another eyra. Of course, we did not succeed, but the time was not wasted. The first thing we ran into was more coatis. These animals were quite common around this area, but, although they sometimes came out onto the open pine, they seemed to prefer the denser growths. We got among a whole troop of them one evening shortly after leaving camp. They were running up and down tree boles, peeking and squeaking at us on all sides. We obtained three and felt well satisfied. It also made Fred feel much better.

This species is reddish-brown on the back and creamy ochre below and on the flanks, with greyish tinges over the shoulders and rump. The long tail, which is often very tattered, is just visibly ringed with dark and light ochrish-brown. The face bears complicated light and dark markings.

Coatis are very prepossessing animals with most competent, bear-shaped little bodies and great control over their forepaws. A tame one which we had for a time, but eventually palmed off on a friend, had some odd tricks. It could not resist cigarettes whether lighted or not, and would grab them out of one's mouth or from packets or boxes, and in a second reduce them to shreds by a furious scratching with the long, slender claws of both its forepaws, which it manipulated like a burrowing dog. Once the cigarettes were destroyed, the coati turned away and paid no further attention to the remains. The animal used the same method for only two other things during the whole time we observed it, a large grub and a bean pod.

We were afforded several opportunities of watching these animals in the wilds, and were fascinated by their eternal activity and great thoroughness. They literally thrashed out every scrap of food from the areas they set upon, on one occasion even chasing an armadillo out of its hole and harrying it on its headlong flight for nearly a hundred feet. I don't think they intended it any harm, but just wanted it out of the way. They are very inquisitive beasts, quite unlike their relations the raccoons, kinkajous, and cacomistles, though they do display some characteristics vaguely reminiscent of the crab-eating raccoon (*Euprocyon cancrivorus*) of South America.

There was one other notable animal which came to us from the neighbourhood of the pine belt and with which Fred was more intimately connected—if I may put it so delicately—than the rest of us. The first specimen was actually brought to us by a local hunter from another district.

We were apprised of this creature's arrival while still under our mosquito nets. Because we had been doing so much night hunting since the acquisition of the first eyra, I had given strict instructions that we were not to be awakened in the morning. This was unfortunate, as it turned out, because by the time we awoke on this particular morning, the new animal had been in camp for nearly two hours. As a result it didn't officially leave the place, in one respect, until we ourselves quit the neighbourhood. In this same respect it is still with us in essence. But let me explain.

I was awakened by Alma prodding me far from gently.

"For the love of zoology must we live with a smell like this?" she was inquiring.

One sniff of the morning air was enough to convince me that we need not, even for the most pressing scientific advancement.

"George!" I bawled, fully awake at once. "What in the devil's that smell?"

"Coming, sir," called George, who came along the path at the double.

For decency's sake the tent was erected at an angle to the path, so that the staff could come in answer to shouts and we could talk to them without being seen or the necessity of going outside. George arrived without, and I was just going to start further inquiries when Alma subsided weakly onto the bed.

"Good Lord, it's George!" she gasped.

"George! Is that you smelling like that?" I inquired.

"Yes, sir," came the astonishing answer.

"Well, do something at once. What on earth is it?"

"Polecat," he announced.

"What do you mean?" I said, forgetting, in my eagerness to get to the bottom of this appalling state of affairs, that this was merely a local misnomer.

"A man brings a 'polecat,' sir."

"Where is he? Why did you let him in?"

"I didn't, sir; he's outside on the path."

"Is Mr. Fred awake?"

"Yes, sir, he's gone out to see the man."

"Heaven help him!" murmured Alma.

"Heaven help us," I came back; "we've got to have breakfast."

I donned some clothes and charged off towards the main tent, which on this occasion was occupied by Fred. As I approached, the smell got worse. I came upon Dick, a most fastidious person, standing disconsolately on the path to the kitchen, wringing his apron and for once without a smile on his face.

"Morning, sir," he said, "a man has a polecat, sir."

"Need you tell me, Dick?"

"It smells plenty," he observed.

"Be serious, Dick, please," I advised him.

"Will you have breakfast, sir?" he said, rather maliciously, I thought.

"How should I know, Dick? Do you feel like eating?"

He laughed dutifully, but I felt rather glum and went on to the tent and thence, following my nose, to the path. The first thing I met was Fred, and it nearly killed me.

"Dear boy," I gasped, reeling backwards, "you're worse than George."

"I'm sorry," he said, looking pained, "I suppose we will get used to it."

"I suppose so. Have you bought it?"

"Not yet. The man wants enough to cover a new outfit of clothes."

This brought me to a halt. I contemplated and rather sympathized with the fellow.

"Get some money, will you? I'm going to see it."

"Be careful, won't you?"

"Is it alive?"

"No, far from it; that's part of the trouble."

I went on and got to the root of the matter. On the path squatted a pleasant, chatty, young, Hinduish-looking fellow in a battered hat. He seemed highly amused by the whole proceeding, having presumably himself become immune to the worst. Beside him lay a small, fat animal.

"Good morning," he said. "It's a polecat."

"Never mind about that," I said, for I can't help arguing about native names even at normal times, and now I felt definitely quarrelsome.

If there is one thing that puts me in a temper, it's inhabitants of small countries' giving their local plants and animals the names of other well-known plants and animals and then having the effrontery to tell you that you are wrong when you correct them. I will never get over the Haitians' insistence on calling bananas "figs"! After heated debate extending over some months, I finally lost my temper and took the trouble to order a case of figs from overseas just to show them. When I did so, and invited the assembled company—which included some educated Jamaicans, I might add—to sample them, they took one look and two sniffs and said, "*Ah! Ce sont des fraises!*" I lost years at that moment.

The matter is not only irritating to the meticulous-minded, it is a real source of danger to a zoologist. In Jamaica they call frogs "toads" and toads "frogs," and get quite rude about it. They also call moths "bats," and insist that "rat-bats" are only another kind. The people of Dutch Guiana, we found, called the tayra "eyra," the eyra "little red jaguar," and the jaguarondi nothing at all. The Belizarians insist upon calling the small deer in their country "antelope," howler monkeys "baboons," jaguars "tigers," pumas "lions," tayras "bush-dogs," tapirs "mountain-cows," agoutis "rabbits," and skunks "polecats." To all of this I object not only on personal grounds, but also upon purely common-sense ones, for all these names are recognized, by more people than have ever lived in British Honduras throughout the whole of its history, as applying to quite other animals.

Nothing is more attractive than *native* names for local animals, and nobody could object to their application, especially when they are as suitable as "night-walker" for the kinkajou, "quash" for the coati, or "gibnat" for the paca, but it is pure laziness and ignorance to persist in calling animals by entirely wrong names, and little short of insolence to get bellicose about it. I'm afraid I got quite heated on this subject with our visitor in the battered hat.

What with the smell, lack of breakfast, and this man's insistence on the subject of polecats I was ready to blow up. Then I looked at the animal again. I stopped short, and my annoyance faded.

"Oh," I said meekly, "are they different, then?"

"Yes," said the man promptly.

"Tell me about it," I implored.

"Well, the skunk smells almost as bad," he began, "but it's smaller and has a big fluffy tail like a squirrel."

"That's what I thought," I said.

"Besides," he went on, "skunks are other colours, sometimes very like this polecat, but never quite the same, and they don't live where this does."

"Where does this live, then?"

"In deep holes in the pine ridges, many together. They make small hills and always stay there."

"What do they do?"

"Oh, just run about at night like skunks, and stink plenty."

I appealed to George, who was standing by. He confirmed this statement, but fell out with the man over the question of the other animal being a skunk. He affirmed that they were both polecats, but agreed that they were different.

"Do you get the other kind here?" I asked them.

One said "Yes" and the other said "No." I tended toward the Hinduish hunter, who was a local man and seemed unusually bright, yet reasonable. He had said "Yes."

This animal was short and very fat, besides being sturdily built. It had a vaguely pig-like appearance, but looked more like a small badger. Its fur was very short, close, and hard, coloured greyish-white above and blackish-brown below. Its tail was a ridiculous little naked thing about a centimetre long. Its feet were long, and carried tremendous claws.

We purchased it at a really moderate price, and prepared it. George was unbearable when he had finished, and remained so for days. Fred was no better, and all of us bore down upon Dick and poor Alma with such power that they almost left us.

We spent a lot of time looking for more of these animals, and made a special trip to the hunter's home to prompt him to further efforts. We were shown two low, raised areas on the pine ridge that had holes in them; these, we were told, were the abodes of the pole-cats, but I could not detect the smell around the place—perhaps because I was myself saturated with it. Fred stayed on in the locality and eventually got another one. It was killed on a main road that ran near the place with the mounds.

This odorous creature nevertheless appears to be but a form of the ordinary skunk, *Conepatus tropicalis,* despite its taillessness and allegations about polecats.

A BASTARD WORLD

Pocket Gophers, a Double Snake, Goofy Bat Traps, Fermenting Fish, and a Woolly Opossum

WHEN we left the pines, we settled down for a time in a cultivated area to study the changes wrought in the fauna of the country by the clearing of lands for agriculture. The most surprising things sometimes occur as a result of this, and very often entirely new animals make their appearance, prompted by the removal of natural enemies or other factors that formerly curbed their increase. Yet again, creatures sometimes appear inexplicably, as if from nowhere.

The second morning after our arrival, George appeared beyond the mosquito screen and, seeing that I was absorbing the morning egg, waited deferentially. Glaring hostilely, I perceived that he held something that moved in his left hand, whereupon I relented and told him to come in.

"Well, what is it, George?" I demanded.

"A ground-mole, sir."

"Oh, good. Let me see," I said, for we had been waiting for one to turn up, knowing that they were to be found at this place.

The pocket gopher, known in British Honduras as the ground-mole, is rightfully a good, individualistic, hard-working American citizen, but extends its range down through Mexico to certain areas in tropical Central America. Owing to my own origins and the exigencies of my travels, I had not previously come across these things alive. This was the first that I had seen, and the very sight of it gave me a violent fit of giggles. This may be incomprehensible to those who have been brought up among these animals, but the sight of it was altogether too much for my complacent British soul.

The countenance of a gopher is beyond all hope. However you view it, be it from above, in profile, from head on, or from below, it looks worse. Its body is no better, especially when alive and out of its native earthy element. Its motions are more ineffectual than those of a fish on dry land, and on this occasion, being firmly held amidships by the sturdy hand of George and raised into the entirely unnatural medium of the lower atmosphere, all its attempts to go places were extremely ludicrous.

"Give it to me at once," I said, holding out my hand.

"Look out, sir, he bite bad, fo' true, sir."

"Never mind, George. This thing I must have. Is it ours yet?" I added.

"Yes, I catch it myself in one of the traps."

"Splendid work," I said as I took it over.

But my hand is not constructed upon any such practical lines as George's, and the power innate in this ridiculous creature was a great deal more than its appearance would suggest. In no time at all it had introduced one of its hind feet between my fingers, and, digging its powerful claws into my palm, was launching out into space. It was becoming very bellicose, and grinding its teeth with rodential rage, so I dumped it on the floor, where it set out at some speed. Its movements irresistibly brought to mind those of a steam-shovel in operation that I once viewed from an aeroplane.

It is perhaps unbefitting to include here a description of an animal that is only too well known to Americans, yet if the extent of my own countrymen's knowledge of the wild life of England is any criterion, it may not be out of place.

These pocket gophers form a family of rodents known as the *Geomyidæ*, which is related to the rats and mice, though distinguished from them by many odd characters. Their headquarters are in western and central North America, but besides being found throughout the uplands of Mexico and Central America, they are also found in Yucatan and, as we now discovered, on the coastal plains of British Honduras.

There are quite a number of different forms of gophers, some of which bear very high-sounding names like *Pappogeomys, Crato-geomys*, and so forth. They do a great deal of damage to crops, sometimes becoming veritable pests, and a tremendous amount is known about them. The habits of all gophers seem to be much alike, and are very singular.

Being subterranean, fossorial animals, their bodies have become mole-like in form. They are stout, and usually about six to eight inches in length. The northern species and those from high altitudes are mostly clothed in thick, silky, woolly fur, whereas the southern and lowland forms have a sparse covering of coarse, hard, hairy fur. The tail is short and usually rather naked, and the skin that covers it is, in the type found in British Honduras, nearly two sizes too big, so that it is loose and wrinkled and can be slipped up and down. The limbs are short and very powerful, and all four feet are naked. The forepaws bear positively gigantic claws for digging.

The most ridiculous part of a gopher, and the most important, is the head. This is very large and broad, flat on top and with a fearsomely underslung jaw. The eyes are minute, and the ears reduced to small ridges. The teeth, on the other hand, have been developed into two pairs of enormous, recurved, ivory chisels, orange in colour, clearly grooved down the front, and sharpened to keen edges.

The mouth almost defies description. It is divided into front and back halves by the hairy skin of the upper jaw, which descends behind the upper front teeth and grows together with what would otherwise be the lower lips. The front upper teeth are thus situated on a false snout, and the mouth is reduced to a small circular hole in the middle of the diaphragm formed by the junction of the lips. The animals can stop up this small hole with their tongues as we can a bottle with a cork. On either side of the mouth lie openings to pouches. These are capacious, fur-lined sacks that extend back under the skin to the shoulders. They are supplied with some musculature, but cannot be completely everted, though the gophers can blow them out to a certain extent when they are frightened or wish to give some other animal a scare. One would have imagined that their normal appearance would be sufficiently appalling without this additional profanity, but then, nature's ethics do not coincide with our own.

Pocket gophers feed upon all manner of roots, nuts, seeds, and underground tubers and have a special predilection for our potato crops. They also thrive on young citrus trees, which they neatly fell during the night, and in Yucatan they can make a sisal plantation look awfully silly in no time at all. The manner of their feeding is odd. They burrow their way to their food like subterranean tanks. The earth is gouged out with their upper teeth, which are used as a pick or adze. It is then scooped back under the body with the powerful front feet, and when the animal has a sufficient pile behind it, it turns round in the hole, places its forefeet side by side under its chin, with the palms facing the pile, and pushes the whole lot along, using its hind legs for propulsion. It erupts the earth into low domes on the surface. When it reaches the food, it attacks it by using its lower jaw with a rapid fore-and-aft motion of machine-like precision and effectiveness.

When the gopher has satisfied its immediate needs, it carves up portions of the food and rounds off the sharper edges by holding the pieces between its forepaws and revolving them, as in a lathe, against its chisel teeth. It then puts the food into its pouches. This it accomplishes by suddenly swiping its forepaws to one side with great rapidity. This motion pushes out the side of the pouch so that the portion of food can be shot in. One pouch is filled first and then the other.

The animal then buzzes off to its storehouse in a most remarkable manner. It goes backwards! Gophers seem to be the only mammals that can do this, and they travel as fast or faster in reverse than they do forwards. The tail is used as a feeler, being possessed of an acute tactile sensitivity which again is a feature unique to these mammals. Like so many fossorial rodents, they collect and store far more food than they really require, and their caches are very numerous and

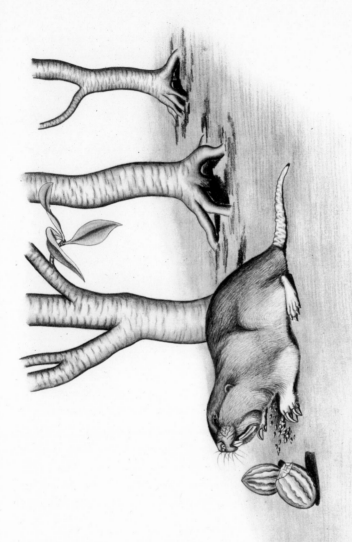

POCKET GOPHER (Heterogeonomys torridus)

large. They get the food out of their pouches by placing the forefeet on either side of the neck and then squeezing them forwards
so that the pieces are tumbled out.

In addition to the storehouses, they construct dwelling quarters.
These are large chambers usually some five or six feet below the
ground, and are often placed under tree roots. Those occupied by
the females are very singular, being surrounded by a circular blind
passageway having but one entrance into the nest. The nests are
lined with grasses and with fur from the mother, who produces
about half a dozen young at a time, and in the tropics keeps at the
job throughout the seasons.

It is said that the gophers of the United States customarily work
from four a.m. to ten o'clock in the morning. Where we were, they
worked throughout the night, but appeared to take an airing above
ground just after sunset. When walking on the surface of the earth,
they are very clumsy, and have to bend their hands inward like an
anteater and walk on their outside edges and on their wrists.

The gophers of this region (*Heterogeomys torridus*) lived in the
upper layers of an alluvial plain in which the water table was but a
few feet below the ground throughout the year, and which was
sometimes flooded for considerable periods. When the water table
rises above the land surface, these fumbling beasts migrate to the
higher land at the sides of this not very wide valley. The strange
fact is that they appear to do this some time before the floods actually
rise. How can subterranean beasts so confidently predict the weather,
or forecast distant cloudbursts?

The appearance of this live gopher had really shocked me. This
was pure lack of experience, for we had heard all about them, seen
plenty of pictures, and handled them in a stuffed or dried condition
many times. The next animal to appear, however, shook my whole
faith in nature, though I now know that this was again only due to
lack of practical experience.

Fred had been out seeing to traps, a line of which was laid along
the junction between the forest and the agricultural lands. At one
point this trap line passed through an area that had previously been

occupied by the thatched house of a small farm. Everything but a pile of conch shells had been cleared away. These conchs are very numerous in the shallow, reef-filled seas along the coast, and are used for many purposes, among others the brewing of excellent-tasting but altogether foul-smelling soups. As usual, Fred was turning over everything movable in search of small fry, and therefore set about dismantling the neat pile of shells. To do this, he removed the outermost shells first, and threw them away upon the principles laid down for the investigation of dead houses.

Picking up a conch, he was just about to hurl it away, when something moving within caught his eye. He turned it up and peered inside, but saw nothing. He then shook it over a clear area, and a small snake's head and fore-body appeared out of the curl where the lip of the shell joins the main spiral. He dumped the shell on the ground, and was preparing to put his machete lightly over the snake's neck, when the after end of another snake also fell out of the shell. He was now in rather a predicament, because the one with its head sticking out looked like a small coral snake, being vividly banded red, cream, and black. Some of these snakes are poisonous. The other snake, however, looked like the little brown *Coniophanes fissidens*, being olive-brown with vague, dark, longitudinal lines. As this latter was one of our spot-types for our distributional work, it was of much importance, so Fred was torn between which of the specimens to grab, as it seemed more than probable that one would escape. He therefore put his machete blade over the brown one and, getting at as respectable a distance as possible, gave the conch a kick in order to remove it and the poisonous coral.

The conch rolled away, and the rest of the brown snake fell out. Fred fell on this and bottled it, keeping half an eye on the conch all the time. In fact, he seems to have paid very little attention to his first capture, as subsequent events will show. He then set to work on the conch, trying to extract the coral. He knew it had not quit, and so when no amount of shaking would bring it out, he broke open the shell. To his amazement there was no snake inside. He tells me he spent some time examining the ground for possible holes, but it was

"DOUBLE SNAKE" (Sibynophis annulata)

hard and perfectly bare, and so, much mystified, he picked up the bottle preparatory to retiring.

When he looked in the bottle, which contained some other previously gathered treasures that would not be harmed by a small snake, he was delighted to find that he had captured, as he thought, both snakes. A moment's reflection, however, convinced him that he was either mad or dreaming, because it is manifestly impossible to pick up two snakes by mistake instead of one, especially when one of them is a vividly coloured and possibly poisonous variety. Utterly amazed, he looked more closely. The result, however, was that he now did think he had gone completely off his chump.

He discovered by revolving the bottle in silent wonderment that the two snakes that had been in the conch shell were in reality but one. Still partly unconvinced that he saw aright, and still seriously shaken over his own mental condition, he stopped his other activities and came bolting home, arriving in a high state of disorder.

"Hey, you!" he said, bursting into the veranda where we were working. "I've got a hybrid snake."

"Eh?" I spluttered. "What on earth are you talking about?"

"I've got two snakes in one."

"How on earth do you know?"

"It's half a coral and half a type C.A. 7."

"Nonsense!" I said. "Absolute rubbish! Here, let me see."

We were working under a mosquito net to ward off bottlas flies, and vision through the net was hazy. Fred held up the bottle for me to see, and I peered at it through the net at close range. What I saw was a mass of snakes and other things, clearly dominated by a small coral snake.

"It looks ordinary enough to me," I said disparagingly. "It's just a young coral."

"It's not, Ivan, look at the other end."

"Here, give it to me," I said, reaching out a hand for the bottle merely because Fred was being so unusually excitable though none the less stubborn.

"It's a coral," I announced after one glance.

"It's not, I tell you; it's two snakes."

"That's what I said," I told him, looking closer at the heaving mass in the bottle.

"No, no! It's two snakes in one."

"Perhaps it swallowed one," suggested Alma.

"Oh, don't be silly," said Fred, now getting very upset. "It's one snake at one end and another one at the other."

"That's *just* what I said," murmured Alma.

By this time, however, I myself was growing quite goggle-eyed. I had traced the coral snake down, and all of a sudden it had changed into something that certainly looked like this *Coniophanes fissidens*.

"By cracky, the fellow's right," I said. "Hi, George, bring a big clean jar and the twelve-inch forceps, quick."

We tipped the snake out into the jar, and then there was no doubt about it at all. This astonishing beast had a black head and was then for the first three inches of its length vivid red, banded with three pairs of narrow black bands enclosing white bands. The body then abruptly became slightly larger in girth, and completely changed colour to a smooth brown with vague, thin dorso-lateral and lateral, *longitudinal* lines of dark brown. This part of the body measured eleven and one-half inches, and the tail eight inches. On the underside, the first part was smooth pink and that of the remainder yellowish-cream. At first sight, the fore-part of the body looked like a coral snake and the latter half like *Coniophanes*, but closer inspection showed that both parts differed considerably in several details.

This snake was of a species known as *Sibynophis annulata*. Conch shells are not a natural feature of this landscape, so its occurrence in one must be looked upon as a coincidence. Under normal conditions, the snake probably lies in the mouth of a hole with the front three inches of its body, which is so vividly coloured, outside. It probably does this for a very special purpose connected with getting its food, or something equally important. There are many snakes whose colouration changes from befront to behind, and there are many with very distinctly coloured tails, but the striking and abrupt alteration displayed by this species is really more than singular.

We were also somewhat stimulated by the question of coral snakes themselves at this place. This group comprises quite a number of forms in Central America. There is, however, a catch about coral snakes. They are also two snakes, in a manner of speaking, there being two entirely different genera of coral snakes that look almost identical. One is poisonous and the other perfectly harmless. It was not until we collected a species of the second and poisonous type, *Micrurus*, that we realized how remarkably similar the two may be.

The only real difference between the representatives of the two genera in this area is that the non-poisonous *Pliocercus* has approximately ten black rings, whereas the *Micrurus* has twenty. The latter is also somewhat slimmer, and displays a few minor details of colouration that help to define it in general appearance. In structure the two animals differ profoundly; in fact they belong to quite different families.

We have from time to time grumbled about the difficulty of collecting bats, more especially the smaller insectivorous species, many of which sleep singly in obscure places. We have devised a whole battery of machines and artifices for coping with this problem, and through these have met with some success, but mostly in caves.

During the past year, we received letters from two kind people offering further suggestions. At first I thought we were having our legs pulled, particularly since both communications hailed from the United States. What they suggested sounded, on the face of it, utterly ridiculous. I passed the letters over to Alma and Fred. There was a nasty silence.

What these kind people suggested was as follows. The first told me that if I provided myself with a catapult or slingshot and some large pellets, and went out into places where insect-eating bats were flying, and lobbed or shot the pellets very slowly not at, but *by* the flying bats, they would think they were insects, swerve, bite at them, and knock themselves out! The oddest thing about this extraordinary suggestion is that the fellow is perfectly right.

The second said that I should provide myself with a long, thin bamboo, the thick end of which I should plant firmly in the ground wherever I saw bats flying. I was then instructed to agitate the bamboo to produce a whirring sound, whereupon (I was assured) the bats would become interested, begin fluttering around, and get knocked out. Once again, the fellow is perfectly right, but unfortunately the device also attracts swallows, swifts, and large nightjars, whose sudden descent is not only superfluous, but very startling.

Of course we didn't believe all this in the beginning, and for some time I was more or less forcibly prevented from trying them out by Fred, who steadfastly forgot to order large shot or a bamboo or even to make me a slingshot. I never was able to persuade him, and had to sneak off myself and obtain the necessaries. The first opportunity to make tests came at this place.

In the absence of bamboos, I got a long, thin sapling, planted it firmly in the ground, and agitated it according to instructions. In no time at all there were two bats fluttering around. It was some time before one got knocked out, during which I discovered that, to gain the desired end, the stick had to be vibrating in a certain manner. Simply shaking it back and forth was not sufficient; it had to be whirred round and round at a certain speed, when it produced a shrill noise. The bats seemed incapable of resisting this.

I tried out the other suggestion with the toy airgun. I shot the pellets past, or, rather, in the general direction of the bats and, sure enough, some of them swerved to grab them. They fell to the ground fluttering violently, but were neither dead nor completely knocked out. I had to be very quick off the mark to retrieve them. Those that I did catch had the pellets gripped in their teeth, with the exception of one which had swallowed his and was gulping hysterically. This experiment explained several things, notably the reason why, in our cave-hunting, we had so often appeared to hit bats at which we had not aimed. I had previously imagined this to be entirely due to bad marksmanship, but it seems that these swift little animals make a dive for the pellets, presumably thinking them to be small, zooming insects.

Bats are a recurring labour to us. They cropped up again at this place. There was a small isolated hill in the valley which was a

last remaining outlier of the limestone cap that covered this whole
area in by-gone geological ages. Like all limestone, it was riddled
with caves, which formed a network of passages running right
through it at present-day ground level. This hill was now being
quarried for surfacing a new road, and a considerable part of it had
already been removed. We are incapable of passing any cave by, so,
with the aid of some friends, a minor *safari* was organized to investigate these.

As a guarantee that blasting operations would not be carried on
while we were inside, we had the supervising engineer in our party.
This wise precaution, coupled with the fact that everybody assured
me that it was Sunday, seemed to make everything perfectly safe.
What we found inside, however, proved so interesting that we subsequently went back without either of these guarantees.

I mentioned above that the effect upon wild animal populations
of clearing land is often strange and unexpected. We now know
that the results of quarrying and blasting, of the proximity of a
towering crusher, and of the presence of a throbbing Diesel engine
in a cave are even less predictable. These were the conditions ap-
pertaining to this hill in question, and yet the wild life inhabiting
the caves appeared to be entirely unaffected. The place not only
swarmed with bats of no less than nine species, but there was fresh
spoor and droppings of at least four other mammals. There were
swallows nesting in the galleries, and lizards, snakes, and a host of
other smaller fry.

The passageways were long and low and tortuous. We wriggled
in with torches and other paraphernalia. At one time Fred and I
were pretty firmly wedged in, in tandem. The others were far away
in other parts of the caves, and it was deathly quiet. We were rak-
ing over the loose rubble on the floor of our passage in search of small
white woodlice, which inhabited some very old cohune nuts that
must have been carried in there by animals. All of a sudden we heard
a plop. This seemed to have originated in water.

We asked each other if we had heard anything, and having decided
that we had, speculated upon the direction from which the noise had

come. We had seen no water so far, nor any side chambers where there might be any. After a time there was another plop, and now there was no doubt about the presence of a pool somewhere about. We spent a most unhappy half-hour passing back and forth like monstrous worms in this narrow tube, searching for the water. We eventually located it.

There was a small hole, through which I could just squeeze, that led through the wall of our passage at the floor level. This opened out into a perfectly spherical little chamber some six feet in diameter. Its symmetry was cut below by a circular pool. This turned out to be the top of another sphere, so that the complete space in the rock was shaped like an hourglass, the lower bulb being full of water. Upon the surface of this water floated a frothy, yellow foam about three inches thick.

I got right inside and, standing up, straddled the pool, which was about four feet wide. I bent down and scooped some of this scum aside. As I did so, I was nearly overcome by a column of powerful, acid-smelling gas which rose up and filled the hole. It was a dreadful smell, but it was not till I finally left the place that I realized its full potency. I felt dizzy and unsteady then, and was sick for hours.

This pool was a kind of natural still, and the liquor it contained was fermenting. When I moved the scum, it effervesced violently, like Perrier water. Yet the pool contained a tremendous quantity of animal life. The walls were so thickly crowded with water snails that I could not put a finger between them anywhere. Swimming in the pool were innumerable small fish. It seemed hardly conceivable that all these creatures could live in this place. There was absolutely no light and practically no air. The water must have been almost devoid of free oxygen apart from that released by the slow fermentation which apparently resulted from the decomposition of a deposit of some fibrous vegetable matter that covered the bottom of the pool. How these snails and fish came to this place in the first instance could not easily be explained, for the whole pool was above the level of the land surface, and this land was itself considerably above the level of the valley floor, so that even the occasional floods never reached such a height. The hole was isolated in the depths of the hill. Its water presumably filtered through the rock and dripped into the pool, because there were no visible cracks in the roof. Stagnant was not the word to describe this pool—nature had simply turned moonshiner.

Fred squeezed through the hole also, and we managed to catch several of the fish with a hand net. These were of three different kinds, all of which are to be found in the streams of the neighbourhood. They were, in fact, billums.

We later found more pools farther in. These were the most disgusting soupy mires, in a deep bed of bat guano in a long narrow crevice, and were devoid of fish. The crevice was literally half full of bats. To go inside was really quite perilous, for the little animals got scared and battered into us continuously. They were all *Carollia*, a common fruit-eating species; or so we thought when we first came out. We had collected a bagful simply by swiping the net back and forth.

When we got back into a big gallery, we sat down to sort out these bats at our leisure, selecting a set of males and females and releasing the others. We were busily employed and getting periodically bitten, when Fred handed me a bat.

"Here, have a look at this, will you?" he said.

"It's a new one on me," I said enthusiastically as soon as I saw it.

"It's the only one here," said Fred.

"We must get some more."

"We will."

"Don't boast, Fred, or we won't," I cautioned.

"Oh, rubbish," he said making a swipe at a passing bat, "you're always an awful pessimist. Here! Here's another," and he tossed me over the bat which he had netted quite by chance.

I opened the net and took out the bat. It *was* another one!

"Here," I stammered, "do that again, will you? You did get one."

"All right, I will," said Fred, still more jocularly, and he nonchalantly made a pass at another bat.

Again he caught it, and again it was one of these special bats. I just sat there goggle-eyed, saying, "Do it some more, please." But although Fred spent the rest of the day in that chamber catching bats with a dogged, British persistency, he never saw another one, nor have we seen any since. The bats were *Chilonycteris rubiginosa*. Coincidences like that rather unnerve you.

Towards the end of our first day's exploration of these caves, we had all congregated in a winding narrow chasm carpeted with smooth wet earth that formed a miniature canyon in the floor of an immensely long gallery. Our chasm was about twelve feet deep and four feet wide. Its sides were draped throughout with the most exquisite stalactitic formations, exactly resembling curtains. These were as thin as paper, translucent, and draped and gathered above just like fabric. They hung most artistically from the lip of the chasm walls.

One of our friends flashed a torch up between these curtains, and happened to spy some quite minute bats (*Myotis nigricans*) concealed therein. He could not get them out, and called for our assistance. We tried everything possible, but could not dislodge them. Then we found that there were many more between all the curtains, and we eventually obtained some by shooting the toy airgun at random up into the small clefts. When we came to skin one, we found that its body was smaller than the terminal joint of our little fingers, in fact it was just about the size of a bumble bee.

Of the nine species of bats that we took in this cave, each kept exclusively to one particular habitat. The *Desmodus* blood-lappers were in horizontal clefts in the walls of dry, smooth, rocky chambers in the depths of the hill; the *Carollia* were crowded together in the long, damp, narrow chambers; the *Artibeus* were on the pitted roofs of large galleries near the exterior; these *Myotis* were only in the curtains; the *Anoura* were only in cavelets where there was some light, and so on. It is remarkable how selective even bats will be in choosing their quarters.

After this bat-hunt, we turned to other objectives. These cleared agricultural lands brought us face to face with many conundrums. They proved to be inhabited by several new forms of animals, just as we had expected, and some of these had come in from the north with man. It was these that we then set out to track down to their original environments, and to do this we had to move north.

Our first stop was on the northern plains of British Honduras near a beautiful lake called by some Skate's Lagoon and by others Kate's Lagoon. Here the work was concerned with dissecting the sundry vegetational zones that were to be found in the area and, secondly, collecting the fauna of each. The camp was laid out in an area of forest almost wholly composed of towering cohune palms and basket-trunked fig trees. This odd and beautiful growth, now so stately and quiet and full of biting insects, appears to be an entirely artificial zone. It has been suggested that it has resulted from ancient Mayan cultivation, and has endured because the cohune palm is almost impossible to eradicate from the land, whereas other plants are not.

You will soon see why, if you cut down a young cohune flush with the surface of the earth, and then erect your bed over it as we did. In a very few days we began to sleep badly, and, after grumbling a bit about this, we happened to make the bed ourselves. The middle of it was raised into a sharp hump. Looking underneath, we saw the cohune growing away happily, a 14-inch white cylinder having appeared out of the centre of the stump. The nuts of the cohune were used by the Mayas and, since their stone axes were quite useless for cutting down the iron-hard trunks of the mature trees, even had they desired to do so, the trees were preserved. Thus, though the other plants have gone, along with the crops once cultivated and the Mayas themselves, the cohunes have thrived mightily, and remain a living memorial to past history.

Bounding the cohune zone there were areas of *akalche*, pure pine, and some other types of forest that need not concern us. The faunas of these zones were distinct, and in each case were dominated by that of the northern type of vegetation of which it formed a part, though the southern forest fauna had not yet petered out. The jungle animals were naturally more prevalent in the vegetation that most closely resembled their southern forest homes. In these there were

kinkajous and *Heteromys* and southern types of bats, whereas out
on the open pines there appeared a quite new congregation of animals that we will meet again presently farther to the north.

Much of the collecting here was done in the pine zone, and was
therefore merely a repetition and a confirmation of previous work.
We found little in the *akalche*, but in the other zones we met a
strange mixture of animals showing that the whole place was not
only a transition area, but also quite unmistakably an overgrown
backlot of an extinct civilization.

Among the small list of animals that were new to us one was particularly outstanding. This was an opossum (*Philander laniger
fervidus*), which was caught alive while sleeping in the head of a
cohune palm. This must be one of the most beautiful and delicately
coloured mammals in existence. It was medium-sized, with a pointed
nose, large naked ears, and a long, rat-like tail of which the basal
half was clothed in fur. It was a rich golden-russet above, and white
below, but this colouration was complicated by the introduction of
delicate mauve-grey on the head and face, and again over the hips
and onto the furred portion of the tail. There were also other markings: a median dorsal line of white-tipped grey hairs between the
shoulder blades, and orange areas in the armpits and on the side of
the neck.

This creature's behaviour was more like that of a kinkajou than
an opossum. It slept rolled up on its side like a cat, and instead of
hissing and spitting like the other opossums, it purred and made a
mewing noise. It only licked bananas and other fruits but gobbled
up any insect or other animal food offered to it. The specimen we
caught was a female, and was carrying four minute young ones in
its lower belly in the depths of a large and well-developed pouch
with a narrow opening directed forwards.

We left Fred to finish off the routine work at Skate's Lagoon, and
Alma and I journeyed on to the cheery little town of Chetumal,
capital of the Mexican Federal Territory of Quintana Roo. To
reach this place we crossed the Rio Hondo.

Part Three

TO YUCATAN

MAYALAND

Yucatan and the Mayas, Akalche and Egrets,
a Zopilote and Special Flies

POLITICAL boundaries are, in six cases out of ten, haphazardly defined lines which have no foundation in fact or in nature. As soon as we had crossed the Rio Hondo, however, we saw that we had indeed passed both a political and a natural boundary of considerable importance, and we realized for the first time that British Honduras was not merely a southward prolongation of Quintana Roo.

This business of Yucatan is rather complicated, especially for those who have had no occasion to visit the country or are not otherwise especially interested in it. Maps and atlases only tend to muddle the issue, because they bear the name in bold lettering right across the whole triangular peninsula that bounds the Gulf of Mexico on the south and then, in more political moods, confine the name to a comparatively small area at the northwestern tip of that peninsula. In the latter case they are endeavouring to convey the confines and position of the present-day Mexican state of Yucatan.

Yucatan is correctly the name of a country which is most distinctive in its inhabitants, fauna, flora, and even its underlying geological structure; it also has clearly defined natural boundaries. This country is a great peninsula bounded on the east by the Caribbean, on the west by the Bight of Campeche, on the north by the rest of the Gulf of Mexico, and on the south by the great sierras that extend from Chiapas in Mexico to Guatemala. The southern part of this peninsula is covered by the real jungle and is in other ways closely related to and confluent with truly tropical Central America. The rest is a very different and distinct kind of country.

British Honduras, which, as will be seen by reference to the map, lies wholly within Yucatan in the real sense of that name, is, however, truly a separate country, though itself also divided into distinct southern and northern portions because the northern limit of the real jungles cuts across its centre. Its northern plains, which are separated from Quintana Roo only by the Rio Hondo, are an old gulf that has only recently been filled in by the sea. The flora and fauna of this latter are noticeably different from those of the rest of Yucatan despite the apparent similarity at first glance.

Yucatan was the "cradle of the Mayan civilization," and, indeed, was entirely the property of that civilization at its fullest maturity. In by-gone days, these charming people were a great deal more numerous than they are today. Moreover, they were great agriculturists, and in their hey-day populated the whole of the country. Because of their system of shifting cultivation, which continued for centuries, they subjected Yucatan, and particularly that portion lying north of the real jungles, to a process of Gargantuan ploughing and harrowing whereby the original vegetation was systematically and completely stripped from its surface time and time again, so that it may truly be said that every stick and stone in the land has at some time been turned by the hand of man.

Such a process had a profound and ineradicable effect upon the fauna and flora, so that the reconstruction of either at the present day is a matter of considerable complexity amounting almost to a sort of biological jigsaw puzzle. The effects upon the fauna were perhaps not so profound as upon the vegetation, for as long as there remained at all times sufficient fallow areas amid the cultivation, the animals could at least continue to exist. That they did so is perfectly obvious, for the wild life of Yucatan today is very extensive and varied; indeed, unusually so for a country that might be thought to be rather inhospitable, being either very arid or completely waterlogged.

After the ordered and beautifully departmental arrangement of the jungles in which we had been working, the investigation of Yucatan proved very novel. However, we could but tackle the matter in the customary way, and so our first operations in Chetumal called for an inspection of the wild life of the town and the assortment of pets kept by its populace. We were surprised to find that both groups were mostly composed of animals we had not seen before.

We discovered that the majority of the pets were brought from the high forests of Peten by the mahogany workers, via the Rio Hondo. We were shown howler monkeys and spider monkeys and kinkajous and even a capuchin monkey, which had arrived by ship from Spanish Honduras. Since these animals were considered enormously valuable by their owners but were practically useless to us, we turned our attention to the small indigenous fauna of the town and its environs.

On the first morning of our visit, I was having my hair badly cut in a small barber shop on the main street. As I reclined in the chair I had a complete view of the street, since the whole side of the place was open. Opposite was a long fence of corrugated sheet iron, in which there were many holes. Idly watching, I saw a small dog's backside retreat out of and then advance into one of these holes no less than three times in succession. Then the dog backed right out, and crouched barking at the hole, from which the sleek, shining, black posterior of a cat then began to emerge. Eventually this also came right out, and crouched beside the dog, spitting and hissing. Now thoroughly intrigued, I ducked beneath the barber's blunt scissors to get a better view, and was just in time to see a large *Didelphis* opossum come out with a rush. The cat bolted, but the dog stood its ground, and the snarling marsupial advanced upon it so that I thought there would be a fight. Then the dog fled. The opossum was left in the glaring noonday sun in sole possession of the sidewalk, and proceeded to snuffle placidly along by the fence.

I pointed this phenomenon out to the barber and those of his assistants who were awake. They all laughed. In my execrable Spanish I indicated that I wanted the beast, and after staring at me in amazement for some time, the assembled company apparently took me at my word. Ensuing events taught me my first real lesson about the contradictory land that is Mexico.

Raising a cry of "*Zorro!*" which is local Spanish for opossum as well as for sundry kinds of dogs, foxes, and other animals, everybody dashed into the street armed with anything that came to hand. In no time at all, shouts were raised on all sides, and several small armies streamed out of doorways. From being a siesta-quiet, orderly street, the place instantly turned into a bloody shambles. Seeing what I had let loose, I hung back, praying for the opossum and kicking myself for what I had so unwittingly precipitated. The crowd surged down the street, driving the luckless animal right into the arms of several wild-looking *hombres* with big hats, who happened to be lying in the road. I don't know what the instruments of death were, but the quarry was dispatched with such thoroughness that I was able to salvage only a rather battered skull. Encouraged by this episode, though the prize obtained could hardly be described as a zoological treasure, we decided to rely upon our own efforts in future.

Chetumal is for the most part built upon a narrow coastal plain separating the mouth of the Rio Hondo from a low escarpment. This plain is clothed in mangroves, but around the town, quite extensive fine-grass pastures have been cut out of the swamps, and upon these, horses and preposterously aggressive cattle graze. Having examined the mangroves and found them to be practically sterile, we turned our attention to these pastures.

In the first that we entered, we found a string of small pans or depressions, filled with a bed of juicy green plants. These latter could be cut along the rim of the pan and rolled back like a quilt. The pans had been ponds, and these quilts were water plants now subsisting on the moist soil below, which they protected from the glaring sun. As we rolled them back, a wonderful little menagerie came to light. Here we had stumbled across a complete representation in concentrated form of the smaller fauna of the little coastal

plain. There were snakes and lizards, frogs and toads, snails, arachnids, and crustaceans of all kinds, as well as worms of many species.
We spent several happy afternoons clearing up these pans, and then
went up onto the plateau beyond the escarpment, where we immediately entered an entirely new world.

The ground below the bone-dry, thorny shrubbery was covered
with dead leaves, and as we walked along, innumerable small lizards
went dashing and rustling over the ground in all directions. When
we finally captured some of these, they turned out to be of two
species (*Sceloporus chrysostictis* and a form of *Ameiva*), which we
had previously met only in the open pine ridges at Skate's Lagoon.
The sexes in the first are marked differently, the females having
black armpits and the males bright red "gills"; they also have different markings and colour patterns on their backs. We kept getting only the females until we found that the males ran up trees
in order to escape danger. Why one sex should do this and not the
other seems beyond comprehension, but it perhaps explains the great
colour differences between the two.

This whole country was dry and inhospitable in the extreme.
Small paths led for miles through the hard, prickly bushes, giving
off little tracks now and then that led to maize milpas. Everywhere
was evidence of former Maya settlements.

We extended our daily explorations as far as we could, starting
from the east by the coast, and gradually working round to the
southwest. The whole of this sector was dry and uninteresting in
the extreme. When we came to the southwestern area, we found,
instead of dry, dusty thorn scrub, a beautiful, cool forest composed
of tall sapodillas and stately palms packed close together, but,
strangely enough, inhabited by the same animals as the dry thorns.
This kept us occupied for many days. Then, beyond this forest
which stretched south to the banks of the Rio Hondo, we one day
reached a great zone of *akalche*.

We had set out at seven o'clock in the morning, and reached the
akalche at about eleven-thirty, after much pounding through the tall
forest and chasing many active animals over piles of fallen logs. The

akalche was as dense as the average hedge, and filled with natural groves of a peculiar kind of terrestrial mangrove with interlocking aerial root systems about ten feet high; these were very difficult to get through. After about an hour's progress of a rather serpentine nature, we came upon a very pretty, placid little river, with amber-coloured water and bordered by reed beds.

Some distance to the right, overhanging the water, there were several gnarled trees among the branches of which a number of white egrets were precariously perched. About an equal distance to the left, the river passed under a natural bridge composed of sedges and rubbish growing upon and entangled in a fallen tree. Small creatures that we thought were birds were flying into and out of the darkness beneath this. When one happened to skim by us, whirling and dipping over the placid waters, we saw that it was a small bat, so we waded down to the mass of rubbish and peered underneath. We saw nothing at first, but when we started to go in, a whole cloud of bats came whizzing out into the sunlight and went swaying away upstream. They all landed together on the under-sides of branches of the trees occupied by the egrets. Then a very unusual thing happened.

The egrets got into a great state of excitement, wobbling about in their stupid, drunken-looking way and side-stepping rapidly along the branches. We thought they were afraid of the tiny mammals, and were therefore considerably surprised when two or three of them reached down with their long necks and adroitly pecked some of the bats off their resting places. The birds held them fluttering in their beaks for a moment, and then very solemnly plunged them under the water. The remainder of the bats left immediately, and came whirling downstream again. They passed between us and went to roost under the original tangle of rubbish once more. This time we were ready for them, and secured two with the airgun.

We were so intent on this that we had taken our eyes off the egrets, but when we again looked they were stabbing repeatedly and vio-lently at the remains of the bats, which they held on the branches with their feet. We waded up to the tree, and had practically to shoo the birds away. One took its bat along with it, but another left the remains on the branch. When we examined this, we found it consisted only of the wings, legs, and tail, joined together by the skin of the back. The head and the body itself had been pecked out and presumably eaten by the bird. The bats were *Rhynchiscus naso,* a diurnal species that customarily sleeps near water.

We were standing discussing this matter, with the river water reaching half-way up our thighs, when Alma stopped talking abruptly, and stared at me in a very curious way. I could not decide whether the look of pained incredulity growing upon her countenance was the result of feeling ill or merely trying to think. I stared back at her for a few seconds and, as she looked more ghastly every moment, I asked what was wrong. She made no reply, but remained rooted to the spot and just pointed downwards into the water.

"What's the matter?" I implored.

"It's got me!" she wailed, again pointing down.

"What? What has?"

"I think it's a croc!"

That was a frightful moment. I stood there feeling utterly foolish, and wondering what on earth I should do. Then all at once my mind and body limbered up, and I plunged down towards Alma's feet, bubbling out a final prayer into the amber-coloured waters. My fingers closed over something hard and smooth lying on the mud. I seized it and pulled. As I appeared into the air again, Alma was projecting herself out into the reeds and the thing I held came to life.

I really thought that I had hold of a crocodile, for it churned the water into an orange foam and was nearly as strong as I. Then I got it out, and found that I was holding a huge river tortoise. I finally landed this amid general sighs of relief. It was a beautifully coloured animal known in British Honduras, where it is much prized as food, as the "hikiti" and to science as *Pseudemys ornata.* Its flesh surpasses that of a turtle in delicacy and flavour. Its skin is striped black and bright yellow, and its shell is smooth and shiny, brown above, yellow-and-black below.

This *akalche* was a happy hunting ground which we explored for several days, but we kept clear of the waters in future as we did see several large crocodiles only a few minutes after we had landed the hikiti.

We extended our explorations as far as we could from Chetumal on daily trips. To go farther afield, however, called for our full equipment, which we did not have with us, because the surrounding country is uninhabited and even lacks paths. As we were making only a preliminary survey at that time, we decided against making a full-fledged trip into the hinterland. Instead, and to obviate the necessity, we took a small ship at Chetumal and sailed round Yucatan to Progreso, whence we travelled to Merida and then from there back towards Chetumal as far as we conveniently could. This brought us, by great good fortune, to a village named Tekom, which, although apparently so far away, actually lay in the climatic belt next to that which we had ultimately reached working out of Chetumal.

Here we established ourselves in a cool thatched house through the kind hospitality of its owner, one Don Jacinto Mukul. We opened our collecting cases and set to work—and it turned out to be very different work from anything we had ever attempted before.

We are accustomed to relying almost entirely upon our own efforts to obtain the animals we want. In towns or areas where there are local hunters, we usually cajole and plead and beg for animals, and many times we have been brought specimens, but these have always been common species, either the ones we wanted least or those that we really didn't want at all. We have always had to search out for ourselves the little obscure creatures that really interest us. In the past, the reason for this was not necessarily indolence on the part of the local inhabitants, for many times they were very keen, but simply that they had never heard of the animals we wanted, did not even suspect their existence, and had no names for them. Here among the Mayas, the position was exactly reversed.

All but a handful of the inhabitants of Tekom spoke nothing but Mayan, and we spoke little Spanish. However, we very fortunately had a Mexican friend with us who spoke perfect English, and there was a very charming and intelligent schoolmaster at Tekom who spoke Mayan, so the four of us—Alma, our friend Riqué Vales, the schoolmaster, and I—sat down surrounded by a closed circle of the local populace, and set to work preparing a somewhat specialized English-Spanish-Mayan vocabulary.

Now we were aware that the Mayas have a very full and advanced language; we knew also that they have names for most plants and animals and other natural objects; and finally we have had personal proof of their sagacity as naturalists. Yet it was not until the second day that we came to realize the true extent of their knowledge or the fullness of their language.

We found out that these people not only knew all of the animals that I had on my list as being likely to occur in the country, but could describe each of them accurately and give it a name in their own tongue. We started with the mammals, and were suspicious of their integrity until we came to the rats, in which we were particularly interested. I asked the schoolmaster the Mayan name for "rat," and he told me it was "tcho." I then mentioned that there were many kinds of rats, and when this had been explained to the assembled company there were hearty assents on all sides, and they began to tick them off on their fingers: "tcho-patch-nail," or "rat of the house"; "spookil-tcho" or "little rat"—i.e., a mouse; "tzub-tcho," "poot-em-poot," and so on. We had each one described via the ring of interpreters, and this was done so accurately and with such detail by these extraordinary people that we were able to put a proper name to it at once from our knowledge of the rats of the peninsula gained previously at Chetumal. As has been mentioned above, the definition of species of rats is a matter of the utmost difficulty, but each rat has in due course turned up in conformity with its Mayan name and our purely scientific definition.

We then discovered that they could classify the Arachnida, an accomplishment that European science did not perfect until the later nineteenth century, and then only after tremendous wrangling. There was no doubt about this, for they had a name for each group and distinctive names for each kind of animal in each group. The

Arachnida are one of the most complex groups of animals. No other native race that we have encountered, and no educated white man that I have ever heard of who was not specifically a zoologist, could classify them, and yet these people must have perfected their opinions on the subject before Columbus discovered America. Not only did they differentiate the various major groups correctly—as, for example, the harvestmen (opilionids), which they call "shaklampoat"; the spiders, which they define as "chingwo"; the Solifugæ as "menché"; the *amblypygi* as "chi-i-tun," etc.—they even divide each into sub-groups bearing an almost exact relationship to our own divisions, which are based upon abstruse morphological details that often cannot be studied except under considerable powers of magnification. These sub-groups are very simply named in Mayan, as, for example, the spiders, where there are the "great spiders" and the "little spiders" and the "herb spiders," but it is almost uncanny to observe that they class a certain tiny trap-door spider common in these parts with the giant hairy mygales in the group designated "no-hoatch-cingwo," or "great spiders." According to our accepted classification, this little beast is, like the mygales, of the arvicularian group.

The deeper we delved into the matter, the more our amazement increased. How is it possible that a people who sometimes do their farming as far as twenty miles from where they live, who do not read or write, and who spend all their waking hours busily employed labouring at the production of their food and other necessities, find time to learn their wild fauna and flora so thoroughly and retain the knowledge? Nor was it only the older men that knew all this; every man and woman and all the children old enough to speak appeared to know all the names! They seemed infallible, and, as far as we could learn, the real Mayas of the country districts are indeed infallible in most respects.

Thus we not only put a Mayan name to every animal on our list, but in addition we compiled a long inventory of animals for which we had only the Mayan names; and I am afraid we were much more stupid than they in our attempts to identify the latter. We therefore

held a council, and it was decided that the populace would co-
operate in a systematic attempt to procure for us at least one specimen of each animal that we had on our lists, both those that we
thought we knew and those which we were quite sure we didn't.
This led us into many amusing incidents, for the Mayan language is
phonetic and, although there is a Mayan academy which is trans-
literating it and there are Spanish-Mayan dictionaries and grammars,
we found it better to ignore even what of these we had, for a
Spaniard's idea of how to spell Shishló—*vide* Xixlodt—for instance, is
not only amusing but would be disastrous to an English-speaking
student.

When we had compiled our dictionary of animal names, we sat
back and waited, while our village friends came to visit us as usual.
Very naturally we began to think that the old history was going to
repeat itself; we thought, in fact, that we had seen the last of local
zoological enthusiasm, and that we would soon have to set to work
to get the animals ourselves. Then things began to happen; little
things happened first.

Riqué and I had been out to inspect a line of traps that we had
laid through an extensive wood of dismally dry thorn trees. It had
been extremely hot work, and we were very thirsty and covered
with warri-ticks that were engaged upon digging themselves in all
over us. In fact, we could think of nothing but hot water by the
bucket, medicated soap, and spongefuls of alcohol, as we trudged
along towards the village. I also longed for the little billums in their
cool, clear streams.

When we reached the house, we found it deserted. Neither Alma
nor any of the myriad members of the Mukul family were anywhere
to be seen. We removed the wicket and entered, praying that there
might at least be water heating on the fire in the outhouse kitchen
beyond.

"Look!" Riqué grabbed me and pointed.

"Good heavens, what is it?" I said, as my eyes fell upon a small,
dome-shaped structure in the middle of the floor.

"It might be a bees' house," said Riqué, with the delightful inconsequence of his otherwise perfect English.

Now, Riqué is a man of great perspicacity. We had known each other only for a few months, but had become the closest companions. He was taking a holiday with us, but had found great interest in our work and had plunged into it with an enthusiasm that almost surpassed our own. Of all the wonderful friends that we have made during our zoological wanderings, I can safely say that we have never received help or co-operation of such a wholeheartedly cheerful nature as we received from him. We had, in fact, as he so naïvely and succinctly put it, "made a very good friendship together." Having lived for many years in the States, his English would perhaps, in the ears of some, sound better than our own, for we, of course, have only the benefit of a British background. Nevertheless, he retained a delicious habit of avoiding the more hopeless English expressions by literally translating their Spanish equivalents.

While I was still wrestling with the etymological conundrum of a "bees' house," the object in question gave a loud squawk, and hopped nimbly towards us, covering about two feet. We both recoiled.

"Look out, Riqué," I cautioned, "this is probably some deep Maya plot."

"I hope not," he said. "They have a wonderful sense of humour, I'm telling you."

"It's not a snake, anyway. What do you think it could be?"

"I tell you what," Riqué suggested, "let's shut the doors and then turn it over with the broom."

"Not on your life, dear boy. What! Be shut up in here with an ocelot or something? No, thank you."

"Look, look; I can see an eye up near the top," Riqué said, shifting his tactics.

This dome-shaped thing was made like a closely woven basket, from stout laths of split sapling sticks, between which there were only a few small chinks. Approaching as close as I dared, I peered into the crack Riqué indicated, and sure enough, there was a very

vicious, shining eye watching us, and occasionally winking like a
camera shutter.

"Riqué, I have an idea. Here, give a hand with this box."

We heaved a heavy collecting box out into the room and, lifting
it, plonked it down on top of the beehive-shaped basket thing, which
sagged slightly and adopted a Fujiyama-like form.

"You hold it steady, while I get a torch," I said.

I got a torch, flashed its beam into the largest chink between the
laths, and peered in. I couldn't see anything at first but darkness;
then something moved, and half of a most evil-looking head fell
athwart the tiny ray of light.

"What is it?" asked Riqué.

"It looks like a miniature dinosaur," I gasped. "Here, you have
a look."

I held the box, and Riqué took the torch. There was a moment's
silence, then he began to giggle. Finally he was roaring with laughter.

"It's a joke, all right," he said. "It's only a zopilote."

"A what?"

"You know, a kind of bird."

"I recognize the name, but what kind of bird?" I inquired, for I
could not get the simple Spanish names sorted out in my mind.

"Ach! What do you call it in English? You know, the black ones
Alma calls turkey buzz-birds."

"Oh," I said, suddenly remembering, "you mean turkey-vultures."

So we overturned the basket, and there, sure enough, stood one
of those wildly staring, rather excited-looking, ugly, black birds
(*Cathartes aura*), covered in dust and with a thick cord attached
to one of its legs. It was no joke, however, for its presence was occasioned by the fact that Mayas do less forgetting than elephants. I
had once mentioned casually that I would like to have one of these
birds for dissection, to ascertain whether it housed any parasitic
worms.

These birds carry scavenging to a fine art. Between times they are
either circling endlessly round and round in the air or squabbling
on roof tops. Much of the drinking water comes from rain water

collected from these roof tops and, except in the homes of the most fastidious, this water is not even boiled before being drunk. There could be no better way for worm eggs to enter the human body, but although we have examined quantities of these "vulturettes" in a variety of countries about the Caribbean, we have so far failed to collect a single worm from any of them. I wanted to include the Yucatan members of this group in our studies, and I was therefore quite pleased with this present. I was hurrying to put the basket over it again, when a fly settled on my wrist.

It was a big black fly, and I was about to swipe it off when it most unexpectedly ran sideways up my arm like a crab, and then flitted onto the bird's back. Staring in surprise, I saw it scuttle sideways into the feathers and disappear. Quite unthinkingly I made a violent lunge and grabbed for the spot. The bird's reaction was natural enough, but took me completely by surprise, as my whole being was concentrated upon the fly. The zopilote very reasonably took the bitterest umbrage at my behaviour. He let out a screech and waltzed about, going for me with everything he had and at the same time losing a lot of feathers. A roar of laughter went up, and, looking round, I perceived the whole Mukul family and Alma clustered in the doorway.

"I knew you'd do that," said Alma.

"Bah, you chump!" I squawked, considerably peeved. "Stop giggling and come and help murder this bird; quick, it's got lovely flies on it."

"Don't be disgusting, dear; the thing's lousy, I know."

"Yes, but it's got huge hippoboscids."

"Poor fellow's mad," said Alma.

"Seems so," said Riqué, and everybody began laughing again because, in a manner of speaking, the gong sounded and the zopilote and I were in the ring again.

I was just about to corner the bird when a fly suddenly appeared on his neck. I made a swipe, but, of course, the zopilote ducked and the fly skipped into the air and landed on my hand. It darted between my closed fingers and tickled my palm, so that I let out a yell and was forced to open my hand. The little devil then scooted round my wrist and started careering up my arm sideways, making for the darkness under my shirt sleeve. I cannot abide being tickled, so I hopped around, screeching and swatting at my arm. Everybody roared with delighted laughter, and the confounded bird added to the clamour.

The fly then suddenly left my arm and flew towards the open door. I saw it going against the pale sky beyond, and gave chase, making furious passes at it. At the door it turned back into the room and made for the zopilote, with me in hot pursuit, swatting at it again and again. The assembled company howled with glee. I yelled at them to help, and then two more of the flies suddenly appeared on my trousers. I made a frantic grab for these with both hands, and missed both. They took to the air, and I flailed about wildly, pleading continuously for assistance, but everybody just rolled about quite speechless with mirth. People came running from neighbouring houses and crowded the doors. This was the first really entertaining show we had put on, and we were the first foreigners that had visited the village within living memory. Besides, it was a distinctly good performance as described to me by Alma and Riqué when they had recovered from their hysterics.

The second act was even more protracted. After chasing the flies back and forth, tripping over the miserable bird, and making sudden grabs at various parts of my anatomy, I seized up a big piece of cloth and took a flying dive at the zopilote. He was completely enveloped and borne to the ground, where I knelt heavily on him. I then cautiously raised a corner of the cloth and began examining his plumage. I saw one of the flies and made a dive for it; I actually had it in my fingers, but it squirmed loose and flew off. I found another and pursued it through the feathers, but it vanished. Then the zopilote pecked me violently, and got loose. I fell back, exhausted, and gave up, almost in tears of frustration. The onlookers let out a cheer, and the dreadful bird hopped away squawking, dragging the basket behind it. Then I began to laugh too, and I didn't stop until long after the others had recovered.

"What on earth were you doing?" Riqué sobbed.

"Chasing flies," I gasped; "they're frightfully important. I must—" and then I was off again.

Finally we regained control of ourselves, and I was able to convince them that there really were very special, semi-parasitic flies living in the zopilote's plumage, and that they had come out and settled on me, flown about the house, and then gone back to their host. It turned out that neither Riqué nor Alma had seen them and, being so convulsed with laughter at my antics, had not taken in what I had said. Our good Mayan neighbours, of course, understood neither what I said nor anything of my intentions. It was small wonder that my performance proved so popular.

When it was explained to them, however, I got real co-operation. Riqué held the bird, and we made a thorough search. We saw some of the flies, but they were too quick for us, and although we actually held one for a moment, it escaped and the others all flew away. It was a terrible disappointment to me, because these creatures are one of my special fancies.

These insects belong to a group of the two-winged flies known as the *Pupipara*, which is a very distinctive collection. They are all parasites on birds, bats, certain other mammals, or bees. They have wide, flattened bodies, and the wings, when present—for there are wingless forms—close over the back, one over the other, like scissors. Their legs are long and spread spider-fashion, and are terminated by rather club-shaped tarsi with powerful claws. They run about their hosts, burrowing into and skidding most dexterously through the fur or feathers, and only fly short distances when pressed to do so. They are extremely quick and active creatures, and I haven't the slightest idea why they interest me so much.

THE FAMILY OF OACH

Diseases of Wild Animals; a Koolu and a Bet on a Rabbit; Ki-Ish-Patch-Oach, a Tzarbin, and the Essence of Skunks

WHEN we had at last convinced ourselves that all the flies had escaped, we killed the bird in the manner prescribed for fowl of all kinds, and then performed an autopsy. Once again there were no worm parasites anywhere throughout the intestinal tract. In fact the whole bird was as clean and healthy-looking as any animal could be, except for its liver. Having made a thorough exploration of everything else, I turned my attention to this organ. The whole left lobe was blackened, constricted, and hard as a rock.

It was ultimately through this vulture's liver that we came to a decision about a matter over which we had deliberated intermittently for many months. During the course of dissection of the animals that come to our skinning tables, we find many strange things. Besides internal parasites and anatomical abnormalities, such as a rat with only one lung, we often meet cases of disease. We have found malignant growths, strange manifestations of deficiency diseases, and many other things most of which we could not identify. In some cases we have preserved specimens of these manifestations, but unfortunately many priceless examples were lost either before or after preservation, owing principally to a most regrettable lack of appreciation on our part of their real value.

The intelligent comprehension of the significance of any series of facts is a strangely slow process. One encounters a succession of examples spread over a considerable period of time before one realizes that they are related. Only then does it dawn upon one's mind as a considerable surprise that they constitute a unity of some importance. Once this has been grasped, how plain it all becomes, and what a fool one feels. That is precisely how the matter of wild animals' diseases has grown upon us. Despite the fact that we had been collecting examples of animal diseases as we met them for some time, it was not till we came to Tekom that we realized the true significance of their occurrence.

There is, I believe, a vague but universal presumption that wild animals in their natural environment do not suffer from diseases such as afflict ourselves and our domestic animals. Tentative questions that we have put to friends certainly confirmed this belief. Inquiries made amongst medical acquaintances have, moreover, convinced us that it is not merely a vague presumption but more nearly a positive assumption that truly wild animals are more or less free from disease. This, however, does not tally at all with what we have ourselves observed. Deeper inquiry in more appropriate quarters then showed that there are quite a number of records of wild animal infections of many forms. Yet the general inference that might be drawn from the number of these still did not in any way coincide with what may be found by the dissection of a large number of wild animals.

During the course of one of our trips, we have occasion to dissect a very great number of animals. The majority of these come from their natural environment in distant and uninhabited places, to which we normally go for our collecting. Were it not for our painstaking search for internal parasites and for certain other studies, we, like most others who collect in such remote places, would not have occasion to dissect our finds in the field. Of the few animal collectors who may have occasion to carry out routine dissections of a detailed nature upon all the specimens that come into their hands in the field, few appear to have made a special study of the examples of diseases that they encounter. Domestic animals, creatures in zoos, and species that are kept and bred for experimental purposes are very extensively studied. Thus we find the majority of the cases of animal disease have been recorded from the latter types. The animals inhabiting populated areas and country surrounding centres of civilization are the next most likely group to be studied, and, being in more frequent contact with domesticated species, are also more likely to be diseased. Truly wild animal populations, on the other hand, seem hardly to have been examined at all in this respect, simply because nobody has had particular reason to study them. This may to a great extent explain the comparative rarity of the records of disease among them.

When we now collected all the scattered records that we already had, the results were more than surprising. By the time all the cases of skin lesions, cysts that could not surely be attributed to worms, samples of liver juices containing protozoan parasites, and other items that came to hand from time to time were added, we found that we had a very considerable list. Since we began to investigate this matter systematically, moreover, many more records have been added. We do not at present know exactly what half these things are, but the very fact that they occur, and the comparative frequency with which they do so in perfectly wild and uncontaminated animals, would, I believe, surprise many medical men.

Here is a phenomenon with aspects of the widest significance. Most of our own diseases and those affecting our domestic animals must have originated in nature. We know that many of them are transmitted by wild animals. The roles played by the mosquito in the transmission of malaria, the tsetse fly in sleeping sickness, and so forth, are common knowledge. Other more abstruse examples, like rabies carried by skunks and by a bat, are also known. In many instances, these diseases have been traced back to some reservoir of infected wild animals. Is it not, therefore, reasonable to deem any study of the known or even unknown diseases of truly wild animals of possible aid in controlling their spread to our own world, and in elucidating some of our present more baffling maladies?

The animals from around Tekom showed an exceptionally high incidence of disease of one kind or another, doubtless because they had lived for so long in such intimate contact with man and his filthy domesticated pets. Almost every animal contained some species of parasitic worm; one housed no less than five distinct forms. And the skins of the animals were at least as frequently infected as their internal organs and tissues.

We were aroused from our hammocks one morning at dawn by a discreet though none the less insistent knocking on our front door. Neither Alma nor I am averse to any excuse for getting out of a hammock, for in our opinion they constitute the most pestilential form of sleeping device yet conceived. I am altogether too long for even the largest, so that I have to sleep doubled up, and invariably awake with a dull ache all over my back. I therefore jumped up with unaccustomed alacrity despite the uncivilized hour.

Poking my blinking visage out into the morning mists, I was confronted by two sturdy chaps clothed in the small, pale blue, striped aprons worn by the Mayas. Between them they carried a large ocelot, its feet tied with sisal ropes.

"*Es muerto?*" I snapped suspiciously, backing into the house.

"*Sí, señor,*" the elder piped, fortunately displaying some knowledge of Spanish.

"Hum, *un momento,*" I said, holding up a hand. Having already established a record for pre-breakfast Spanish, I retired to rouse Riqué.

"Hi, Riqué," I bawled, as I gave his hammock a slap, "get up, there's a tiger outside."

I hadn't meant the pronouncement to be so portentous and had quite neglected to take into account my friend's condition. The poor chap came uncoiled like a watch spring.

"Tiger! A tiger! Where?" he yelled, lashing about in the darkened room.

Having completely mistaken my meaning, naturally, and thinking that it was the middle of the night, he was in a ferment.

"It's all right, Riqué," I consoled him; "it's only an ocelot and some Indians have got it outside, *dead*."

"Phew!" he said, subsiding into his hammock and scratching his head. A few tense seconds ticked by, for Riqué has a highly commendable Latin temper. We then opened the door and got down to bargaining. In due course the ocelot became ours, and we went back to bed.

When we came to deal with it later we found that the whole top of its head was devoid of fur, and the naked skin bright pink and tumid. The poor brute had been suffering from a severe infection of mange. It had been caught in a small cave only a few miles from the village, and had undoubtedly been attacked by hunting dogs at some time, for it bore scars on its hind legs and nose.

It was the same two hunters who quite unwittingly put us on the spot a few days later. We had been steadily working down our list of animals, ticking them off by their Mayan names as they came in. The village populace, quite contrary to all expectation, had gone to work with a persistence befitting their Mongolian affinities. A constant stream of creatures had been brought to us by them while we had been very busy ourselves searching the countryside by day, hunting by night, and trapping widely all over the place. Most of the animals to which we could confidently assign proper names had already come to hand, but there remained quite a number of creatures for which we had only Mayan names. It appeared, as far as we could make out, that most of these were carnivores. Therefore, when any competent-looking hunters with guns came to the house, we besought them to get us any of these. We also put prices upon each of them which varied greatly, according to what we imagined the animals might be or the degree of our inquisitiveness.

There are at least sixteen carnivorous mammals known to inhabit the peninsula. We had a list of twelve Mayan names, which left us with three blanks apart from the otter, which is not found in that area. We were sure of the identity of seven of our Mayan names, and were left with five names—choolea, cap-ko, koolu, sa-an-hole, and tzarbin—for nine animals. As days went by and none of these blanks was filled in, we kept raising the ante, particularly on the cap-ko and koolu, for reasons which I would now be ashamed to mention.

We were just coming to what we thought was the end of a day of back-breaking labour, during which we had dealt with over a hundred animals, a considerable number of which were new types calling for photography, drawing, and other tedious routine work. It was nearly midnight, and we had closed the front door in the hope of warding off any more of the contributions that the younger members of the populace kept bringing to us at all hours and as long as they could get into the house. We were just sitting back and giving vent to sighs of thankfulness, when there came a knock at the door. Riqué called out an inquiry in his best Mayan. A shout of "Koolu!" came back, and we made a concerted dash for the door, all our tiredness instantly forgotten.

Outside were the two men who had brought the ocelot. They carried a sack and, as was usual upon such occasions, the darkness behind them was filled with happy faces, all of whose owners streamed into the house as soon as the doors were opened. The inhabitants of Tekom were the most charming and friendly people that it has ever been our luck to dwell among; they took the keenest interest in our endeavours, and felt with us every excitement and disappointment. Everybody was now very enthusiastic, because we had been so insistent upon this matter of the koolu. The bag was untied in the centre of a quietly palpitating circle.

The animal that tumbled out, however, was the very greatest disappointment to us, for it was nothing but a raccoon. In any other country one would instantly have suspected the hunters of playing a trick upon the stupid foreigners, with the tacit consent of the onlookers, but at Tekom there could be no question of such dishonesty. The raccoon was the "koolu," and we had offered a very handsome price for a koolu and so the men got an awful lot of money, which made it quite unnecessary for them to do any further hunting until long after we left. We in turn had a raccoon on our hands.

By hard work and a string of intermediate interpreters, we made it quite clear that we didn't want the animal a bit but that we paid the stipulated price nevertheless on grounds of honesty and business integrity. We then pleaded even more strongly for the choolea and the cap-ko, and raised the ante on the latter still further. Everybody seemed satisfied and began to leave.

As the men turned to go, I spotted a pair of long mammalian ears sticking out of a leather bag slung across the back of a young hunter. I made a grab for the youth before he vanished into the night, and seized hold of the ears.

"Riqué, ask him what he's got here," I implored, for the hunter was not sure of my intentions and looked somewhat peeved.

When the question had got over we were informed that it was only a "tŭ-ool," and further inquiry brought to light the fact that this was a rabbit. A tremendous palaver then ensued, taking the following form, with Riqué and the secretary of the village council acting as intermediaries.

"For heaven's sake, can't I buy it?" I asked.

"No," came the answer.

"Why not? Doesn't he want to sell it?"

"No," once more came the answer, without embellishment.

"But why?" I pleaded.

"He wants to eat it."

"But good heavens, I'll give him much more money than the cost of a meal."

"He still wants to eat it. He says it's his rabbit; he shot it and he's going to eat it."

"But he can't eat the fur."

"No," came the answer.

"Tell him I'll buy the skin if I may skin it."

"No," came the answer again.

"Why not?"

"Because he doesn't like bad meat and he says it will be rotten by the time *you* finish skinning it."

"Nonsense!" I said, now in the highest dudgeon. "I'll have it skinned in half an hour if he'll wait." After this there was a heated discussion in which I could not join. It was obviously a matter of hard cash, and I naturally assumed that a price was being fixed. It was not so simple as that, however, for Riqué began to laugh, and turned to me.

"He says that if you skin it in half an hour he will take a peso for it, but if you take longer you must pay two pesos and fifty centavos."

I was quite dumbfounded. I had never heard of such a proposal since I left Africa.

"Does this man come from Tekom?" I promptly asked, bringing an old trick into play.

"No," came the answer, "he's from another place."

"Ah-ha!" I said triumphantly. "I thought nobody of Tekom would behave in such a way."

"Oh, yes, we would!" came a positive chorus.

"Oh, really?" I gasped, when the full significance of this outcry had been explained to me. "All right then, gentlemen, place your bets."

And they did. Soon there was quite a decent little pot, containing not only coins of small denominations in several small piles, but a very handy hunting knife contributed by the hunter himself. Seeing this I tried to hedge a bit.

"Tell them I accept the challenge, but that I refuse to part with *my* hunting knife."

"That's agreed," finally came the reply, "you just buy a new one for the man from the store."

I looked at the hunter, and he grinned most openly and pleasantly. The whole thing was done in the best spirit possible, but I felt very mean, for half an hour is an outrageously long time for skinning a rabbit. I got out my skinning tools, cleared the table, had the company sit down. Cigarettes and light refreshment were brought, and I then set to work while Riqué acted as time-keeper.

The rabbit was a type new to us, as it is an extremely rare animal farther to the south. This specimen proved to be a female. It

Yucatecan Rabbits (Sylvilagus floridianus yucatanicus)

was very fat, and when I laid it out to start work I suddenly realized how very neatly and completely I had been tricked.

You know what rabbits are over the little matter of reproducing themselves. Wild species are no less wholehearted about the business than tame ones. They have litters the size of football teams, and a battery of mammary glands extending from their chests to their groins with which to suckle them. Tropical rabbits also have incredibly thin skins. For the benefit of those who have not skinned animals, it must be explained that the milk glands adhere to the inside of the skin rather than to the underlying musculature. Skinning a pregnant tropical rabbit, therefore, is about as simple a job as performing an eye operation blindfolded.

As the minutes ticked by, I laboured away with wads of cotton-wool everywhere and my hands, the table, and the whole skin bathed in a sea of milk. How or when the skin began to tear, I never really knew, but long before I had it separated from the body along the underside where the mammary glands lay, I had made three large, sickle-shaped rents, one of which was almost big enough to be mistaken for the primary cut along the belly. As the time drew short, the assembled company began to get restive. There was much happy chatter, and, I had no doubt, a considerable amount of the more subtle forms of Mayan humour. When the skin was separated from the whole body and turned back over the head, my heart again sank, for I saw that the shot had shattered the skull. The head within was a mass of blood and bone fragments.

It was a close race, and the other side was very generous. At first they even declined to collect their money, and the hunter insisted that a matter of five minutes over my allotted time didn't call for an extra one-peso-fifty and a new knife. Among such charming people the white man's burden is indeed not a heavy one to bear, and the amount that I lost was well worth the fun and entertainment that we all got out of the thing. The store-keeper's son happened to be on hand, and went at once to get a new knife. The man got his meat and his two-pesos-fifty, a price that one would not consider paying in ordinary circumstances. I got the skin and skull. It was, all in all, a rather expensive evening. We never got the milk properly washed out of the fur, and, in trying to remedy this, kept it damp too long, so that it rotted. The skull was so broken that it was useless, and during the excitement we got so tired that we had to leave the koolu for attention next day. In the meantime it went bad, and the skin was ruined.

We always seem to have bad luck with porcupines. The first one I owned when I was a child, and it escaped into the woods surrounding our home in England, where it was promptly shot by a gamekeeper on the plea that it was a "varmint." I lost the next one in Java and never obtained another specimen of that species. Several of our carefully preserved ones went rotten in Africa owing to the overenthusiasm of a minion who plunged the skins into a brine tank during our absence. We bought a fine specimen of the island representative in Trinidad, and carried it carefully with us to Surinam. This one escaped on the boat, and got jammed in the inner recesses of the emergency steering apparatus. In extricating it I got a score of quills in my hand, and by the next evening had two badly swollen fingers and a septic-looking thumb. This same animal subsequently escaped in Surinam, and in our mad search for a torch with which to chase it, we dropped a case and broke a valuable microscope, but never recaptured the animal. Another that turned up on our roof in a jungle house in the same country ate its way out of a box and escaped.

One of our principal desiderata in Yucatan was a species of porcupine (*Coëndou mexicana*) that differs from the South American tree porcupines in several respects, the most noticeable being its covering of long, thick, black hair that hides the armament of short, black-tipped, white quills. The first one we got was a baby, which was welcome, but of little use to us. The next was a fine adult male, and was brought to us by our host, Don Jacinto Mukul, who had captured it in an area of tall thorn scrub in which he was clearing a new milpa some ten leagues south of Tekom.

We were exceedingly pleased with the acquisition of this animal, and spent the afternoon taking its portrait from all angles and constructing a cage for it that not even a porcupine could gnaw through in one night. We then went off to have dinner at another house some distance away, as was our custom, leaving the "ki-ish-patch-oach," as the Mayas call this species, in its cage, inside the house, with all doors shut and barred. As there were no windows, we felt that everything possible had been done, but our bad luck held.

We got back from dinner to find the cage empty and the animal gone. With devilish cunning, the porcupine had first overturned the cage and then forced apart the boards that constituted the floor, and so made good its escape. This was the one weak part of the structure which, of course, we had overlooked. The only possible way in which the animal could have left the house was by squeezing through the eaves between the top of the wall and the bottom of the very solid thatching. A careful search convinced us that this is just what it had done, so we collected some friends, armed ourselves with torches, and set out upon a rather hopeless search.

The house in which we lived stood in a large compound which was free of undergrowth and surrounded by a low stone wall. There were a number of large trees standing about, among them a few palms. The latter afforded the only real cover, but it seemed unlikely that a porcupine would ascend one of these, because they were isolated. Somebody produced a very satisfactory small dog, whose cooperation really began from the moment when we showed him where the porcupine had got through the roof. The thatch had been pushed apart, and there were scratches on the white plaster wall and several quills lying on the ground beneath. The little dog picked up the scent and went charging off into the night, giving a very fair imitation of a hound. We all followed at the double.

Our compound was the last one at that side of the village. Beyond its wall at one end lay the open country, which at this point most unfortunately consisted of a very thick tangle of dry scrub and thorn bushes. The scent, of course, led directly into this. The dog went in, and we followed as best we could.

Seeing that the chase was veering to the right, where I had a line of traps and where I knew the thorns to be of great length and potency, I hung back and started to circle round to the left along a small trace. I began running, as it was some distance by this longer route to the point where the others were charging about.

As I rounded a sharp bend in the path, I skidded to a sudden stop, for there in the middle of the road was Old Man Porcupine, sitting up on his hind legs, his paws held out before him like a pugilist, sniffing the air with his ridiculous, inflated nose and peering myopically into my torch-light with his bulging bright eyes. I had no time to call out for assistance, but made a dive for him. He swivelled around, got down on all fours, and started trundling off up the path. Had he gone to either side into the tangle it would have been hopeless. As it was, his recapture was no trouble at all. I simply got hold of his spineless tail and hoisted him off the ground.

Provided you keep "dumping" this kind of porcupine once you have him suspended in the air by his tail, he can't climb up himself and get at you. After a time he gets tired of being bounced up and down, and just hangs, snuffling pathetically and resignedly, with his limbs spread-eagled. While I was getting him into this state, I had time to consider the situation and came to the rather idiotic conclusion that it might be amusing to refrain from informing the others that I had caught the runaway. I had inflated visions of their faces when they got home empty-handed, to be met by a self-satisfied me with the animal back in its cage. I therefore dashed back to the house, filled with an inane conceit.

Having dumped the porcupine into the cage, I securely nailed the bottom on and put a heavy case on top of the whole structure. Then I lit a cigarette and sat down as calmly as possible to get on with the work. Faint sounds of the search were just audible in the far distance.

A quarter of an hour passed, but nobody returned. Ten minutes later a fellow came dashing past the house, and called out something in very rapid Mayan. Five minutes later he returned at the gallop with a friend, and followed by quite a pack of assorted hounds. He again called out to me, and then passed on into the night once more.

Yucatecan Weasel (Mustela frenata perda)

I waited for a further quarter of an hour, and then could bear it no longer, so took a torch and went out to look for the others.

This time I had to navigate the thorns, but there was no sign of the intrepid hunters. Dogs were barking on all sides, but there were two distinct major uproars, one far to the left and the other far to the right. I chose the right-hand one, and took a dreadful beating on my way towards it. When I arrived, covered from head to foot with burrs and scratches, bathed in perspiration, and completely out of swear words, I found three men and two boys trying, with most inadequate pieces of rope and without a light, to get a large bull out of a pen. They stopped in amazement when I appeared out of the bush, but as none of them understood Spanish, our encounter resolved itself into a series of grins and gesticulations, out of which I bowed myself with what good grace I could muster, for I disliked the look in the bull's eye.

I found a small road, and eventually regained the house, where I found a considerable crowd and had some difficulty getting in.

"Ah, there you are," said Alma. "Where have you been?"

"Where have *you* been?" I naturally asked.

"Out the back, making a hunt," said Riqué.

"And Marciano wants five pesos," Alma informed me.

"What on earth for? He didn't catch the darned thing."

"Yes he did, dear, and you know you promised five pesos for one."

"Yes, but darn it all, I've paid for it once to Don Jacinto."

"How could you? He's been with us all the time."

"Listen," I said, with some heat, "is this some sort of joke? Did somebody let it out of the cage? I put it there myself."

"What d'you mean?" said Riqué. "Look! Look, Ivan; this. This is a tzarbin. Marciano killed it with a stone," and he indicated something on the table partly covered by a cloth.

I needed some time to take in the situation. Then I looked more carefully, and my confidence in everything was more than restored, for there lay a most beautiful little animal, long and thin, with a golden belly, a bushy black tail, and black-and-white markings on its face. It was a weasel of the species *Mustela frenata perda*, which settled several conundrums in our list of animals and added a new item to our collections.

They told me that the stalwart little dog had picked up the scent of this animal and nearly caught it. They had seen it go humping and jumping away in the loop-caterpillar fashion that these animals adopt, and go to ground under a pile of stones. The little dog had then refused to budge, so they had sent for more dogs, surrounded the place, cleared the ground, and then removed the stones. When the tzarbin came out, another chase had ensued, and Marciano, one of our local friends, had deftly dispatched it with a well-aimed stone.

Such luck is exceptional, and I should imagine killing a weasel with a stone to be almost unexampled. We all crowded round the little corpse, examining it and listening to several very good tales about tzarbins in general. For the moment I completely forgot the porcupine. When I did remember it, I hinted gently that the assembled company should inspect the cage. I thought my moment of now rather second-hand triumph had come. Riqué went over and peered into the box.

"Did you mend it?" he asked with great innocence.

"Yes, I did. But look inside and tell me what you see."

"I don't see anything," he said, "do you, Alma?"

"No," she said, going over, "what's inside, Ivan?"

"How do you mean?" I said, jumping up. "Here, let me see." Then, "Good Lord, where's it gone?"

"Where's what gone?" they asked.

"The porcupine. I caught the porcupine and put it back in there again!"

"Nonsense!" said everybody. "We don't believe you."

"I did, I swear I did!" I implored them to believe me, but they only tittered.

Our Mayan friends asked what was the matter, so Riqué told them and everybody began to talk. I couldn't believe it. I squatted down and examined the cage, but it was indeed empty. What was more, the cage door was not fastened. I thought furiously, and had

YUCATECAN SKUNK (Spilogale angustifrons yucatanensis)

just come to the positive conviction that I had forgotten to fasten it, when there was a commotion. Looking up, I saw a small boy standing quietly beside me, holding the porcupine by the tail.

"Where did you get that?" I asked tartly.

This was translated, and the answer came back.

"I caught it in the road outside."

I will never be sure whether they believed me when I told them that I had caught it, and I didn't really press the point, as the more I thought about it the more sure I became that I had indeed forgotten to make the cage door fast after so very carefully nailing up the floor boards. However, this incident must have broken the spell, for we have managed to keep several porcupines since.

It is interesting to note that the Mayas, by calling the porcupine the "ki-ish-patch-oach," class it with several other medium-sized mammals that might well confound naturalists having the fauna of one limited country only upon which to base their classifications. All the opossums are called something-"oach," the whole family being now called "bolsa-oach" or "pouched oaches." This group in the Mayan system also includes another animal, the classification of which might easily puzzle a primitive, i.e., the skunks which they call "pie-oach." These observant and intelligent people are fully conversant with the mysterious variety of colour patterns displayed by skunks. They affirm, quite rightly, that the differences in the arrangement and extent of the white markings on these animals are purely adventitious.

We were very eager to get some local skunks, and so raised the price offered for them to the high figure previously offered for the tzarbin. This had the desired effect. In a short time, a man arrived with a very pretty little skunk and, like our hunter farther south, demanded the price of a new outfit of clothes in return for it. The matter was quickly arranged, with much hilarity on all sides, and I retired to the garden in solitary state to get the skinning done.

This was a good, all-round skunk (*Conepatus tropicalis*) with a bushy white tail and a broad white band along its back which started on the crown and was split centrally by a narrow black wedge which ran forward from the base of the tail and petered out on the nape of the neck. The skin was in a filthy condition, the animal having been dragged in the mud and dust by the hunter, who had brought it attached to the end of a long pole. I gave it a bath in soap and water, and got the white parts to glisten like well-washed bed linen.

The smell of a skunk is undoubtedly terrific, and it clings with a persistency only a little short of that of a dead whale, but, to be perfectly frank, I don't dislike it. It is neither nauseating nor fuggy; it's just a good, irrepressible stink. When, therefore, I came to the scent glands in the process of skinning the beast, I was overcome by an unconquerable desire. With inexcusable secretiveness, I squeezed the contents of both glands into a two-by-one-inch tube, which the clear yellow liquid just filled. I then corked it up carefully, sealed it with paraffin wax, wrapped it in damp cotton-wool, and securely screwed it down in a small air-tight jar. I believed and subsequently proved without a shadow of doubt that a chap in possession of a bottle of skunk essence is in a very strong social position indeed. I had to wait some weeks for this proof, but the opportunity, when it came, could not have been a better one for the experiment.

Alma and I were living at another village in a small, isolated house. It was a nice village, but the inhabitants were as exceptionally unpleasant as the average Maya is charming. They were an indolent, rude lot, thoroughly spoiled by the unwonted ministrations of generations of stupid tourists, and without even the redeeming features of cheerfulness or good humour. On the second night of our stay in their village, they had a dance and the whole lot got noisily and nastily drunk.

We were awakened at five o'clock next morning—after a night made hideous with their music and fire-crackers, and intolerable by the multitude of jigger fleas and ticks that infested their filthy village—by our flimsy front door being broken in. A band of the locals had apparently decided that it would be fun to turn the newly arrived "gringos" out of their hammocks. This was not done in fun nor in real malice, but just to see what we would do. Sitting up in dazed early-morning surprise, I found the small house filling with horribly drunken men, covered in grime and stinking to high heaven. I yelled at them in no uncertain Spanish and what Mayan I could muster, but they were too far gone to heed me. Then I had an idea.

The collecting case was just under my hammock. I reached down, heaved out the tray, got the screw-topped bottle, and, with shaking hands, extracted the precious tube of skunk essence just as the more forward of the men came lurching towards me. I got the cork out and, holding up the tube, blew across its open mouth right into their faces with a whole lungful of air.

The result was perfectly marvellous. I have never been vouchsafed a more glorious moment in my life. The "borachos" reeled back. There was a thunderstruck pause, and then pandemonium broke out in their ranks. They sniffed like sick opossums, they gasped once or twice, and then reeled out of the house in a body. Within a few seconds no less than three were violently sick, for it seemed that their particular brand of liquor did not mix at all well with my precious essence.

They scattered immediately, and from that time until we left, nobody would come near our house. They never brought us any animals and they wouldn't even carry water for us at any price, but apart from the all-pervading aroma in which we had to live until we left, we were well satisfied.

ZOOLOGICAL NIRVANA

A Night of Frogs; Podogona and Other Underground Difficulties

OUR stay at this horrible little place was a painful contrast to our sojourn at Tekom, where everyone was so clean, charming, and dignified, and where we had made so many friends. Nevertheless, there are always compensations for such things in our work, and this place was no exception. Our traps brought us a fine series of one of the rats that we especially desired, as well as a surprising number of other animals. We collected in the course of two days no less than five species of bats that we had not seen before.

The rats trapped at this place were most interesting. Of the five species caught, four were really representatives of species that we had first taken in central British Honduras. Had we not collected these animals at intervals throughout the two hundred miles of country that lay between our first camps and this place, we would never have known that they were in any way related, for they had changed step by step along with the vegetation and the climatic conditions. Their form, their size, their fur texture, their colouration, and even certain details of their anatomy, had completely altered; in fact, they were now quite different rats.

Each of the four species belonged to a distinct genus. They represented four parallel clines occasioned by the same physical factors, yet the changes wrought in each of them were different. The grey-and-white tree-rats of the forest (*Tylomys*) had got smaller, lighter, and sleeker. At the same time, the *Sigmodon* had become larger and darker in general colour and the fur had become longer, thicker, and more fluffy. The *Heteromys* were now all in the lightest phase, with white shoulders and tail tips, and the little *Peromyscus* had gradually changed into sturdy little rats with long, plume-like reddish-golden fur. It is surprising how the same changes in environmental conditions can have quite contrary effects upon different rats merely because of their genetical make-up.

We had one unforgettable evening at this beastly place. The first proper storm of the wet season broke in mid-afternoon, and there were three hours of continuous deluge. The whole countryside had been as dry as parchment, and as the land surface was composed of patches of dusty red soil interspersed with great areas of bare limestone, it might well have been a desert but for the thick growth of bushes and trees that it supported. Except in deep wells, there was no water anywhere, nor was there any appreciable dew at night, so that one began to wonder whether the animals could get along entirely without liquid refreshment.

As the sun was setting that night, the whole countryside came to life in a manner that we had not previously witnessed. By the time darkness had descended, the air was a humming, ringing cacophony of jumbled sounds. Starting from our very doorstep and extending away as far as the ear could hear, there was a continuous uproar. There were birds and beasts and all manner of insects contributing to the symphony, but above all rose the chorus of the frogs.

From time to time we had heard an occasional toad croaking away in some damp recess, and once, after a brief spattering of rain during a thunderstorm at Tekom, there had been some half-hearted amphibian outcries from well-heads, but apart from that the dry nights had been unusually quiet for the tropics. This night was bedlam.

It all started with a sudden burst from just behind our house; a deafening crescendo that made one's eardrums buzz furiously, and sounded something like the grinding of a monstrous knife. Riqué and I dived out the back door, and the noise promptly stopped. In the unexpected though purely localized silence that followed, we were nearly blasted out of our skins by a tremendous outbreak of those non-functional automobile self-starters in a small tree not more than a yard from our heads. We dashed back for torches, and began a search. Presently we each had a handful of wriggling tree-frogs of the species *Hyla baudinii*. All these were identical with those that we caught in the northern part of British Honduras, being in the dull brown colour phase with the odd, irregular, hollow, dark brown markings. None was in the bright, plain yellow coat adopted by those of the tall southern forest, and none showed the remarkable vivid green markings on a silvery-grey base spotted with chocolate such as we noted on all those frogs of this species that we caught up in the Maya Mountains.

We got small bags and went back for more, and while we were struggling with a mass of thorns in an attempt to reach a pair that clung to a tall slender twig, the knife-grinding blast started again at our feet. Looking down, we saw a number of circular pot-holes in the surface of a big area of open limestone-marl. The noise was coming from these.

We both crawled under the bushes and found that these pot-holes were spherical below and full of water, with a layer of mud and decayed leaves at the bottom. As we thrust the torches into the holes, things flipped and splashed, but when the ripples died away nothing was to be seen but clear amber-coloured water and lots of leaves. We switched off the torches and waited quietly for several minutes, but nothing happened. We were just about to give it up, when I heard a little splash in my pool and, flashing on the light, saw a small, more or less spherical frog, coloured orange and brown like a dead leaf, floating on the water. I made a grab and caught him.

This wonderful little creature, which was only an inch and a quarter long, had produced all that noise, as we presently found out, for he gave us a prolonged chorus as soon as he was housed in one of our jars. This species (*Hypopachus inguinalis*) is a fossorial ani-mal, and spends the dry season dug deep in the mud or moist earth at the bottom of these pot-holes. Its body is pear-shaped, the head minute and sharply pointed, with small eyes and mouth. The arms are tiny and the hind limbs very short, though stout. Its whole underside is marbled black and white.

Encouraged by these captures, we had a hurried dinner and then set out into the uproarious night to search in earnest. We located the areas of greatest uproar, and found that they were all open spaces of bare rock in which there were many of these pot-holes filled with water. As we quietly approached them, the din was so terrific it seemed to get right inside our heads, and we could hear frogs shaking the surrounding bushes and plopping into the pools. Standing silently with the lights out, we listened to all manner of small frog talk.

The majority of the inmates of these natural baths, which had so suddenly and invitingly appeared in this parched land, were an odd species (*Triprion petasatus*) which has a very flattened head covered by a hard, armoured shield with sharp ridges and modified in front into a hard, overhanging beak. The front of the head, in fact, looks something like that of a small shark, the mouth being far back under the snout. The animal is really a tree-frog, and is supplied with finger and toe disks for climbing. In colour, the females are deep olive-green above, with large black spots. The males, which are less than half the size of the females, are generally lighter in colour, being almost yellow with pale greenish spots at night.

All these frogs were very busily mating. The pools were full of spawn in irregular strings. These creatures must know very well when the rains are coming. At any rate, the females have the eggs ready and well advanced in their oviducts, so that they can be fertilized and deposited the moment the first rains fall. Since that night we have never found any more spawn or mating couples; it would seem, then, that this species, like most other frogs, disposes of this business all in a rush at one time. It has been shown that even the frogs of temperate climes do this, and that they select only the exact weather conditions that they need, and only the first occasion that such conditions occur after a certain date each year.

In the low-lying places, where there was soil rather than rock, small, temporary swamps had formed, and in these we found the toads. They could be detected from afar by their endless rolling, rattling growls, or by the furious trilling of the smaller species (*Bufo valliceps*). The armour-headed or spoon-billed tree-frogs gave vent to an intermittent croaking not unlike that of a bullfrog. We soon got to know the various calls, and these guided us in our searches.

While we were messing about with the toads, we heard a strange call in a big tree close at hand. It was a very loud rattle which started on one pitch and changed to another just before it ceased. It was repeated about half a dozen times, and then there was a pause of nearly a minute before it recommenced. This gave us time to track it down, or, rather, up, for it proved to be near the top of an almond tree, which was fortunately quite easy to climb. The perpetrator was not at all put out by our approach, and continued to give vent to his call until Riqué spotted him pressed flat against a perpendicular leaf.

This was one of the most beautiful tree-frogs imaginable. Its whole upper side was smooth, vivid, apple-green, with a sprinkling of raised pure white spots, while its enormous eyes were pure unblemished red, like the lighter toned and less valuable rubies. These eyes, indeed, looked more like gems than like part of an animal. When we captured this specimen (*Agalychnis callidryas*) and stretched out its legs, we saw that its flanks were vertically banded with yellow and pale mauve, while the underside ranged from mauve at the head to yellow under the body and flame-orange under the limbs. The "hands" and feet were vivid golden-yellow. The eyes, strangely enough, retained their colour in the fluid in which the animal was preserved, which is most unusual.

We were finally drawn toward the middle of the village by yet another distinct frog chorus. This was a very high-pitched trilling that rose into a positive screech before breaking off and starting again. We traced it to a patch of herbs and grass which filled a runway from the stone water trough at the well. It took us a long time to find the choristers, principally because they were so very much smaller than we had expected. They were tiny frogs (actually a hitherto undescribed species of *Eleutherodactylus*) that stuck upside down under the leaves, and were coloured a disagreeable dirty yellow, relieved only by vivid green ocular swellings. While we were bottling these, a thick white mist suddenly rolled down upon us, so that our torch beams became practically useless. We decided to go home, and were just wondering which way that might be in the general clammy obscurity, when far away in the distance we heard a long and mournful wail.

"Whaaaw. Whaaaaw. Whaaaaw," it went.

Now, we knew about the creatures that made this noise, and had for long hoped to see one, so we set out at once to track the sound to its source. By strange good fortune, we found a small path that led straight through the thick bush to the very place where this gloomy creature was proclaiming itself.

The mist had cleared a bit when we reached an area of bare rock pitted with many water-filled pot-holes. The whaaawing had, of course, stopped, and the whole place was positively littered with all kinds of frogs. They plopped into the pools and constantly attracted our attention by shaking the bushes as they jumped about. We searched the pools systematically, and every now and then, when we were quiet, this thing would whaaaw at us. But the sound came and went so suddenly, and had such a strange, all-pervading quality, that we never knew in which direction it lay. Knowing the perpetrator to be a digging frog, we set to work and scooped out all the mud and rubbish from several of the pools, but still we got whaaawed at, at irregular intervals.

We were standing disconsolately by an especially large pool waiting for the next wail, when Riqué suddenly made a dive. I don't know to this day whether he slipped or whether his whole performance was intentional, but he went into the pool head first, showering me with muddy water. He landed flat on his face, and when he tried to raise himself on his hands to get out, his arms sank into the deep liquid mud at the bottom of the pool, so that his head barely remained above water. I got him by the collar and heaved him up, gasping and spluttering. He had no visible face; it was covered in a mask of black mud, with dead leaves sticking out of it.

"Look, I've got it," he bubbled, holding out a lump of mud.

I took this and washed it and, sure enough, he had. It was one of the whaaawing frogs (*Rhinophrynus dorsalis*) called by the Mayas "Whaw-Mooch." With one possible exception, this is the most hopeless kind of frog you could find. It is a loose, dark grey bag, with a line of golden spots straight down the back which make it appear as if it had been split open and then sewn up again. Its upper side has a few irresponsibly arranged white flecks. The head is disproportionately small and pointed, and the eyes are not much larger than pin-heads. The small mouth has a circular depressed area in front like a bell-push. The limbs are there all right, but they are completely enclosed in the sack-like skin, which extends almost directly from the wrists to the ankles. The creature blows itself up until it is practically spherical, and floats in water, a shapeless, inert mass, with its pointed snout sticking out into the air.

This was how Riqué had noticed it. We had both been staring at it for some time but had not realized what it was. He had seen it move, and had made quite sure that he would capture it!

Despite our fine catches, we left this place with few regrets. We left in a barely credible Model-T Ford truck, and proceeded over a road that cannot be described. What is even more remarkable, we arrived in due course at a village which, surprisingly for Mexico, was actually the very one for which we had set out. This was the village of Kawa.

Once several years ago, when we were leaving on a real expedition to West Africa, we were asked, by way of a zoological joke more than anything else, to bring back some little animals called Podogona. This gibe caused hearty laughter on all sides. How well I remember the scene, and my own gusty contribution to the general mirth. Podogona happened to be just about the rarest and most pointless creatures known to zoological science, and we could have counted on the fingers of our hands all the specimens then existing in all the collections of the world.

These animals form a distinct group of the Arachnida, and have

"Whaw-Mooch" (Rhinophrynus dorsalis)

no close affinities with any of the other groups. The first specimen was discovered in West Africa just over a century ago. It was named *Cryptostemma*, and since it was an entirely new kind of animal, the new order Podogona or Ricinulei was created for its reception into zoological classification. The next specimen was found by the famous naturalist Bates during his travels up the Amazon in 1874, and was named *Cryptocellus*. From that time until 1938, only thirteen more came to light from the whole of the New World. These, moreover, came from six different tropical American countries, and required the creation of six new species.

In 1938, descriptions of a new American species were published. These had been found deep in two caves of Yucatan. One of these caves was reported to be called Oxolodt and to be situated at Kawa, and the other to be named Bala-am, and to be at Chichen-Itza. When it was at last decided that we should leave England not for the Orient, as we had thought, but for Central America, final attention of course had to be given to the question of *Sphærorhynchus* (which is also an arachnid). While we were thus occupied one day, the scene that I have mentioned above, complete with the same zoological joke, was re-enacted. Once again we were asked to get some of the Podogona, but on this occasion none of us laughed quite so heartily because by dint of great good fortune, somewhat helped, I like to believe, by a year's hard work, we had managed to collect five hundred *Cryptostemma* in Africa and to bring twenty of them home to England alive in a biscuit tin.

So here we were, after another year of ceaseless endeavour, once more face to face with these obscure arachnids that seem to plague my life at intervals. How many caves we had descended, and how many acres of leaves we had raked over, and how many ants' nests and other likely habitats we had searched for some sign of Podogona, I would not like to guess. This, however, was the very spot from which they had been reported. It was our last hope.

Kawa seemed to be a decent sort of place. We arrived at sundown, and the *Presidente del Municipio* made us very welcome in the equivalent of the city hall, while the more interested section of the populace crowded in to discuss the local fauna and look us over. When they discovered that we had the Mayan names of the animals more or less pat, most of them left, as they saw they were to be deprived of their principal object in coming, namely, to pull the legs of the "gringos" with tales of wonderful and improbable beasts. Of those who remained, we presently singled out a small body of friendly young men who showed genuine interest and enthusiasm.

The first thing we learned was that there was no cave named Oxolodt, but there was one name Shishló which might conceivably be transliterated by a Spaniard as Xixlodt. This was not at Kawa, but five miles distant. There was, however, a very extensive system of caves and grottoes and passages honeycombing the earth below the village. This underground network was simply referred to as *Las Grutas*. We subsequently learned that Bala-am Cave was not precisely at Chichen-Itza, either, but such mistakes are minor details in Mexico! By further inquiry, we elucidated the fact that this Shishló cave, although big, was perfectly open and dry. It didn't sound like a haunt of the moisture-loving Podogona, so we decided, more in despair than in hope, to visit *Las Grutas* the next day.

The following morning we were conducted to the only feasible entrance to this remarkable system of caves by a band of new friends. The leader was a very large and portly gentleman, a man of great intelligence, personal charm, and initiative, who insisted upon accompanying us. The identity of the others remains hazy in my mind for several reasons. Our own team consisted of Alma, Riqué, myself, and our good friend the *Presidente* of Tekom, who happened to be there at the time. We carried a formidable assortment of machines and instruments, ranging from gasoline pressure lamps to small lenses and tubes. Our new friends brought along something else, but we didn't know that at the time. To them this excursion was as good an excuse as another for having a *fiesta*.

The entrance to the caves was only a few hundred yards beyond the last house at the western end of the village. It was a circular hole some thirty inches in diameter which led vertically downward

through the crust of the earth under an overhanging bank. Down
this a crudely fashioned, twenty-foot ladder was dropped, and we descended into a circular, domed chamber about twelve feet in diameter. From this, a low-roofed passage sloped down into the bowels
of the earth. We experienced considerable difficulty in getting our
large friend through the first hole; in fact, we probably never would
have done so had he not been stung by a wasp at the crucial moment
when he became securely wedged amidships. He then came down
with a rush. We lit the pressure lamps and the torches and set off
down the passageway.

Yucatan is a great plateau of consolidated limestone-marl and is
honeycombed with caves, underground rivers, lakes, passages, and
tunnels. Unlike the majority of caves in the more ancient and solid
rock formations of other countries, which are usually formed by
cracks and crevices between huge shifting blocks of the country
rock, those of Yucatan are water-worn tunnels of various dimensions, smooth and domed above, and with level, cave-earth floors.
All that we have visited, and these at Kawa in particular, are arranged like the strands of a giant fish net; the passageways, in plan,
would divide the rock into square, oblong, or diamond-shaped
blocks. This arrangement is often repeated at different levels, so that
at the junctions of passages there are sometimes holes in the floor
leading down to another whole set of caves lying below. This is repeated downwards until the water level is reached, and it probably
continues far below that, for we have been told that during some
exceptional droughts people have descended into two further levels
that are normally filled with water. This would have brought them
to sea level, below which the water table presumably can never fall.

The life of these underground waters is strange and plentiful.
There are blind shrimps, catfish, blind fish, water snails, and many
other creatures that have presumably spent the last epochs of their
evolution down in these eerie depths. The life of the drier passages is
no less numerous and diverse. In this cave we found many crickets,
thrips, and other insects, large red millepedes, *amblypygi*, small
web-spinning spiders, small white isopods, or "woodlice," and a

small black platyhelminthine worm. Even a few hours' careful search would doubtless have extended this list to cover a whole page.

The first part of the passage was very dry. The floor was composed of dusty earth and many loose boulders. Further on came patches of bare, damp earth. We spent some hours grovelling about, turning over boulders and squirming into small, low side chambers. Our principal difficulty was a total lack of any precise suggestions as to where this particular species of Podogona should be sought. We knew by experience that these little creatures are uncannily touchy about their environment. In West Africa they lived only in an unusual damp layer of leaf mould, sandwiched between two dry layers in one special kind of forest which was itself a rarity in that very exceptional kind of jungle. The endless variety of habitats in a series of caves of these dimensions would sound incredible if I attempted to enumerate them.

While we were thus occupied, our Mexican friends, led by the ever-enthusiastic Riqué, went on into the earth, and our party was soon spread out along many hundreds of yards of passageways. Our own labours were tedious and prolonged; they were far too Anglo-Saxon, almost Teutonic, in nature for the vivacious Latins. Now that I come to look back on that day, the whole performance was a very literal demonstration of the possibilities of co-operation between the two mentalities, explaining why the Nordic so seldom makes a discovery, and the Latin so seldom follows one up!

We began to despair of the place. We talked it over and asked our portly friend, who alone had stayed behind with us, whether there were wetter parts farther down. He said there might be, but he knew nothing of the caves beyond this point, and doubted whether anybody in the party had ever been farther. We then bawled for Riqué, but got no answer. I had to leave Alma to continue the search, while I went ahead to look for him.

The place was a veritable maze of tunnels, all looking exactly alike. The only things to guide me were occasional footprints in the damp earth floor and, following these, I walked or crawled forward, bawling lustily every now and then. Finally I got a reply, and presently came upon a small party seated round a flickering lantern.

"*Dond' esta Riqué?*" I called.

"*Adelante, señor, muy lejos.*"

"Oh," I said, and stumbled onward.

"*He! Señor, quiere tomar?*" they called, extending in my direction a whole battery of small bottles containing a suspiciously cloudy white liquid.

I contemplated the offering, but decided to risk giving offence by refusing the well-meant invitation. Excusing myself and murmuring politenesses, I pushed on and eventually came out into a fair-sized gallery where a whole block of rock had been dissolved away between four tunnel cross-junctions. I spotted a small bat sleeping in a pot-hole on the roof, and, being without the airgun, chucked a rock at it. Of course I missed. The quarry flitted off down a tunnel and came to rest on a low arch. I got another rock and crept forward, took careful aim, and let fly again. This time I missed the bat by several feet. The rock sailed on into the darkness beyond, and burst like a bomb.

"Whow! *Nombre de—*" et cetera. A whole chorus of voices sprang from the depths.

It seemed fairly plain that I had found some more of our friends. The chief difficulty under which I laboured was that I never knew how many were in the cave. I was again offered a drink. Once more I refused politely, and inquired after Riqué. This second party also pointed onwards, and so on I went. Next I came upon Don Jenero, the *Presidente* of Tekom, and one other. The latter also had a bottle. I again declined an offer of a drink, but as I was perspiring freely from the bad air and was a bit weary, I sat down for a smoke.

The local man was a young and intelligent-looking fellow. He was in rather a shaken condition, and seemed inordinately keen to get Riqué back. He was also firmly against my going any further, saying that the caves were endless and that it was easy to get lost. I pointed out that we were probably all lost already and as we all seemed to have plenty of time, who should he be to care. But it wasn't only that, he told me with great solemnity, and he got up and pointed to the low, arching roof of the cave. The rock was white limestone marl, but here all the prominences depending from the roof and all the lower arches were stained with red earth; the points were rounded and polished and there were long scratches and great smears of discolouration.

"That," the man announced, "is caused by the passing of huge and terrible beasts that live in these caves. They are so tall that their backs rub along these low places as you can see."

"What do they look like?" I asked.

"They are as big as cows," he began, "but they are shaggy and higher in front than the back. They have jaws like dogs and great claws."

When pressed for further details, he went on to build this imaginary animal into the best and most detailed description of an extinct cave bear (*Spelarctos*) that you could wish—which was doubly absurd because these animals are not known in the fossil state from this part of the world. The peculiar marks on the roofs, of course, are probably caused at times of flood by logs and other rubbish being washed along. I stupidly suggested this explanation, and was glared at. Then even more stupidly I pressed the point by observing that these great beasts seemed to leave no footprints on the soft cave earth below. After that I became definitely unpopular. It is an interesting superstition, nevertheless, and I would like to know from what dim recess of Mayan primeval history such a vivid description presumably of some extinct pleistocene mammal might have come to his mind. Perhaps there are rock drawings of giant extinct ground sloths somewhere, descriptions of which may have been handed down to him; yet his mythical beast didn't sound like one of those animals.

I then went on in search of Riqué, but as the air was getting worse, I refrained from further calls. I had gone a long way and was not only getting really worried about Riqué's disappearance, but was beginning to consider seriously my own predicament. Suddenly my blood nearly froze in its leisurely tracks. It was a momentary sensation, but in the deathly stillness among the eerie shadows deep down there in the earth it was stark terror. I like to believe that the bad air had something to do with my fright, but I fear there can be no disguising the fact that the sensation was pure reflex.

What had frozen me to the marrow was the most blood-curling and Gargantuan growl or snort some way ahead in the depths of the shadows. I waited hardly breathing, and not knowing whether to flee or emulate the ostrich. I think I would have simply remained rooted to the spot out of pure terror, if there had not been a disturbance of quite a different nature to my left. You can have no idea how these other noises relieved the strain. They were so obviously solid and real, that I knew if this was indeed the shaggy, cave-dwelling monster, it was at least tangible.

I flashed on the torch, and behold, there was an extremely pale Riqué peering over a rock like some remnant of our prehistoric and troglodytic ancestry.

"Riqué," I called, "was that you?"

"Ivan," he gasped, clutching the stone, "did you hear it too?"

"Wasn't it you?" I ran down the tunnel towards him. "What on earth is it?" I asked.

"I don't know," wailed Riqué, "I got lost chasing bats, and first I thought it was you people, but when I got here it sounded so huge I've been listening to it ever since."

"Listen, Riqué, have you been hearing stories of these great beasts that live in these caves?" I asked.

"Oh, the cave cows! Yes, I've heard of those, but they're——"

Then another frightful growl came echoing along the passage, followed by a tumultuous splashing.

"Good heavens, Riqué, it must be a crocodile in a cenote."

"Yes, it might be," he said doubtfully, but the thought that it might be just an ordinary very dangerous animal made us both feel much better.

So we set out to track down the sounds. As the noises grew louder, they certainly became more formidable and blood-curdling. One needed no imagination whatever to conjure up a vision of some monstrous bear wallowing in a pool. On the other hand, I wanted to know if crocodiles really did live in underground waters. The sounds certainly resembled some of the worse outcries of those reptiles.

As we went on, the air became fresher and damper, and the whole cave came alive. Many bats flitted around us, and the walls became crowded with insects. We turned a sharp corner into a small gallery, and as we entered, the hideous, gurgling growls suddenly blasted out at us almost from our feet. We leaped around.

There was a long pause before they were repeated, but we then found that they were issuing from a small hole leading into the wall at floor level. This hole was only a foot high, and about two feet broad. We could hear water splashing about within, apparently at a lower level. After some debate and soul searching, we decided that I, being the slimmer, should squeeze in with a torch and see if I could catch a glimpse of whatever was causing the blood-curdling disturbance. With some trepidation, I began to wriggle into the hole.

The tiny passage was very short, and gave into a round chamber. I got far enough in to poke my head over the lip and look down. Sure enough, there was water below, now agitated into small waves that lapped against the sides. I was manœuvring the torch further forward to have a better view when—*wham!*—something caught me squarely across the back of the head, jabbing my chin down onto the rock. I knew positively that my hour had come, and I started to fight with the desperation of the doomed. I yelled; I clutched wildly, and then my hand got a hold on something cold and hard, which I instantly let go.

The torch had gone out, and I was waiting for the end, being now firmly jammed into the hole with my legs lashing about in the cave behind, and my head dangling over the waters. There was a splosh and a splash, and I had visions of a pair of great jaws coming up to get me. In my frenzy I slewed round and looked up.

Far, far above was a small, circular spot of light, and in the centre a small round thing that bobbed in and out. Puzzled, I looked again, for I could not make any sense out of what I was seeing. Then, slowly, it all began to dawn on me. I nearly fell into the water as a result; in fact, I probably should have done so if I hadn't clutched the rope, though this came away with a rush.

I was in the bottom of a deep well; the little dot above me was an unsuspecting Mayan lady drawing water; the cold hard thing that had biffed me on the back of the head was a bucket whizzing downward to the water level; the frightful noises were the banging of the concave base of the bucket when it hit the water, and the blood-curdling gurgles and growls, the filling of the bucket magnified a thousand times and muffled out of recognition by the small sound-box leading into the cave. The disturbance in our breasts proved to be as nothing compared to the effect upon the lady above, when piercing and unearthly shrieks issued from her well and her rope was suddenly yanked out of her hand. She let go of everything and bolted, and we heard later that she was several hours recovering from her ordeal.

"Riqué," I yelled, "pull me back! It's only a well, and I'm stuck and half knocked out by a bucket."

Riqué got me by the legs and pulled me back. As I went slithering in, my face dragged over the ground. I clutched the torch, which lit up the little hole, and I suddenly saw something.

"Riqué, Riqué," I screamed, "stop! For goodness' sake, stop! I've got one."

"Got one what?" he called, letting me go again.

"A Podogona! Wait a minute; give me a tube."

"Here, on your left," he said, pushing one in to me.

I cornered the little beast and manœuvred it into the tube; then I wriggled back and jumped up in triumph, my battered head completely forgotten. We executed a war dance; we yelled and shouted with glee; we howled and bawled for the others. The effect of this above ground was, we later learned, to send the eastern half of the village charging off to the local church in a body. Hearing these sounds greatly magnified above, they imagined that some horrible ancestors were coming to life, and that an intraterranean invasion was imminent.

Then began a frightful time. We had to find the others and we had to find more Podogona, for where there is one animal there must always be more. At first we both ran off to look for assistance, but we soon realized that we were lost, and that we might easily lose the Podogona. I called out to Riqué to go back to the well and start to work while I set out in search of the others.

After prolonged wandering, I got to the big chamber where the first bat had been and stumbled across Don Jenero and the romancer. They were perched on two rocks like gargoyles. I called to them to come and help and, because of my insistence but despite my patchy Spanish, I think they imagined Riqué had been killed by one of the cave beasts. They jumped up and came at the double. I then pushed on, calling for the next lot.

Answering shouts came from all sides. Yells seemed to issue from every tunnel and passage, and among them I heard Alma's feminine screech. I made tracks in that direction, and found her alone and somewhat disturbed.

"Thank goodness you've come," she said when I reached her; "I'm utterly lost and thought you had gone for good. Where have you been?"

"I've got one; a Podogona."

"Really? Where? Show me, please," she begged.

I held up the bottle in triumph. It was a great moment, and we executed another war dance on the strength of it, and shouted some more. We were answered from all sides.

"Listen, dear, where are the others?" I asked. "I want all the help we can muster. We must get more and I want to spend a long time going into these things."

"I don't know where they are, Ivan; they're all as drunk as owls."

This brought me up sharp. "They're all drunk?" I queried.

"Yes; I've never seen people so drunk in my life, not even at a bottle-party."

PODOGONA

"Good gracious!" I gasped, as the full significance of the many little bottles dawned upon me. "We'll never get them out of here. The place is endless and full of pot-holes. Are they all separated?"

"Yes, they're all over the place, and I found one asleep just now."

"How many are there?"

"I've no idea. They kept wandering back and forth, and some went back for more habanero."

"So it was habanero—in this bad air! I wonder we *didn't* meet a cave bear!"

"Let's get hold of Riqué."

And as usual, when things got too complicated, that is what we did. We finally mustered around the well our own party and the man who told me about the cave beasts. Having been in the fresher air near this vent, we were all perfectly all right, and even the story-teller, who had finished his bottle, was now quite sober. We asked Riqué what we should do about the others. He shrugged his shoulders and said simply that they were all free, Mexican, and twenty-one, so hadn't we better look for Podogona. And we did.

We soon found that these strange little animals were to be found only within a few yards of the well. Here the air was fresh and moist though generally not too cold, thus creating an environment matching very closely that which I have described as being chosen by their African congeners. They were all under stones, so that they were also in a damp stratum between two dry ones, the top one being drier than the bottom one, just as in the leaf mould in West Africa.

There was little that we could discover about their habits. None was moving about; they all appeared to be resting, and mostly on the underside of the stones rather than on the earth below. Some carried a single, crystal-clear, yellowish egg under the cephalo-thorax, held by the two terminal spines on the palpi just as we had found the African *Cryptostemma* to do with their rather larger, pale mauve eggs. This species (*Cryptocellus pearsii*) also hated the light, and made away from it with all speed. They were, however, much more active and less timid than the others we had seen. Also, they lacked the peculiar habit of bunching up all their limbs and lying inert when alarmed, which was so characteristic of the other species.

In searching for these animals, we found a very odd kind of large mite under the same stones. They lived in small communities and were quite colourless, so that their internal organs showed through their skins. They were large and active and excessively soft and easily crushed.

It was a most exceptional cave in many ways, and the presence of this well created a very novel environment. We found that many wells penetrated other passages, and that the big cenote, or underground lake, under the central plaza of the village also joined it. We were later told that there was a belief that one could travel for miles underground by way of these caves, and come up in almost any of the cenotes or villages in the country that one desired.

This did not augur well for the next job we had on hand, namely, rounding up *los fiesteros*. We have been called upon to do many queer things during our travels, but nothing to date has surpassed that job for pure bizarrerie.

We each got lost in turn. Sometimes we were all lost together, sometimes all at once but separately. We would find a roisterer and drag him back to what we thought was the main passage, only to find that it wasn't, and, while searching for the real one, would find another drunk. Whenever we made an attempt to conduct two at once, a violent argument would break out as to the route to be followed, and one drunk would stagger off one way and the other to another side. Giving up in despair, one decided to take charge of only one of them, and promptly met a sober leading another drunk in the contrary direction. Once we had five drunks in a clutch under the care of Don Jenero, but Riqué and Alma were lost. When I had found Alma and brought her back, all the drunks and Jenero had gone. Another time we had a huge party clustered in a small chamber. There were many more of us than had left the village, and yet I knew there were still two missing.

"Where have they gone?" we pleaded.

"They went home," everybody chorused.

"Which way is that?" we asked.

"There," they shouted, pointing in various directions.

For answer, there was a terrified shout from the depths of the earth, followed by a splash. We all dashed off, thinking somebody had gone down a well, but found a fellow we had never seen before sitting in a shallow puddle. When I looked round, half our precious convoy had gone again.

Finally we collected all we could, and at last made our way back to the entrance. Here we found two very tipsy gentlemen struggling with the primitive ladder. They had broken half the rickety rungs already, and it was only by great luck and much exertion that we got out at all. Just as the last man emerged from the hole, somebody yelled, "Where's Carlos?" There was an awful silence, then, with one accord, the whole lot dived back into the hole, falling pell-mell into the rubble below and roaring with laughter. Then it all began again.

The fresh air had sobered them considerably, however, and they clung together rather desperately. What is more, they soon found Carlos, who turned out to be the story-teller. He embraced me fondly, for he had been in a patch of bad air. Then we all scrambled back again into the sunlight.

"Señor," said Carlos, embracing me again, "you saved me; look what I've got for you."

He held up a small and infinitely dilapidated bat. I took it gratefully, and wondered, as I often do yet, if I had any other friends down there clutching tender little tributes. I turned it over in my hand, and then I saw something in its ear.

It was a *Sphærorhynchus,* but after all that had happened it seemed so trivial that its discovery passed almost unnoticed, and left no impression on us at the time.

THE END

INDEX

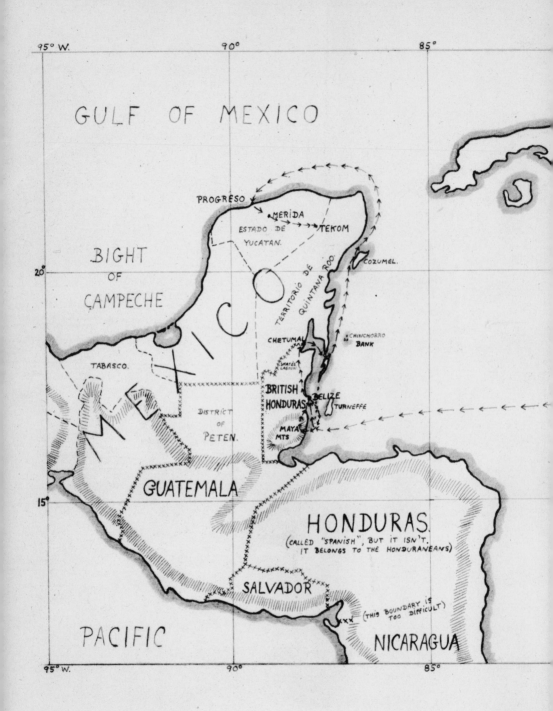

GULF OF MEXICO

95° W.   90°   85°

BIGHT
OF
CAMPECHE

20°

PROGRESO
MERIDA
ESTADO DE TEKOM
YUCATAN.

COZUMEL.

TERRITORIO DE
QUINTANA ROO

CHETUMAL

CHINCHORRO
BANK

TABASCO.

WATÉS
LAGOON

BRITISH
HONDURAS
BELIZE
TURNEFFE

DISTRICT
OF
PETEN.

MAYA
MTS

GUATEMALA

15°

HONDURAS.
(CALLED "SPANISH", BUT IT ISN'T.
IT BELONGS TO THE HONDURANEANS)

SALVADOR

(THIS BOUNDARY IS
TOO DIFFICULT)

PACIFIC

NICARAGUA

95° W.   90°   85°